GENERAL CHEMISTRY
PROBLEM SOLVING

II

Gaseous Equilibria, Acid-Base
Equilibria, Titrations,
Indicators, Solubilities,
Thermodynamics,
Electrochemistry

STEVEN S. ZUMDAHL
University of Illinois, Urbana

. Heath and Company
ngton, Massachusetts/Toronto

TO THE STUDENT

The purpose of this book is to help you learn to solve chemistry problems of various types. The principles are illustrated in sample problems, which are worked out for you in detail. Then there are tests to help you evaluate your understanding of the concepts. Complete solutions to the tests are given at the back of the book.

To get the maximum benefit from this book, be sure to study the introductory material and the sample problems thoroughly before attempting the test that follows that material. Be sure you do not look at the solutions to the tests too soon. Try hard to do the test on your own. If you cannot do a problem on a test, review the written material and sample problems and then try the test again. After you have completed the chapter tests, do the exercises at the end of the chapter. The answers for the exercises and multiple choice questions are given in the back of the book.

INSTRUCTOR

Because the material covered in this book is treated at various levels of sophistication in general chemistry courses depending on the needs of the students, special care has been taken to make this book useful to students at all levels. The topics are organized so that the fundamental material is separated from the more advanced material. The concepts that are appropriate in a course for chemistry majors but possibly not appropriate in a service course are presented in sections which can be used at the instructor's option.

In the treatment of equilibrium, the more advanced topics have been placed in Chapter 5. The instructor can use all, none, or specific sections of Chapter 5 as is appropriate for a particular course, without effect on the material presented in Chapters 1 to 4.

In addition, equilibrium is presented in a way which allows the instructor to choose the level of mathematical sophistication appropriate for his/her students. Fundamental concepts are treated using only basic algebra. More complicated mathematical procedures are used only in the optional sections.

Chapter 6 deals with the Second Law of Thermodynamics. This topic can be presented in many different ways, and thus it is difficult to treat in a problem-solving book, which should be compatible with any general chemistry textbook. Chapter 6 was organized with two goals in mind:

1. to provide the student with some insight concerning the significance of entropy, free energy, and the Second Law of Thermodynamics; and
2. to provide drill in using the various thermodynamic functions.

The instructor who does not wish to expose his/her students to a treatment of this material with a different emphasis from that of the course textbook may use only the sections in the chapter that provide drill in the use of the thermodynamic functions.

Chapter 7 covers electrochemistry. Because some instructors may wish to de-emphasize the relationship between electrochemistry and thermodynamics, the first part of this chapter is devoted to the practical aspects of electrochemistry: construction of electrochemical cells, calculation of the cell voltage, prediction of the direction of current flow, etc. The more theoretical aspects of electrochemistry are presented later in optional sections, where the relationship between thermodynamics and electrochemistry is explored.

CONTENTS

COMPLETE SOLUTIONS TO TESTS

ANSWERS TO MULTIPLE-CHOICE QUESTIONS

1

EQUILIBRIA INVOLVING GASEOUS REACTANTS AND PRODUCTS

Chapter Objectives

1. Define equilibrium, equilibrium constant, and equilibrium position.

2. Write equilibrium expressions using the Law of Mass Action.

3. Calculate the value of K from a given set of equilibrium concentrations.

4. Learn to interconvert between K (in units of concentration) and K_P (in units of pressure).

5. Solve for equilibrium concentrations, given the initial concentrations and one equilibrium concentration.

6. (optional) Solve for equilibrium concentrations (or pressures), given the initial concentrations (or pressures) and the value of K.

7. Use Le Chatelier's Principle to predict shifts in equilibrium position.

1.1 INTRODUCTION

When substances react, the concentrations of reactants and products change continuously until the system reaches chemical equilibrium. At equilibrium, no further changes occur in the concentrations of any reactants or products as a function of time.

Equilibrium occurs because chemical reactions are reversible. To illustrate this concept, consider the very important chemical reaction for the synthesis of ammonia from dinitrogen and dihydrogen:

$$N_2(g) + 3H_2(g) \rightleftarrows 2NH_3(g) \tag{1-1}$$

The double arrows in this equation indicate that $N_2(g)$ and $H_2(g)$ not only can react to

1

form $NH_3(g)$, but that $NH_3(g)$ can decompose to form $N_2(g)$ and $H_2(g)$. When $N_2(g)$ and $H_2(g)$ react in a closed container, the concentrations of these gases will initially decrease, and the concentration of $NH_3(g)$ will increase. As the concentrations of $N_2(g)$ and $H_2(g)$ decrease, fewer $N_2 \cdots H_2$ collisions occur, so that the forward reaction will slow down. At the same time, the increase in NH_3 concentration results in more $NH_3 \cdots NH_3$ collisions and the reverse reaction speeds up. Eventually the forward and reverse rates will become equal, and no further changes occur in the concentrations of either reactants or products. For example, NH_3 is being formed at the same rate as it is being used up, so that no change in its concentration occurs.

The following diagram shows concentration changes for the reaction just described:

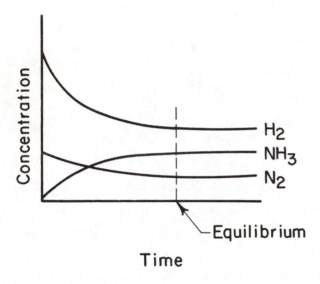

1.2   THE EQUILIBRIUM CONSTANT

One of the most striking properties of equilibrium is its consistency. For example, at equilibrium the concentrations of the substances in reaction (1) always obey the expression

$$K = \frac{[NH_3]^2}{[N_2][H_2]^3}$$

where the square brackets indicate *equilibrium* concentrations in moles/liter. The **equilibrium constant**, K, is a number which is *constant* for this reaction at a particular temperature. At 500°C, its measured value is $K = 6.0 \times 10^{-2} \ \ell^2/mole^2$, which means that for this reaction system at 500°C equilibrium will be achieved when the concentrations are such that

$$\frac{[NH_3]^2}{[N_2][H_2]^3} = 6.0 \times 10^{-2} \frac{\ell^2}{mole^2}$$

Sample Problem 1–1

For a particular experiment involving reaction (1–1), the equilibrium concentrations at 127°C are observed to be

$$[NH_3] = 3.05 \times 10^{-2} \text{ mole}/\ell$$
$$[N_2] = 8.47 \times 10^{-1} \text{ mole}/\ell$$
$$[H_2] = 3.05 \times 10^{-3} \text{ mole}/\ell$$

Calculate the value of K at 127°C.

Solution

The equilibrium expression for this reaction is

$$K = \frac{[NH_3]^2}{[N_2][H_2]^3} = \frac{(3.05 \times 10^{-2})^2}{(8.47 \times 10^{-1})(3.05 \times 10^{-3})^3}$$
$$= 3.87 \times 10^4 \frac{\ell^2}{\text{mole}^2}$$

For a general reaction

$$aA + bB \rightleftarrows cC + dD$$

the equilibrium expression is written

$$K = \frac{[C]^c[D]^d}{[A]^a[B]^b}$$

where the bracketed capital letters represent concentrations of chemical species and the small letters represent the coefficients in the balanced equation. This expression is the **Law of Mass Action,** which states that the equilibrium constant expression is given by the product of the concentrations of the chemical products divided by the product of the concentrations of the reactants, each concentration being raised to the power corresponding to the coefficient of that substance in the balanced chemical equation.

Sample Problem 1–2

A. Consider the reaction

$$2NOCl(g) \rightleftarrows 2NO(g) + Cl_2(g)$$

at 35°C, when 3.00 moles NOCl(g), 1.00 mole NO(g), and 2.00 moles $Cl_2(g)$ are mixed in a 10.0 ℓ flask. After the system has reached equilibrium the concentrations are observed to be:

$$[Cl_2] = 1.52 \times 10^{-1} \text{ mole}/\ell$$
$$[NO] = 4.00 \times 10^{-3} \text{ mole}/\ell$$
$$[NOCl] = 3.96 \times 10^{-1} \text{ mole}/\ell$$

Calculate the value of K for this system at 35°C.

Solution

From the balanced equation for the reaction, the equilibrium expression can be written using the Law of Mass Action:

$$K = \frac{[Cl_2][NO]^2}{[NOCl]^2}$$

Substitute the measured equilibrium concentrations:

$$K = \frac{(1.52 \times 10^{-1} \text{ mole}/\ell)(4.00 \times 10^{-3} \text{ mole}/\ell)^2}{(3.96 \times 10^{-1} \text{ mole}/\ell)^2}$$
$$= 1.55 \times 10^{-5} \text{ mole}/\ell$$

B.   Calculate the value of K for the reaction:

$$Cl_2(g) + 2NO(g) \rightleftarrows 2NOCl(g)$$

Solution

The equilibrium expression for this reaction is

$$K = \frac{[NOCl]^2}{[Cl_2][NO]^2}$$
$$K = \frac{(3.96 \times 10^{-1} \text{ mole}/\ell)^2}{(1.52 \times 10^{-1} \text{ mole}/\ell)(4.00 \times 10^{-3} \text{ mole}/\ell)^2}$$
$$= 6.45 \times 10^4 \text{ } \ell/\text{mole}$$

An easier way to solve this problem is to note that the reaction considered in this problem is the reverse of the reaction in part A, so that the equilibrium expression is the reciprocal of that in part A:

$$K = \frac{1}{1.55 \times 10^{-5} \text{ mole}/\ell} = 6.45 \times 10^4 \text{ } \ell/\text{mole}$$
$$\nwarrow K \text{ value from part A}$$

Problem 1–2 illustrates a useful general principle: When a reaction is reversed,

$$K_{\text{reverse}} = \frac{1}{K_{\text{forward}}}$$

The Equilibrium Constant in Terms of Pressures

Equilibria involving gases can be described in terms of either pressures or concentrations. The relationship between pressure and concentration can be seen from the ideal gas law, $PV = nRT$. Rearrangement of this equation gives

$$P = \frac{n}{V} RT = CRT$$

where $\frac{n}{V}$ represents the concentration of the gas in moles per liter (C). From this expression, it can be seen that

$$P = CRT$$

and

$$C = \frac{P}{RT}$$

For the synthesis of NH_3,

$$K = \frac{[NH_3]^2}{[N_2][H_2]^3} = \frac{C^2_{NH_3}}{C_{N_2} \cdot C^3_{H_2}} = \frac{\left(\dfrac{P_{NH_3}}{RT}\right)^2}{\left(\dfrac{P_{N_2}}{RT}\right)\left(\dfrac{P_{H_2}}{RT}\right)^3} = \frac{P^2_{NH_3}}{P_{N_2} \cdot P^3_{H_2}} \cdot (RT)^2$$

$$= K_P \cdot (RT)^2$$

In this book, K will always represent the equilibrium constant in units of concentration, and K_P will represent the equilibrium constant in units of pressure. In general, K and K_P will not be the same number, since the units are different. The only exception occurs when the sum of the coefficients for the products and the sum of the coefficients for the reactants are the same. In this case, the RT term cancels out. For example, for the reaction

$$H_2(g) + F_2(g) \rightleftharpoons 2HF(g)$$

we find that

$$K = \frac{C^2_{HF}}{C_{H_2} \cdot C_{F_2}} = \frac{\left(\dfrac{P_{HF}}{RT}\right)^2}{\left(\dfrac{P_{H_2}}{RT}\right)\left(\dfrac{P_{F_2}}{RT}\right)} = \frac{P^2_{HF}}{P_{H_2} \cdot P_{F_2}} = K_P$$

Note that K has no units.

Substitution of $P = CRT$ into the equilibrium expression for a general reaction leads to the general relationship between K and K_P:

$$K_P = K(RT)^{\Delta n}$$

where Δn is the sum of the coefficients of the *gaseous* products minus the sum of the coefficients of the *gaseous* reactants.

Sample Problem 1–3

Consider the reaction

$$2NOCl(g) \rightleftarrows 2NO(g) + Cl_2(g)$$

At 25°C a particular experiment showed the equilibrium pressures to be

$$P_{NOCl} = 1.2 \text{ atm}$$
$$P_{NO} = 5.0 \times 10^{-2} \text{ atm}$$
$$P_{Cl_2} = 3.0 \times 10^{-1} \text{ atm}$$

Calculate the values of K_P and K.

Solution

$$K_P = \frac{P_{Cl_2} \cdot P_{NO}^2}{P_{NOCl}^2} = \frac{(3.0 \times 10^{-1} \text{ atm})(5.0 \times 10^{-2} \text{ atm})^2}{(1.2 \text{ atm})^2} = 5.2 \times 10^{-4} \text{ atm}$$

In order to use the Law of Mass Action,

$$K = \frac{[Cl_2][NO]^2}{[NOCl]^2}$$

we must convert the given pressures to concentrations. Using $PV = nRT$, concentration (moles/ℓ) $= \dfrac{n}{V} = \dfrac{P}{RT}$. For example,

$$\text{concentration of } Cl_2 = [Cl_2] = \frac{n_{Cl_2}}{V} = \frac{P_{Cl_2}}{RT}$$

Substituting the appropriate expressions into the equilibrium constant expression,

$$K = \frac{[Cl_2][NO]^2}{[NOCl]^2} = \frac{\left(\dfrac{P_{Cl_2}}{RT}\right)\left(\dfrac{P_{NO}}{RT}\right)^2}{\left(\dfrac{P_{NOCl}}{RT}\right)^2} = \frac{P_{Cl_2} \cdot P_{NO}^2}{P_{NOCl}^2}\left(\frac{1}{RT}\right) = \frac{K_P}{RT}$$

$$R = 0.08206 \frac{\ell \cdot atm}{K \cdot mole} \qquad T = 25°C + 273 = 298 \text{ K}$$

Thus

$$K = \frac{5.2 \times 10^{-4} \text{ atm}}{RT} = \frac{5.2 \times 10^{-4} \text{ atm}}{\left(0.08206 \dfrac{\ell \cdot atm}{K\text{-mole}}\right)(298 \text{ K})} = 2.1 \times 10^{-5} \frac{\text{mole}}{\ell}$$

Now solve this problem using the formula $K_P = K(RT)^{\Delta n}$. In this case, $\Delta n = (2 + 1) - 2 = 1$, so that

$$K_P = K(RT)$$

or

$$K = \frac{K_P}{RT} = 2.1 \times 10^{-5} \text{ mole}/\ell$$

as calculated above.

Reactions Involving Pure Solids or Liquids

When *pure solids* or *liquids* participate in a chemical reaction, they are not included in the equilibrium expression. For example, for the reaction

$$CaCO_3(s) \rightleftarrows CaO(s) + CO_2(g)$$

the equilibrium expression is simply

$$K = [CO_2]$$

The solids, $CaCO_3$ and CaO, are not included.

TEST 1–1

A. Define equilibrium.

B. Write the equilibrium expression for each of the following reactions:
   1. $2SO_2(g) + O_2(g) \rightleftarrows 2SO_3(g)$
   2. $3O_2(g) \rightleftarrows 2O_3(g)$
   3. $4NH_3(g) + 7O_2(g) \rightleftarrows 4NO_2(g) + 6H_2O(g)$
   4. $Fe_2O_3(s) + 3H_2(g) \rightleftarrows 2Fe(s) + 3H_2O(g)$

C. Consider the hypothetical reaction

$$A(g) + 2B(g) \rightleftarrows 3C(g) + 2D(g)$$

   1. Write the equilibrium expression.
   2. A set of equilibrium concentrations for this system at 298 K is
       $[A]$ = 0.35 mole/ℓ
       $[B]$ = 0.20 mole/ℓ
       $[C]$ = 1.0 mole/ℓ
       $[D]$ = 0.50 mole/ℓ
      a. Calculate K for this system at 298 K.
      b. Calculate K_P for this system at 298 K.

1.3   SOLVING FOR EQUILIBRIUM CONCENTRATIONS

So far the problems that have been illustrated have involved the calculation of the value of an equilibrium constant from given equilibrium concentrations. Another common type of problem involves calculation of one or more equilibrium concentrations.

These problems will be classified into two categories that require different mathematical manipulations. Your instructor will indicate which types of problems you should be able to solve.

Type I   The given information is:
   1. the initial concentrations (*the concentrations before the system adjusts to come to equilibrium*), and
   2. one equilibrium concentration.
These problems can be solved by using the stoichiometry of the balanced chemical equation. No algebra is required.

Type II   The given information is:
   1. the initial concentrations, and
   2. the value of the equilibrium constant.
The solution of these problems requires algebraic manipulations.

In solving both types of problems, these steps will be followed:
   1. Write the reaction and the equilibrium constant expression.
   2. Write down the initial concentrations.
   3. Determine the change required to reach equilibrium.
   4. Calculate the equilibrium concentrations by applying the change to the initial concentrations.

1.4   SOLVING EQUILIBRIUM PROBLEMS—TYPE I

Principles for solving equilibrium problems will be developed in this section by considering examples where the given information consists of:
   1. the initial concentrations, and
   2. the equilibrium concentration of one reactant or product.
Using these data, the equilibrium concentrations of the remaining reactants and products and the value of the equilibrium constant will be calculated.

Consider again the synthesis of ammonia:

$$N_2(g) + 3H_2(g) \rightleftarrows 2NH_3(g)$$

Sample Problem 1–4

In a certain experiment, 1.000 mole of $N_2(g)$ and 1.000 mole of $H_2(g)$ were placed in a 1.000 ℓ flask at 500°C and allowed to react. After the system had reached equilibrium, the flask was found to contain 0.921 mole of N_2. Calculate the equilibrium concentrations of H_2 and NH_3.

Solution

Since the equilibrium constant expression involves concentrations and not moles, first convert from moles to moles/ℓ. This is a trival operation in this case since the volume is 1.000 ℓ:

$$\text{Initial concentration of } N_2 = [N_2]_0 = \frac{1.000 \text{ mole}}{1.000 \; \ell} = 1.000 \text{ mole/}\ell$$

The subscript "$_0$" means that the concentration is an initial rather than an equilibrium concentration.

For H_2 and NH_3, the initial concentrations are

$$[H_2]_0 = \frac{1.000 \text{ mole}}{1.000 \; \ell} = 1.000 \text{ mole/}\ell$$
$$[NH_3]_0 = 0$$

After the system has reached equilibrium, 0.921 mole of N_2 remains:

$$\text{Equil. concentration of } N_2 = [N_2] = \frac{0.921 \text{ mole}}{1.000 \; \ell} = 0.921 \text{ mole/}\ell$$

The equilibrium concentrations of H_2 and NH_3 are still unknown and must be calculated. This can be done by using the stoichiometry defined by the balanced equation

$$N_2(g) + 3H_2(g) \rightleftarrows 2NH_3(g)$$

This equation shows that 1 mole of N_2 reacts with 3 moles of H_2 to produce 2 moles of NH_3.

In this problem, how much N_2 has been consumed? The amount of N_2 changes from 1.000 mole to 0.921 mole as the system proceeds to equilibrium. Thus $1.000 - 0.921 = 0.079$ mole of N_2 has reacted. The number of moles of H_2 consumed can be calculated using normal stoichiometric procedures:

$$0.079 \text{ mole } N_2 \times \frac{3 \text{ moles } H_2}{1 \text{ mole } N_2} = 0.237 \text{ mole } H_2 \text{ consumed}$$

Similarly, the amount of NH_3 produced can be calculated:

$$0.079 \text{ mole } N_2 \times \frac{2 \text{ moles } NH_3}{1 \text{ mole } N_2} = 0.158 \text{ mole } NH_3 \text{ produced}$$

What are the equilibrium concentrations of NH_3 and H_2? The flask originally contained no NH_3, so the amount of NH_3 present at equilibrium is 0.158 mole. Since the volume is 1.000 ℓ, at equilibrium

$$[NH_3] = [NH_3]_0 \text{ plus} \left(\begin{array}{l} \text{the change needed to} \\ \text{reach equilibrium} \end{array} \right) = 0 + 0.158 \text{ mole}/\ell$$

The original 1.000 mole of hydrogen present has been reduced by 0.237 mole; at equilibrium

$$[H_2] = [H_2]_0 \text{ plus} \left(\begin{array}{l} \text{the change to reach} \\ \text{equilibrium} \end{array} \right) = 1.000 \text{ mole}/\ell - 0.237 \text{ mole}/\ell$$
$$= 0.763 \text{ mole}/\ell$$

Note that the change in H_2 is negative since H_2 is consumed to reach equilibrium.

TEST 1–2

In a certain experiment, 1.000 mole of NH_3 was placed in an empty 1.000 ℓ flask at 500°C. After equilibrium was reached, 0.399 mole of N_2 was found to be in the flask. Calculate the concentrations of NH_3 and H_2 at equilibrium.

Sample Problem 1–5

In an experiment, 2.00 moles of N_2, 1.00 mole of H_2 and 3.00 moles of NH_3 were mixed in a 1.00 ℓ flask at 500°C. At equilibrium, 2.77 moles of H_2 were found to be present in the flask. Calculate the concentrations of N_2 and NH_3 at equilibrium.

Solution

In this experiment, the amount of H_2 changes from 1.00 mole to 2.77 moles. Thus 2.77 − 1.00 = 1.77 moles of H_2 have been formed as the system proceeds to equilibrium. For this to occur, NH_3 must have been consumed to produce N_2 and H_2. The number of moles of N_2 produced can be calculated:

$$1.77 \text{ moles } H_2 \times \frac{1 \text{ mole } N_2}{3 \text{ moles } H_2} = 0.590 \text{ mole } N_2 \text{ produced.}$$

Since the volume is 1.00 ℓ, 0.590 mole/ℓ of N_2 was formed to reach equilibrium. The concentration of N_2 at equilibrium is given by the initial concentration plus the change to reach equilibrium:

$$[N_2] = [N_2]_0 + \text{change} = 2.00 \text{ moles/}\ell + 0.590 \text{ mole/}\ell$$
$$= 2.59 \text{ moles/}\ell$$

The number of moles of NH_3 consumed is given by

$$1.77 \text{ moles H}_2 \times \frac{2 \text{ moles NH}_3}{3 \text{ moles H}_2} = 1.18 \text{ moles NH}_3 \text{ consumed.}$$

Since the volume is 1.00 ℓ, 1.18 moles/ℓ of NH_3 are consumed. At equilibrium:

$$[NH_3] = [NH_3]_0 \text{ plus change} = 3.00 \text{ moles/}\ell - 1.18 \text{ moles/}\ell$$
$$= 1.82 \text{ moles/}\ell$$

Summary

In doing problems of the type considered above, it is best to proceed as follows:
1. Write the equilibrium constant expression.
2. Write down the initial concentrations.
3. Calculate the change required to reach equilibrium.
4. Apply the change to the initial concentrations to obtain the equilibrium concentrations.

Calculations Involving Pressures

Note that equlibria involving pressures rather than concentrations can be solved using the procedures introduced above, since at constant T, pressure is proportional to concentration for an ideal gas.

TEST 1–3

A quantity of $N_2O_4(g)$ is introduced into a flask at an initial pressure of 2.0 atm at temperature T. After the $N_2O_4(g)$ has decomposed to $NO_2(g)$ and has come to equilibrium, the pressure of N_2O_4 is 1.8 atm. Calculate the value of K_P for the process

$$N_2O_4(g) \rightleftarrows 2NO_2(g)$$

at temperature T.

A. Set up the expression for K_P in terms of the pressures of $N_2O_4(g)$ and $NO_2(g)$.

B. Calculate the pressure of $N_2O_4(g)$ consumed when the reaction comes to equilibrium and the equilibrium pressure of $N_2O_4(g)$.

C. What is the pressure of $NO_2(g)$ formed to reach equilibrium?

D. Calculate K_P using the equilibrium pressures of $NO_2(g)$ and $N_2O_4(g)$.

1.5   THE EQUILIBRIUM POSITION

It is important to recognize that although the special *ratio* of the concentrations of products to reactants defined by the equilibrium constant expression is constant, the equilibrium concentrations will not always be the same. To illustrate this point, consider the results of the calculations carried out in Sample Problems 1–4 and 1–5 and in Test 1–2. These are summarized in Table 1–1.

TEST 1–4

Show that the ratio $\dfrac{[NH_3]^2}{[H_2]^3[N_2]}$ is constant at equilibrium for each of the situations shown in Table 1–1.

Table 1–1   Initial and Equilibrium Concentrations in the Ammonia Synthesis Reaction

Experiment	Initial Concentrations	Equilibrium Concentrations
I	$[N_2]_0 = 1.000$ mole/ℓ $[H_2]_0 = 1.000$ mole/ℓ $[NH_3]_0 = 0$	$[N_2] = 0.921$ mole/ℓ $[H_2] = 0.763$ mole/ℓ $[NH_3] = 0.158$ mole/ℓ
II	$[N_2]_0 = 0$ $[H_2]_0 = 0$ $[NH_3]_0 = 1.000$ mole/ℓ	$[N_2] = 0.399$ mole/ℓ $[H_2] = 1.197$ moles/ℓ $[NH_3] = 0.202$ mole/ℓ
III	$[N_2]_0 = 2.00$ moles/ℓ $[H_2]_0 = 1.00$ mole/ℓ $[NH_3]_0 = 3.00$ moles/ℓ	$[N_2] = 2.59$ moles/ℓ $[H_2] = 2.77$ moles/ℓ $[NH_3] = 1.82$ moles/ℓ

From the results of Test 1–4, note that the ratio $\dfrac{[NH_3]^2}{[N_2][H_2]^3}$ is constant within errors caused by round-off for these experiments, even though the equilibrium concentrations are quite different for different experiments.

Each set of equilibrium concentrations is called an **equilibrium position.** It is very important to distinguish between an equilibrium position and the equilibrium constant. The equilibrium position depends on the initial concentrations, but the equilibrium constant is always the same at a given temperature. There are an infinite number of equilibrium positions, depending on the initial conditions, but only one equilibrium constant for a given reaction system at a given temperature.

TEST 1–5

Consider the reaction

$$2SO_2(g) + O_2(g) \rightleftarrows 2SO_3(g)$$

at 600°C.

A. In a certain experiment, 2.00 moles of SO_2, 1.50 moles of O_2, and 3.00 moles of SO_3 were placed in a 1.00 ℓ vessel. After the system reached equilibrium, 3.50 moles of SO_3 were found to be present.
Calculate
1. The equilibrium concentrations of O_2 and SO_2.
2. K.
3. K_P.

B. In a different experiment at the same temperature (600°C), 0.500 mole of SO_2 and 0.350 mole of SO_3 were mixed in a 1.000 ℓ container. When the system reached equilibrium, 0.045 mole of O_2 was found to be present.
Calculate
1. The equilibrium concentrations of SO_2 and SO_3.
2. K.

1.6   THE REACTION QUOTIENT

The strategy that has been developed for solving equilibrium problems involves writing the initial concentrations and then defining the change in concentration needed to reach equilibrium. To do this, the direction of the shift from initial to equilibrium concentrations must be known.

Determination of the direction of the shift is easy when the initial concentration of a reactant or a product is zero. On the other hand, in problems where all initial concentrations are non-zero, the direction of the adjustment to equilibrium may not be obvious.

To determine the direction of the shift in such cases, the **reaction quotient**, Q, will be used. The reaction quotient has the same form as the equilibrium constant expression except that *initial* concentrations are used instead of equilibrium concentrations. For the synthesis of ammonia, $N_2(g) + 3H_2(g) \rightleftarrows 2NH_3(g)$,

$$Q = \frac{[NH_3]_0^2}{[N_2]_0[H_2]_0^3}$$

To determine in which direction the system will proceed from the initial concentrations toward equilibrium, one needs to compare Q and K.

1. Q is greater than K.

    If Q is greater than K, the ratio of initial concentrations of products to reactants is too large. To reach equilibrium, products must be changed to reactants. The system proceeds to the left (consuming products, forming reactants) to reach equilibrium. In this case, the system shifts to the left.

2. Q is less than K.

    If Q is less than K, the system must proceed in the direction of more products to reach equilibrium. In this case, the system shifts to the right.

3. Q is equal to K.

    The initial concentrations are equilibrium concentrations. No shift will occur.

Sample Problem 1–6

For the synthesis of ammonia, the value of K is 6×10^{-2} ℓ^2/mole^2 at 500°C. In an experiment, 0.50 mole of $N_2(g)$, 1.0×10^{-2} mole of $H_2(g)$, and 1.0×10^{-4} mole of $NH_3(g)$ are mixed at 500°C in a 1.0 ℓ flask. In which direction will the system proceed to reach equilibrium?

Solution

The initial concentrations are:

$$[NH_3]_0 = 1.0 \times 10^{-4} \text{ mole}/\ell$$
$$[N_2]_0 = 5.0 \times 10^{-1} \text{ mole}/\ell$$
$$[H_2]_0 = 1.0 \times 10^{-2} \text{ mole}/\ell$$

Calculate the reaction quotient:

$$Q = \frac{[NH_3]_0^2}{[N_2]_0[H_2]_0^3} = \frac{(1.0 \times 10^{-4})^2}{(5.0 \times 10^{-1})(1.0 \times 10^{-2})^3} = 2.0 \times 10^{-2} \text{ } \ell^2/\text{mole}^2$$
$$K = 6 \times 10^{-2} \text{ } \ell^2/\text{mole}^2$$

Thus Q is less than K and the system will proceed to the right (N_2 and H_2 consumed, NH_3 formed) to reach equilibrium.

TEST 1–6

Consider the reaction

$$2NOCl(g) \rightleftharpoons 2NO(g) + Cl_2(g)$$

where $K = 1.55 \times 10^{-5}$ mole/ℓ at 35°C. In an experiment, 1.0×10^{-1} mole of $NOCl(g)$, 1.0×10^{-3} mole of $NO(g)$, and 1.0×10^{-4} mole of $Cl_2(g)$ are mixed at 35°C in a 2.0 ℓ flask. In which direction will the system proceed to reach equilibrium?

1.7   SOLVING EQUILIBRIUM PROBLEMS—TYPE II (optional)

In this section, techniques will be developed for solving problems where the given information is:
1.   the initial concentrations, and
2.   the value of K.

Sample Problem 1–7

At 700 K, carbon monoxide reacts with water to form carbon dioxide and hydrogen:

$$CO(g) + H_2O(g) \rightleftharpoons CO_2(g) + H_2(g)$$

The equilibrium constant for this reaction at 700 K is 5.10.

Consider an experiment in which 1.00 mole of $CO(g)$ and 1.00 mole of $H_2O(g)$ are mixed together in a 1.00 ℓ flask at 700 K. Calculate the concentrations of all species at equilibrium.

Solution

The first step in solving equilibrium problems is to write the equilibrium expression. In this case

$$K = \frac{[CO_2][H_2]}{[CO][H_2O]} = 5.10$$

Next write down the initial concentrations:

$$[CO]_0 = \frac{1.00 \text{ mole}}{1.00 \ell} = 1.00 \text{ mole}/\ell$$
$$[H_2O]_0 = \frac{1.00 \text{ mole}}{1.00 \ell} = 1.00 \text{ mole}/\ell$$
$$[CO_2]_0 = 0$$
$$[H_2]_0 = 0$$

It is clear that for this system to reach equilibrium it must proceed to the right (some CO_2 and H_2 will be formed by consuming some CO and H_2O). The key question is: How much CO_2 and H_2 will form as the system comes to equilibrium?

To consider this question systematically, use algebraic techniques. As is customary in algebra, assign the symbol x to the unknown quantity. In this problem, the amounts of CO_2 and H_2 formed to reach equilibrium are the unknown quantities. Let x equal the number of moles per liter of CO_2 formed to reach equilibrium.

If x moles per liter of CO_2 have been formed, how much H_2 will be present? Since CO_2 and H_2 are formed in equal amounts, x moles/ℓ of H_2 will be formed.

How much CO is consumed to form x moles/ℓ of CO_2 and H_2? Since all the coefficients in the balanced equation are 1, x moles/ℓ of CO are consumed, as well as x moles/ℓ of H_2O. Thus, at equilibrium, the concentrations of reactants and products present are:

Concentration of substance at equilibrium = concentration initially present + change

$$[CO] = [CO]_0 - x = 1.00 \text{ mole}/\ell - x \text{ mole}/\ell$$
$$[H_2O] = [H_2O]_0 - x = 1.00 \text{ mole}/\ell - x \text{ mole}/\ell$$
$$[CO_2] = [CO_2]_0 + x = 0 + x \text{ mole}/\ell$$
$$[H_2] = [H_2]_0 + x = 0 + x \text{ mole}/\ell$$

The ratio of these equilibrium concentrations must give the equilibrium constant:

$$K = 5.10 = \frac{[CO_2]\,[H_2]}{[CO]\,[H_2O]} = \frac{(x)\,(x)}{(1.00 - x)\,(1.00 - x)} = \frac{x^2}{(1.00 - x)^2}$$

Taking the square root of both sides gives

$$\frac{x}{1 - x} = \sqrt{5.10} = 2.26$$
$$x = 2.26 - 2.26x$$
$$3.26x = 2.26$$
$$x = 0.69 \text{ mole}/\ell$$

Thus the equilibrium concentrations are

$$[CO_2] = x = 0.69 \text{ mole}/\ell$$
$$[H_2] = x = 0.69 \text{ mole}/\ell$$
$$[H_2O] = 1.00 - x = 0.31 \text{ mole}/\ell$$
$$[CO] = 1.00 - x = 0.31 \text{ mole}/\ell$$

TEST 1–7

Consider the reaction at 700 K:

$$CO(g) + H_2O(g) \rightleftarrows CO_2(g) + H_2(g), \qquad K = 5.10$$

Calculate the equilibrium concentrations of all reactants and products in an experiment where 3.00 moles of $CO(g)$ and 3.00 moles of $H_2O(g)$ are mixed in a 1.00 ℓ flask at 700 K.

Sample Problem 1–8

Consider the reaction

$$H_2(g) + F_2(g) \rightleftarrows 2HF(g)$$

at a temperature where $K = 1.15 \times 10^2$. In an experiment, 3.00 moles of H_2 and 6.00 moles of F_2 are mixed in a 3.00 ℓ container. Calculate the equilibrium concentrations of H_2, F_2, and HF.

Solution

The equilibrium constant expression is

$$K = 1.15 \times 10^2 = \frac{[HF]^2}{[H_2][F_2]}$$

The initial concentrations are

$$[H_2]_0 = \frac{3.00 \text{ moles}}{3.00 \ \ell} = 1.00 \text{ mole}/\ell$$

$$[F_2]_0 = \frac{6.00 \text{ moles}}{3.00 \ \ell} = 2.00 \text{ moles}/\ell$$

$$[HF]_0 = 0$$

Now define the change required to reach equilibrium. In this case, since no HF is initially present, some H_2 and F_2 will react to form HF.

Let x be the concentration of H_2 consumed. Using the stoichiometry of the reaction:

$$H_2 \quad + \quad F_2 \quad \rightarrow \quad 2HF$$
$$x \text{ mole}/\ell \ H_2 + x \text{ mole}/\ell \ F_2 \rightarrow 2x \text{ moles}/\ell \ HF$$

These are the changes in concentration required to reach equilibrium.

Now write the equilibrium concentrations:

$$[H_2] = [H_2]_0 + \text{change} = 1.00 \text{ mole}/\ell - x \text{ mole}/\ell$$
$$[F_2] = [F_2]_0 + \text{change} = 2.00 \text{ moles}/\ell - x \text{ mole}/\ell$$
$$[HF] = [HF]_0 + \text{change} = 0 + 2x \text{ moles}/\ell$$

To solve for the value of x, substitute these concentrations in the equilibrium expression:

$$K = 1.15 \times 10^2 = \frac{[HF]^2}{[H_2][F_2]} = \frac{(2x)^2}{(1.00 - x)(2.00 - x)}$$

Note that this expression cannot be solved by taking the square root of both sides, since the denominator is not a perfect square.

To solve for x, first multiply out the terms:

$$1.15 \times 10^2 = \frac{(2x)^2}{(1.00 - x)(2.00 - x)} = \frac{4x^2}{2.00 - 3.00x + x^2}$$
$$(1.15 \times 10^2)(2.00 - 3.00x + x^2) = 4x^2$$
$$(2.30 \times 10^2) - (3.45 \times 10^2)x + (1.15 \times 10^2)x^2 = 4x^2$$

Subtracting $4x^2$ from both sides and rearranging gives

$$(1.11 \times 10^2)x^2 - (3.45 \times 10^2)x + (2.30 \times 10^2) = 0$$

This is a quadratic equation, which has the general form

$$ax^2 + bx + c = 0$$

The solutions to an equation of this type can be obtained from the formula

$$x = \frac{-b \pm \sqrt{b^2 - 4ac}}{2a}$$

where a and b are the coefficients of x^2 and x, respectively, and c is the constant in the general equation. In the quadratic equation above,

$$a = 1.11 \times 10^2$$
$$b = -3.45 \times 10^2$$
$$c = 2.30 \times 10^2$$

Thus

$$x = \frac{-(-3.45 \times 10^2) \pm \sqrt{(-3.45 \times 10^2)^2 - (4)(1.11 \times 10^2)(2.30 \times 10^2)}}{2(1.11 \times 10^2)}$$

$$= \frac{3.45 \times 10^2 \pm \sqrt{1.19 \times 10^5 - 1.02 \times 10^5}}{2.22 \times 10^2}$$

$$= \frac{3.45 \times 10^2 \pm \sqrt{1.7 \times 10^4}}{2.22 \times 10^2} = \frac{3.45 \times 10^2 \pm 1.30 \times 10^2}{2.22 \times 10^2}$$

The two roots are

$$x = \frac{3.45 \times 10^2 + 1.30 \times 10^2}{2.22 \times 10^2} = 2.14 \text{ moles}/\ell$$

$$x = \frac{3.45 \times 10^2 - 1.30 \times 10^2}{2.22 \times 10^2} = 0.968 \text{ mole}/\ell$$

In this situation, there is only one correct value of x (there is only one equilibrium position which results from these initial concentrations). Which value of x is correct?

The correct value can be chosen by looking at the equilibrium concentrations. Since

$$[H_2] = 1.00 - x$$

the value $x = 2.14$ gives a negative number for the concentration of H_2. This is physically impossible. Therefore, $x = 0.968$ mole/ℓ must be the correct root.

Now compute the equilibrium concentrations:

$$[H_2] = 1.00 - x = 1.00 - 0.968 = 3.2 \times 10^{-2} \text{ mole}/\ell$$
$$[F_2] = 2.00 - x = 2.00 - 0.968 = 1.03 \text{ mole}/\ell$$
$$[HF] = 2x = 2(0.968) = 1.94 \text{ mole}/\ell$$

After solving the quadratic equation, it is wise to check the correctness of the computed concentrations. This can be done by substituting into the equilibrium constant expression:

$$\frac{[HF]^2}{[H_2][F_2]} = \frac{(1.94)^2}{(3.2 \times 10^{-2})(1.03)} = 114$$

The given value of K is 115. Thus there is agreement within the error caused by round-off, and the calculated concentrations are shown to be correct.

TEST 1–8

Consider the reaction

$$H_2(g) + I_2(g) \rightleftarrows 2HI(g)$$

at a temperature where $K = 60.0$. In an experiment, 1.50 moles of H_2 and 2.50 moles of I_2 are placed in a 1.00 ℓ flask. Calculate the equilibrium concentrations of H_2, I_2, and HI.

Next, problems in which none of the initial concentrations are zero will be considered. To solve these problems:
1. calculate the reaction quotient, Q,
2. determine the direction of the shift to equilibrium,
3. define the change required to reach equilibrium, and
4. calculate the equilibrium concentrations.

Sample Problem 1–9

Consider the reaction

$$2HF(g) \rightleftarrows H_2(g) + F_2(g)$$

where $K = 1.0 \times 10^{-2}$ at some very high temperature. In an experiment, 5.00 moles of HF(g), 0.500 mole of $H_2(g)$, and 0.750 mole of $F_2(g)$ are mixed in a 5.00 ℓ flask and allowed to react to equilibrium.

A. Write the equilibrium constant expression.

Solution

$$K = \frac{[H_2][F_2]}{[HF]^2} = 1.0 \times 10^{-2}$$

B. Calculate the initial concentrations.

Solution

$$[HF]_0 = \frac{5.00 \text{ moles}}{5.00 \ \ell} = 1.00 \text{ mole}/\ell$$

$$[F_2]_0 = \frac{0.750 \text{ mole}}{5.00 \ \ell} = 0.150 \text{ mole}/\ell$$

$$[H_2]_0 = \frac{0.500 \text{ mole}}{5.00 \text{ } \ell} = 0.100 \text{ mole/}\ell$$

C. Calculate Q and determine in which direction the reaction will shift to reach equilibrium.

Solution

$$Q = \frac{[F_2]_0[H_2]_0}{[HF]_0^2} = \frac{(0.150)\,(0.100)}{(1.00)^2} = 1.50 \times 10^{-2}$$

Q is larger than K. To come to equilibrium, the system must shift to the left (i.e., the numerator must get smaller and the denominator larger).

D. Define the change required to reach equilibrium.

Solution

Let x be the moles/ℓ of H_2 consumed to reach equilibrium. Note that x moles/ℓ of F_2 will also be consumed and that $2x$ moles/ℓ of HF will be formed.

E. Define the equilibrium concentrations of all species.

Solution

$$[H_2] = [H_2]_0 - x = 0.100 - x$$
$$[F_2] = [F_2]_0 - x = 0.150 - x$$
$$[HF] = [HF]_0 + 2x = 1.00 + 2x$$

F. Solve for x and calculate the equilibrium concentrations.

Solution

$$1.00 \times 10^{-2} = \frac{[H_2]\,[F_2]}{[HF]^2} = \frac{(0.100 - x)\,(0.150 - x)}{(1.00 + 2x)^2}$$

Multiplying and collecting terms gives

$$0.960x^2 - 0.290x + 5.00 \times 10^{-3} = 0$$

This is a quadratic equation where

$$a = 0.960$$
$$b = -0.290$$
$$c = 5.00 \times 10^{-3}$$

Use the quadratic formula to solve for x.

$$x = \frac{-b \pm \sqrt{b^2 - 4ac}}{2a} = \frac{-(-0.290) \pm \sqrt{(-0.290)^2 - 4(0.960)\,(5.00 \times 10^{-3})}}{2(0.960)}$$

Solving for x gives the roots

$$x = 0.284 \text{ mole/}\ell$$
$$x = 0.018 \text{ mole/}\ell$$

Since $[H_2] = 0.100 - x$, the root $x = 0.284$ cannot be correct. Thus

$$x = 0.018 \text{ mole/}\ell$$

is the appropriate root. The equilibrium concentrations are

$$[H_2] = [H_2]_0 - x = 0.100 \text{ mole/}\ell - 0.018 \text{ mole/}\ell = 0.082 \text{ mole/}\ell$$
$$[F_2] = [F_2]_0 - x = 0.150 \text{ mole/}\ell - 0.018 \text{ mole/}\ell = 0.132 \text{ mole/}\ell$$
$$[HF] = [HF]_0 + 2x = 1.00 \text{ mole/}\ell + 2(0.018 \text{ mole/}\ell) = 1.04 \text{ mole/}\ell$$

TEST 1–9

Consider the reaction:

$$PCl_5(g) \rightleftarrows PCl_3(g) + Cl_2(g) \qquad K = 5.0 \times 10^{-2} \text{ mole/}\ell \text{ at } 240°C.$$

In an experiment, 0.200 mole of $PCl_5(g)$, 0.500 mole of $PCl_3(g)$, and 0.300 mole of $Cl_2(g)$ are mixed in a 2.00 ℓ vessel.

A. Calculate the initial concentrations.

B. Calculate Q using these initial concentrations.

C. Which way does the system adjust to reach equilibrium?

D. Define the change needed to reach equilibrium in terms of x.

E. Define the equilibrium concentrations in terms of x.

F. Substitute the equilibrium values into the equilibrium expression and solve for x.

G. Calculate the equilibrium concentrations of $PCl_5(g)$, $PCl_3(g)$, and $Cl_2(g)$.

Calculations Involving Pressures

Sample Problem 1–10

Consider the reaction

$$N_2O_4(g) \rightleftarrows 2NO_2(g)$$

at a temperature where $K_P = 0.131$ atm. A flask initially contains $N_2O_4(g)$ at 1.000 atm pressure. Calculate the pressures of $NO_2(g)$ and $N_2O_4(g)$ at equilibrium.

Solution

Note that the usual steps are followed for this problem, but are condensed:

$$N_2O_4(g) \rightleftarrows 2NO_2(g) \qquad K_P = \frac{P_{NO_2}^2}{P_{N_2O_4}} = 0.131$$

Initial Pressures   *Equilibrium Pressures*

$P_{N_2O_4}^0 = 1.000$ atm $\xrightarrow[\text{of NO}_2 \text{ to come to equilibrium}]{\text{Let } x \text{ atm of N}_2\text{O}_4 \text{ react to form } 2x \text{ atm}}$ $P_{N_2O_4} = 1.000 - x$

$P_{NO_2}^0 = 0$ $P_{NO_2} = 2x$

$$0.131 = K_P = \frac{P_{NO_2}^2}{P_{N_2O_4}} = \frac{(2x)^2}{(1.000 - x)}$$

Multiplying and collecting terms gives the quadratic equation:

$$4x^2 + 0.131x - 0.131 = 0$$

where $a = 4$, $b = 0.131$, and $c = -0.131$. Use of the quadratic formula gives

$$x = 0.165 \text{ atm (and an } extraneous \text{ root, } x = -0.198 \text{ atm)}$$

The equilibrium pressures are:

$$P_{N_2O_4} = 1.000 - x = 0.835 \text{ atm}$$
$$P_{NO_2} = 2x = 2(0.165) = 0.330 \text{ atm}$$

1.8   LeCHATELIER'S PRINCIPLE

A system will remain at equilibrium unless disturbed in some way. Since certain types of "disturbances" often occur, it is useful to be able to predict in which direction the position of the equilibrium will shift when disturbed. This prediction may be made in terms of LeChatelier's Principle:

If a stress is applied to a system at equilibrium, the position of the equilibrium will shift in the direction which reduces the stress.

Several types of stresses (disturbances) will be considered:
A.   Addition or removal of reactants or products.
B.   Change in pressure by
    1.   change in volume or
    2.   addition of an inert gas.
C.   Change in temperature.
The effects of these stresses are explained in the following problem.

Sample Problem 1–11

A 1.000 ℓ vessel contains $N_2(g)$, $H_2(g)$, and $NH_3(g)$ at equilibrium. The reaction is exothermic (heat is produced).

$$3H_2(g) + N_2(g) \rightleftarrows 2NH_3(g)$$

The concentrations are:

$$[N_2] = 0.921 \text{ mole/}\ell$$
$$[H_2] = 0.763 \text{ mole/}\ell$$
$$[NH_3] = 0.158 \text{ mole/}\ell$$

A.   Predict the effect on the equilibrium position of adding 1.000 mole of H_2.

Solution

The stress is the added H_2 which, according to LeChatelier's Principle, will cause the position of the equilibrium to shift to the right, consuming H_2 and relieving the stress. This effect can be rationalized in terms of the reaction quotient. Immediately after addition of H_2, the system is no longer at equilibrium. The concentrations at that point can be considered to be initial concentrations:

$$[N_2]_0 = 0.921 \text{ mole/}\ell$$
$$[NH_3]_0 = 0.158 \text{ mole/}\ell$$
$$[H_2]_0 = 0.763 \text{ mole/}\ell + 1.000 \text{ mole/}\ell$$
$$Q = \frac{[NH_3]_0^2}{[N_2]_0[H_2]_0}$$

Since $[H_2]_0$ is greater than the concentration of H_2 in the system formerly at equilibrium, Q will be smaller than K, and the system will adjust to the right.

Experimental results confirm this conjecture. The new equilibrium concentrations show an increase in $[NH_3]$ and a decrease in $[N_2]$. The details are summarized below.

Equilibrium Position I		*Equilibrium Position II*
$[NH_3] = 0.158$ mole/ℓ	add	$[NH_3] = 0.378$ mole/ℓ
$[N_2] = 0.921$ mole/ℓ	$\xrightarrow{\text{1.000 mole}}$	$[N_2] = 0.811$ mole/ℓ
$[H_2] = 0.763$ mole/ℓ	H_2	$[H_2] = 1.433$ moles/ℓ

Note that this shows the shift to the right (toward NH_3).

B. Predict the effect of adding 1.000 mole of $NH_3(g)$ to the system.

Solution

The equilibrium position will shift to the left, since the stress is applied to the right side of the equation (Q will be larger than K).

C. Predict the effect of suddenly halving the volume (increasing the pressure).

Solution

The stress applied is reducing the volume. To relieve this stress, the system will shift in a direction which reduces its own volume. This can be done by a shift to the right, since the right side of the equation involves fewer molecules of gas, and thus lower volume.

D. Predict the effect of increasing pressure by adding $He(g)$. Assume ideal behavior for all gases.

Solution

There will be no effect on the equilibrium position. Ideal gas molecules have negligible volumes. Thus the addition of $He(g)$ does not change the volume, and since He is not involved in the reaction, the concentrations of reacting molecules are unaffected. The equilibrium position remains unchanged.

E. Predict the effect of increasing the temperature.

Solution

The equilibrium will shift to the left.

This situation is more complicated than those discussed above because the *value of K* changes with temperature. The other disturbances which have been considered (addition or removal of reactants or products and change in pressure) *do not* change the value of K. However, LeChatelier's Principle can be used in this case by considering heat to be a reactant or product. The reaction is exothermic, which can be shown by treating heat as a product.

$$3H_2(g) + N_2(g) \rightleftarrows 2NH_3(g) + \text{Heat}$$

The temperature is increased by adding heat. LeChatelier's Principle predicts that the equilibrium position will shift to the left, consuming some of the added heat. Note that this shift to the left will decrease $[NH_3]$ and increase $[H_2]$ and $[N_2]$ so that K becomes smaller as the temperature is increased. (The opposite effect occurs for an endothermic reaction, where heat may be considered a reactant.)

TEST 1–10

Consider the reaction system

$$2NO_2(g) \rightleftarrows N_2(g) + 2O_2(g)$$

which is exothermic. A vessel contains $NO_2(g)$, $N_2(g)$, and $O_2(g)$ at equilibrium. Predict how each of the following stresses will affect the equilibrium position.

A. $NO_2(g)$ is added.

B. $N_2(g)$ is removed.

C. The volume is halved.

D. $He(g)$ is added.

E. The temperature is increased.

Exercises

1. Give the equilibrium constant expression for each of the following.
   a. $2H_2(g) + O_2(g) \rightleftarrows 2H_2O(g)$
   b. $SnO_2(s) + 2H_2(g) \rightleftarrows Sn(s) + 2H_2O(g)$
   c. $4NH_3(g) + 7O_2(g) \rightarrow 4NO_2(g) + 6H_2O(g)$

For exercises 2–5, consider the reaction

$$PCl_3(g) + Cl_2(g) \rightleftarrows PCl_5(g)$$

2. Write the equilibrium expression.

3. At a certain temperature, the following equilibrium concentrations were observed:

$$[Cl_2] = 2.0 \times 10^{-3} \text{ mole/}\ell$$
$$[PCl_3] = 3.0 \times 10^{-1} \text{ mole/}\ell$$
$$[PCl_5] = 6.7 \times 10^{-3} \text{ mole/}\ell$$

   a. Calculate the value of K at this temperature.

   b. Calculate the value of K for the reaction

$$PCl_5(g) \rightleftarrows PCl_3(g) + Cl_2(g)$$

   at the same temperature.

4. $Cl_2(g)$, $PCl_3(g)$, and $PCl_5(g)$ are mixed at the following concentrations at the same temperature as in exercise 3:

$$[Cl_2]_0 = 5.0 \times 10^{-4}\ \text{mole}/\ell$$
$$[PCl_3]_0 = 6.3 \times 10^{-2}\ \text{mole}/\ell$$
$$[PCl_5]_0 = 3.8 \times 10^{-3}\ \text{mole}/\ell$$

In which direction will the system shift to reach equilibrium?

5. $Cl_2(g)$, $PCl_3(g)$, and $PCl_5(g)$ are in a vessel at equilibrium. In which direction will the position of the equilibrium

$$PCl_3(g) + Cl_2(g) \rightleftarrows PCl_5(g)$$

shift if the total presure is increased by halving the volume?

6. For the reaction

$$2SO_2(g) + O_2(g) \rightleftarrows 2SO_3(g)$$

$K = 4.00 \times 10^2\ \ell/\text{mole}$ at 750°C. What concentration of SO_2 must be in equilibrium with the concentrations $[O_2] = 2.0 \times 10^{-1}\ \text{mole}/\ell$ and $[SO_3] = 3.0\ \text{mole}/\ell$?

7. The synthesis of ammonia,

$$N_2(g) + 3H_2(g) \rightleftarrows 2NH_3(g)$$

is exothermic. The value of K for this equilibrium at 600 K is 4.1 $(\ell/\text{mole})^2$.
   a. Calculate K_p at 600 K.
   b. Will the value of K be larger or smaller than 4.1 $(\ell/\text{mole})^2$ at 700 K?

For exercises 8 and 9, consider the reaction

$$H_2(g) + I_2(g) \rightleftarrows 2HI(g)$$

8. $H_2(g)$ and $I_2(g)$ were mixed at 490°C and allowed to reach equilibrium. The following equilibrium concentrations were found:

$$[H_2] = 2.00\ \text{moles}/\ell$$
$$[I_2] = 2.49 \times 10^{-2}\ \text{moles}/\ell$$
$$[HI] = 1.50\ \text{moles}/\ell$$

   a. Calculate K.
   b. Calculate K_p.

9. In another experiment at 490°C, 1.00 mole of H_2, 5.00 moles of I_2 and 2.50 moles of HI were mixed in a 1.00 ℓ vessel. When equilibrium was reached, the concentration of H_2 was found to be 1.00×10^{-1} mole/ℓ. Calculate the equilibrium concentrations of I_2 and HI.

10. Calculate the value of K at 25°C for the reaction

$$CO_2(g) + H_2(g) \rightleftarrows CO(g) + H_2O(\ell)$$

    if the *equilibrium* concentrations of $CO_2 = H_2 = CO = 0.10\ M$.

11. Consider the reaction

$$CaCO_3(s) \rightleftarrows CaO(s) + CO_2(g)$$

    for which $K = 8.0 \times 10^{-3}$ mole/ℓ at 750°C.
    a. 1.00 mole of $CaCO_3(s)$ is sealed into a 5.0 ℓ flask at 750°C. Calculate the equilibrium concentration of $CO_2(g)$.
    b. What fraction (by moles) of the original $CaCO_3(s)$ has decomposed?
    c. How many moles of $CaO(s)$ are produced?
    d. Calculate K_P for this reaction at 750°C.

For exercises 12–14, consider the exothermic reaction

$$2NO(g) + O_2(g) \rightleftarrows 2NO_2(g)$$

A study of this system at 25°C found the equilibrium concentrations to be

$$[NO] = 1.0 \times 10^{-3}\ \text{mole}/\ell$$
$$[O_2] = 1.0 \times 10^{-6}\ \text{mole}/\ell$$
$$[NO_2] = 1.3\ \text{moles}/\ell$$

12. Calculate K at 25°C.

13. Calculate K_P at 25°C.

14. Predict the effect on the equilibrium position of the following stresses.
    a. Increase the temperature.
    b. Decrease the pressure by increasing the volume.
    c. Increase the pressure by adding $Ne(g)$.
    d. Add 1.0 mole of $O_2(g)$.

15. A 10.0 ℓ flask contains 1.0 mole of $PCl_5(g)$, 0.30 mole of $PCl_3(g)$, and 0.80 mole of $Cl_2(g)$ at equilibrium. Calculate K for the reaction

$$PCl_5(g) \rightleftarrows PCl_3(g) + Cl_2(g)$$

16. Consider the reaction

$$2NH_3(g) \rightleftarrows N_2(g) + 3H_2(g)$$

at a temperature where $K = 3.0 \times 10^{-8}$. In an experiment, 1.0×10^{-3} mole NH_3, 1.0×10^{-1} mole H_2, and 1.0 mole N_2 are mixed in a 5.0 ℓ vessel.

a. Is this system at equilibrium?
b. If not, in which direction must the system shift to reach equilibrium?
c. Define the change needed to reach equilibrium in terms of x.
d. Represent the equilibrium concentrations in terms of the initial concentrations and x.

17. $N_2O_4(g)$ decomposes to $NO_2(g)$ according to the following equation:

$$N_2O_4(g) \rightleftarrows 2NO_2(g)$$

Pure $N_2O_4(g)$ was placed in a closed flask at 127°C at a pressure of 4.38×10^{-2} atm. After the system reached equilibrium, the *total* pressure was found to be 7.43×10^{-2} atm. Calculate the value of K_P for this reaction.

Verbalizing General Concepts

Answer the following in your own words.

18. What is chemical equilibrium?

19. How does an equilibrium position differ from an equilibrium constant?

20. What is the reaction quotient and how is it used?

21. What is LeChatelier's Principle?

22. Using LeChatelier's Principle, state how a change in volume of the reaction vessel of a system at equilibrium affects the equilibrium position.

23. The addition of an inert gas to a system at equilibrium has no effect. Explain.

MULTIPLE CHOICE QUESTIONS

Questions 24–28 deal with the following equilibrium:

$$PCl_5(g) \rightleftarrows PCl_3(g) + Cl_2(g) \qquad \Delta H = 125 \text{ kJ}$$

6.0 moles of $PCl_5(g)$ are placed in an empty 10.0 liter reaction vessel at 230°C and the reaction is allowed to come to equilibrium. When equilibrium is reached, an analysis of the mixture indicates that 1.0 mole of $Cl_2(g)$ is present.

24. How many moles of $PCl_5(g)$ are present at equilibrium?
    a) 0.0 mole
    b) 1.0 mole
    c) 5.0 moles
    d) 5.6 moles
    e) 6.0 moles

25. What is the molar concentration of $Cl_2(g)$ at equilibrium?
    a) 0.1 mole per liter
    b) 0.2 mole per liter
    c) 0.5 mole per liter
    d) 1.0 mole per liter
    e) 2.0 moles per liter

26. The value of the equilibrium constant, K, is
    a) $\dfrac{0.1 \times 0.1}{0.5}$

    b) $\dfrac{1 \times 1}{5}$

    c) $\dfrac{1 \times 1}{6}$

    d) $\dfrac{5}{1 \times 1}$

    e) $\dfrac{0.5}{0.1 \times 0.1}$

27. The numerical value of the equilibrium constant, K, for this reaction may be expected to
    a) increase as temperature is increased to 250°C and pressure is held constant.
    b) increase as pressure is increased and temperature is held constant.
    c) increase if some additional Cl_2 is injected, temperature and pressure being held constant.
    d) remain unchanged no matter how conditions are altered.

28. Which of the following would surely increase the amount of $PCl_3(g)$ present at equilibrium?
    a) Decrease the volume at constant temperature.
    b) Inject some $Cl_2(g)$ into the system at equilibrium.
    c) Decrease the temperature at constant pressure.
    d) Remove some $PCl_5(g)$ from the system at equilibrium.
    e) Inject some $PCl_5(g)$ into the system at equilibrium.

29. Calculate the equilibrium constant, K_P, for the following reaction:

$$2NOBr(g) \rightleftharpoons 2NO(g) + Br_2(g)$$

given that a 1.0 liter vessel was initially filled with 4.0 atm of pure NOBr, and after equilibrium was established, the partial pressure of NOBr gas was 2.5 atm.

a) 0.45   b) 0.27   c) 0.18   d) 0.75   e) none of these

30. After equilibrium has been attained in the reaction system in question 29, decreasing the total pressure (by increasing the volume) will result in
a) an increase in the equilibrium constant.
b) a decrease in the equilibrium constant.
c) a shift of the equilibrium position to the right.
d) a shift of the equilibrium position to the left.
e) none of these.

31. In the reaction

$$C(s) + CO_2(g) \overset{1000 \text{ K}}{\rightleftharpoons} 2CO(g)$$

if one mole of solid carbon is added to the system at equilibrium, the result when equilibrium is reattained will be
a) to increase the quantity of CO by two moles.
b) to decrease the quantity of CO by two moles.
c) no change.
d) none of these.

For questions 32–35, consider the reaction

$$Fe_2O_3(s) + 3H_2(g) \rightleftharpoons 2Fe(s) + 3H_2O(g)$$

where $\Delta H° = 15$ kJ.

32. The equilibrium expression is

a) $K = \dfrac{[Fe]^2 [H_2O]^3}{[Fe_2O_3] [H_2]^3}$

c) $K = \dfrac{[H_2O]^3}{[H_2]^3}$

b) $K = \dfrac{1}{[H_2]^3}$

d) none of these

33. The equilibrium concentrations under certain conditions were found to be

$$[H_2O] = 1.0 \text{ mole}/\ell \text{ and}$$
$$[H_2] \ \ = 2.5 \text{ mole}/\ell$$

Calculate K.

a) 0.40   b) 0.064   c) 15.6   d) insufficient information to calculate

34. K_P is
    a) less than K
    b) greater than K
    c) equal to K
    d) insufficient information to predict

35. Using the following choices
    a) shift left
    b) shift right
    c) no change
    d) not possible to predict

    indicate the effect of each of the following stresses on the position of this system at equilibrium:
    1) Decrease the volume of the container.
    2) Add $Fe_2O_3(s)$.
    3) Remove $H_2O(g)$.
    4) Increase the temperature.

36. For the reaction

    $$4NH_3(g) + 5O_2(g) \rightleftarrows 4NO(g) + 6H_2O(g)$$

    $\Delta H°$ is negative. The position of this equilibrium would be shifted to the left by
    a) removing $NO(g)$.
    b) adding $O_2(g)$.
    c) increasing the pressure by decreasing the volume of the container.
    d) decreasing the temperature.
    e) none of these.

37. Calculate the equilibrium constant for the following reaction:

    $$2A(g) \rightleftarrows B(g) + 3C(g)$$

    given that a 1.0 ℓ vessel was initially filled with 5.0 atm of pure A and the partial pressure of gas A was found to be 3.5 atm at equilibrium.
    a) 1.1 atm²
    b) 0.70 atm²
    c) 3.8 atm²
    d) 0.48 atm²
    e) none of these

38. Increasing the volume of the reaction vessel in question 37 would have what effect?
    a) Increase the equilibrium constant.
    b) Force the reaction to proceed to the right.
    c) Force the product ratio [C]/[B] to be greater than 3.
    d) Only (a) and (b) are correct.
    e) (a), (b), and (c) are correct.

39. Consider the following equilibrium system:

$$SnCl_2(s) + Cl_2(g) \rightleftarrows SnCl_4(\ell) + 195 \text{ kJ}$$

The position of this equilibrium could be driven to the *right* by
a) compressing the system in the reaction chamber.
b) increasing the temperature in the reaction chamber.
c) adding more $SnCl_4(\ell)$ to the reaction mixture.
d) adding more $SnCl_2(s)$ to the reaction mixture.
e) All of the above would drive the reaction farther to the right.

40. Given the following equation:

$$A + B \rightleftarrows 3C + D$$

where initial concentrations of A and B are each equal to 1.2 moles/ℓ with no C or D present. At equilibrium, the concentration of D is found to be 0.30 moles/ℓ. Calculate K.
a) 0.27   b) 0.33   c) 0.010   d) 0.030   e) none of these

41. For the gas phase oxidation of CO to CO_2 by means of O_2:

$$2CO + O_2 \rightleftarrows 2CO_2$$

the equilibrium constant expression is

a) $K = \dfrac{[CO_2]^2}{[CO][O_2]}$

b) $K = \dfrac{[CO_2]^2}{[CO]^2[O_2]}$

c) $K = \dfrac{[CO]^2[O_2]}{[CO_2]}$

d) $K = \dfrac{[CO]^2[O_2]}{[CO_2]^2}$

e) $K = \dfrac{[CO][O_2]}{[CO_2]}$

42. Two moles of NH_3 gas are introduced into a previously evacuated 1.0 liter container in which it partially dissociates at high temperature:

$$2NH_3(g) \rightleftarrows N_2(g) + 3H_2(g)$$

At equilibrium, 1.0 mole of $NH_3(g)$ remains. What is the equilibrium constant for the above reaction?
a) 0.42   b) 0.75   c) 1.5   d) 1.7   e) none of these

43. Which of the following affects the *value* of K for gaseous reactions?
a) Change in pressure of reactants or products.
b) Change in concentration of reactants or products.
c) Change in temperature.
d) Change of volume of the container.
e) None of these.

For exercises 44–48, consider the equilibrium:

$$H_2O(g) + CO(g) \rightleftarrows H_2(g) + CO_2(g)$$

For this reaction, $\Delta H° = -40$ kJ. Using the following choices
   a) shift to the right
   b) shift to the left
   c) no change
   d) not enough information to predict
give the effect of each of the following stresses on the position of the equilibrium
for this reaction.

44. 1.0 mole of $H_2(g)$ is added.

45. 1.0 mole of $CO(g)$ is removed.

46. 1.0 mole of $He(g)$ is added.

47. The pressure is doubled by halving the volume.

48. The temperature is decreased.

49. In which reaction will a decrease in volume at constant temperature favor
    formation of the products?
    a) $CaCO_3(s) \rightleftarrows CaO(s) + CO_2(g)$
    b) $H_2(g) + Cl_2(g) \rightleftarrows 2HCl(g)$
    c) $2NO(g) + O_2(g) \rightleftarrows 2NO_2(g)$
    d) $COCl_2(g) \rightleftarrows CO(g) + Cl_2(g)$

50. Given the equilibrium equation

$$A_2(g) + B_2(g) \rightleftarrows 2AB(g)$$

where the equilibrium concentrations in moles/ℓ are

$$[A_2] = 0.40$$
$$[B_2] = 0.40$$
$$[AB] = 1.20$$

what is the value of the equilibrium constant?
   a) 0.11   b) 0.13   c) 1.8   d) 9.0

51. For the equilibrium system $N_2(g) + 2O_2(g) \rightleftarrows 2NO_2(g)$ where the forward
    reaction is endothermic, which of the following statements is *not* true?
    a) A decrease in volume will shift the position of the equilibrium to the right.
    b) An increase in temperature will shift the equilibrium to the left.
    c) The equilibrium expression is $K = \dfrac{[NO_2]^2}{[N_2][O_2]^2}$
    d) A decrease in the concentration of N_2 will shift the position of the equi-
        librium to the left.

52. For the reaction $2CO(g) + O_2(g) \rightleftarrows 2CO_2(g)$, the initial concentrations for CO, O_2, and CO_2 are each 0.10 mole/liter. $K = 4 \times 10^{-16}$ at 500°C. To establish equilibrium, the system will
   a) proceed to the right.
   b) proceed to the left.
   c) not change.
   d) cannot tell; insufficient information

53. The equilibrium constants K_I and K_{II} for the reactions

$$\text{I.} \quad N_2(g) + 3H_2(g) \rightleftarrows 2NH_3(g)$$

$$\text{II.} \quad \tfrac{1}{2}N_2(g) + \tfrac{3}{2}H_2(g) \rightleftarrows NH_3(g)$$

are related as
   a) $K_I = 2K_{II}$
   b) $K_I = \dfrac{1}{K_{II}}$
   c) $K_{II} = \sqrt{K_I}$
   d) $K_I = \sqrt{K_{II}}$
   e) none of these

Note:
   The following problems require the solution of quadratic equations.

54. Consider the reaction

$$PCl_3(g) + Cl_2(g) \rightleftarrows PCl_5(g)$$

at a temperature where $K = 11$ ℓ/mole. If 1.0×10^{-3} mole of $Cl_2(g)$, 1.26×10^{-1} mole $PCl_3(g)$, and 7.6×10^{-3} mole of $PCl_5(g)$ are mixed in a 2.0 ℓ vessel, calculate the equilibrium concentrations of $Cl_2(g)$, $PCl_3(g)$, $PCl_5(g)$.

55. 1.00 mole of $N_2O_4(g)$ is placed in a 10.0 ℓ vessel and allowed to reach equilibrium. The reaction of interest is

$$N_2O_4(g) \rightleftarrows 2NO_2(g)$$

where $K = 8.1 \times 10^{-2}$ mole/ℓ. Calculate the equilibrium concentrations of $N_2O_4(g)$ and $NO_2(g)$.

For questions 56 and 57, consider the reaction

$$N_2(g) + 3H_2(g) \rightleftarrows 2NH_3(g)$$

where $K_P = 1.7 \times 10^{-3}$ atm^{-2} at 600 K.

56. 0.10 atm of N_2 is mixed with 0.50 atm of H_2 in a 1.0 ℓ flask at 600 K. Calculate the equilibrium pressures of $N_2(g)$, $H_2(g)$, and $NH_3(g)$.

57. 0.0200 atm of $H_2(g)$, 0.0800 atm of $N_2(g)$, and 0.100 atm of $NH_3(g)$ are placed in a 1.00 ℓ flask at 600 K.
    a)   In which direction will the system shift to come to equilibrium?
    b)   Calculate the equilibrium pressures of $N_2(g)$, $H_2(g)$, and $NH_3(g)$.

For questions 58 and 59, consider the reaction

$$H_2(g) + I_2(g) \rightleftarrows 2HI(g)$$

at a temperature where $K = 38.6$.

58. 1.800 mole of H_2, 1.800 mole of I_2, and 2.600 moles of HI are mixed in a 2.000 ℓ vessel. Calculate the equilibrium concentrations of H_2, I_2, and HI.

59. 1.00 mole of I_2 is added to the system at equilibrium in problem 58.
    a)   In which direction does the position of the equilibrium shift?
    b)   Calculate the new equilibrium concentrations.

60. Consider the equilibrium mixture from question 15. Now 1.00 mole of $PCl_5(g)$ is added to this mixture in the 10.0 ℓ vessel. Calculate the new equilibrium concentrations of Cl_2, PCl_3, and PCl_5.

61. Consider the reaction

$$2HI(g) \rightleftarrows H_2(g) + I_2(g)$$

at 620°C where $K = 1.63 \times 10^{-3}$. In an experiment, 0.600 mole of $H_2(g)$, 0.300 mole of $I_2(g)$, and 0.800 mole of HI(g) are added to a 2.0 ℓ vessel. Calculate the equilibrium concentrations of HI, H_2, and I_2.

62. Consider the reaction

$$2ClO(g) \rightleftarrows Cl_2(g) + O_2(g)$$

at a temperature where $K = 6.4 \times 10^{-3}$. In an experiment, 1.00×10^{-1} mole of ClO(g), 1.00 mole of $O_2(g)$, and 1.00×10^{-2} mole of $Cl_2(g)$ were mixed in a 4.00 ℓ flask.
    a)   Is the system at equilibrium?
    b)   If not, in which direction must the system proceed to reach equilibrium?
    c)   Calculate the concentrations of ClO(g), $Cl_2(g)$, and $O_2(g)$ at equilibrium.

2

ACID-BASE EQUILIBRIA

Chapter Objectives

1. Define acid, base, K_a, K_b, pH, and buffer.

2. Understand the concept of acid strength.

3. Recognize the major species in solutions containing acids and/or bases.

4. Calculate the pH of a solution containing an acid and/or a base.

5. Learn to deal with buffered solutions, including:
   a. calculation of the pH of buffered solutions.
   b. calculation of the change in pH when OH^- or H^+ is added to a buffered solution.

6. Learn to approach complicated problems in a systematic way.

7. Learn to make reasonable assumptions to simplify the calculations involved in acid-base problems.

2.1   INTRODUCTION

Acids and bases in aqueous solution are most often defined in terms of the **Brønsted-Lowry model:** An acid is a proton (H^+) donor and a base is a proton acceptor. In general terms, the reaction that occurs when an acid is dissolved in water can be represented as

$$\underset{\text{acid}}{HA(aq)} + \underset{\text{base}}{H_2O(\ell)} \rightleftarrows \underset{\substack{\text{conjugate} \\ \text{acid}}}{H_3O^+(aq)} + \underset{\substack{\text{conjugate} \\ \text{base}}}{A^-(aq)} \qquad \text{(2–1)}$$

where "aq" means that the substance is hydrated (water molecules are attached).

Note that this is an equilibrium system that involves competition for the proton between two bases, H_2O and A^-. If H_2O is a much stronger base than A^-, it will combine with most of the H^+ and the position of the equilibrium will be to the right. If A^- is a much stronger base than H_2O, the equilibrium position will be to the left.

The equilibrium constant expression is

$$K_a = \frac{[H_3O^+][A^-]}{[HA]} = \frac{[H^+][A^-]}{[HA]}$$

where K_a is called the **dissociation constant** for the acid. Note the following important points:

1. The symbols "$H^+(aq)$" or simply "H^+" are often used to represent the hydrated proton, $H_3O^+(aq)$.
2. The condensed phase, H_2O, the concentration of which remains essentially constant, is not included in the K_a equilibrium expression. Because $[H_2O(\ell)]$ is not included, the form of the K_a equilibrium expression is the same as if the reaction were a simple dissociation:

$$HA(aq) \rightleftarrows H^+(aq) + A^-(aq)$$

The water molecules are very important in causing an acid to "dissociate" (the H^+ ions are transferred to H_2O molecules). However, since $[H_2O(\ell)]$ is constant and does not enter into the equilibrium calculations, the reaction of an acid in water is often represented as a simple dissociation, neglecting the role of water.
3. The reaction corresponding to K_a *always* involves formation of H^+ and a conjugate base. The conjugate base is everything left after the removal of H^+ from the acid. Knowing this fact allows one to write the K_a reaction even for an unfamiliar acid.

Acid Strength

The strength of an acid is determined by the position of the "dissociation" equilibrium. A **strong acid** dissociates completely in water. A **weak acid**, on the other hand, dissociates only to a slight extent. Several general statements can be made concerning strong and weak acids:

Strong Acid
1. K_a is very large.
2. $[H^+] = [HA]_0$, where $[HA]_0$ represents the number of moles of acid dissolved per liter of solution.
3. A^- is a weak base relative to H_2O.

The common strong acids are hydrochloric, $HCl(aq)$; nitric, $HNO_3(aq)$; and sulfuric, $H_2SO_4(aq)$.

Weak Acid
1. K_a is very small.
2. $[H^+] \ll [HA]_0$. ($\ll$ means "much less than")
3. A^- is a stronger base than H_2O, and remains for the most part bound to the proton.

It is very important to focus on the relationship between the strength of an acid and the strength of its conjugate base. A strong acid implies a very weak conjugate base (one with very small affinity for H^+ compared to H_2O). A weak acid, on the other hand, has a conjugate base that is strong compared to H_2O.

TEST 2–1

A. Describe in words what reaction is associated with K_a and what K_a means.

B. Write the K_a expression for
    1. HCN
    2. $C_6H_5NH_3^+$
    3. $Al(OH_2)_6^{3+}$
    Hint: Although acids 2 and 3 may be unfamiliar to you, simply apply the definition of a Brønsted acid.

C. The K_a for HCN is 6.2×10^{-10}. State the value of K for the reaction

$$H^+ + CN^- \rightleftarrows HCN$$

D. Consider the following acids:

Acid	K_a
HIO_3	1.7×10^{-1}
HNO_2	4.0×10^{-4}
HF	7.2×10^{-4}
HOCl	3.5×10^{-8}

1. Which of the anions IO_3^-, NO_2^-, F^-, and OCl^- is the strongest base? (Hint: Recall the relationship between acid strength and the strength of the conjugate base.)
2. Order these anions according to decreasing base strength.
3. Order the acids according to increasing acid strength.

2.2   GENERAL PRINCIPLES

Water as an Acid and Base

A substance is said to be **amphoteric** if it can react as either an acid or a base. Water is the most common amphoteric substance. This property can most clearly be seen in the **autoionization** of water:

$$H_2O(\ell) + H_2O(\ell) \rightleftarrows H_3O^+ + OH^-$$

In this reaction, one molecule of water furnishes a proton, behaving as an acid, and a second molecule accepts a proton, behaving as a base. The equilibrium expression for this process is

$$[H_3O^+][OH^-] = [H^+][OH^-] = K_w$$

At 25°C, experiment shows that

$$[H^+] = [OH^-] = 1.0 \times 10^{-7}\ M$$

Substituting these concentrations into the equilibrium constant expression gives a value of 1.0×10^{-14} for K_w. Thus in any aqueous solution at 25°C, the *product* of the $[H^+]$ and $[OH^-]$ must be 1.0×10^{-14} at equilibrium.

Note that there are an infinite number of combinations of $[H^+]$ and $[OH^-]$ which when multiplied together will give 1.0×10^{-14}. For example, $(1 \times 10^{-5})(1 \times 10^{-9}) = (1 \times 10^{-4})(1 \times 10^{-10}) = (5 \times 10^{-3})(2 \times 10^{-12}) = 1 \times 10^{-14}$. Recall from Chapter 1 that there are an infinite number of equilibrium positions but only one equilibrium constant at a given temperature.

Sample Problem 2–1

In a certain acidic solution at 25°C, the $[H^+] = 1.0 \times 10^{-2}$ M. What is the $[OH^-]$ in this solution?

Solution

We know that

$$[H^+][OH^-] = K_w = 1.0 \times 10^{-14}$$

Since $[H^+] = 1.0 \times 10^{-2}$,

$$[H^+][OH^-] = (1.0 \times 10^{-2})[OH^-] = 1.0 \times 10^{-14}$$
$$[OH^-] = \frac{1.0 \times 10^{-14}}{1.0 \times 10^{-2}} = 1.0 \times 10^{-12} \text{ M}$$

The pH Scale

Because the concentration of H^+ in most aqueous solutions is small (for example, it is 1.0×10^{-7} M in pure water), a quantity, called **pH**, is defined to designate the $[H^+]$, where

$$pH = -\log[H^+]$$

A similar type of notation is used for other quantities, for example:

$$pOH = -\log[OH^-]$$
$$pK = -\log K$$

Sample Problem 2–2

A.   Calculate the pH of pure water.

Solution

The $[H^+] = 1.0 \times 10^{-7}\ M$, so

$$pH = -\log[H^+] = -\log(1.0 \times 10^{-7}) = -(-7.00) = 7.00.$$

B.   Calculate the pOH of pure water.

Solution

The $[OH^-] = 1.0 \times 10^{-7}\ M$

$$pOH = -\log[OH^-] = -\log(1.0 \times 10^{-7}) = 7.00.$$

TEST 2–2

A.   Calculate the pH of a solution in which the $[OH^-] = 2.0 \times 10^{-4}\ M$.

B.   Calculate the pOH of a solution containing $5.0 \times 10^{-3}\ M\ H^+$.

Solving Acid-Base Problems: Some General Considerations

Acid-base problems tend to be more complicated than gas-phase equilibrium problems because aqueous solutions typically contain several components. It is, therefore, important to approach acid-base problems systematically and with care.

One of the most important steps in solving an acid-base problem is deciding which components are important and which can be ignored. In fact, knowing what simplifications can be made lies at the heart of the methods for solving many types of chemistry problems. Chemical systems tend to be very complex, and many are impossible to treat exactly. Thus, in order to obtain some kind of answer, reasonable approximations must be made. Much of chemistry involves the art of making intelligent approximations.

One way to approach chemistry is to memorize every problem you can find and then hope that test questions are exactly the same. This is a poor strategy that is likely to produce only frustration and anger. Instead of wasting time memorizing problems, homework should be used to practice the application of chemical concepts. In approaching a chemistry problem, do not try to force it into the mold of some previously memorized solution. Do not worry if you cannot immediately see the entire solution to the problem. Approach the problem in a step-by-step fashion, and *let the problem guide you* toward a solution. Don't fight the problem; it will often win.

In treating acid-base problems, the emphasis will be on the need to be systematic, yet flexible, and to look at each problem with an open mind. The methods illustrated for solving these problems may seem awkward at first, but they will pay dividends as the problems become more complicated. Remember, the key is to read the problem carefully and let the information given be the guide to the solution.

2.3   CALCULATING THE pH FOR SOLUTIONS CONTAINING STRONG ACIDS

Recall that a strong acid is an acid that is completely dissociated in water. Methods for dealing with strong acids will be developed by doing the following sample problem.

Sample Problem 2–3

Calculate the $[H^+]$ and the pH in a 1.0 M solution of HCl.

Solution

The following steps should always be used when doing an acid-base problem:

1. Note the substances used to prepare the solution (HCl and H_2O in this case) and then list the *major species* in the solution. This is a critical step; the ground rules must be carefully established. The major species:
   a) are the components of the solution present in relatively large amounts.
   b) are written as they actually occur in solution.

   To illustrate: What components are present in 1.0 M HCl?
   Since HCl is a strong acid (essentially completely dissociated), the solution contains no HCl molecules; rather, it contains H^+ and Cl^- ions. The label "1.0 M HCl" tells how the solution was prepared (1.0 mole HCl(g) per liter of solution), not that it actually contains 1.0 mole/ℓ of HCl molecules. The solution also contains $H_2O(\ell)$, which dissociates to a slight extent to produce H^+ and OH^-.

   Thus the solution contains

   $$H^+, \ Cl^-, \ OH^-, \ H_2O$$

   Which of these are major species?
   Note that H_2O, H^+, and Cl^- are present in relatively large quantities, and therefore are classified as major species. Since OH^- is present in very small quantities, it will be ignored for now.

2. Write reactions for the substances that produce (or consume) H^+. In this case, there are two sources of H^+:
   a) $HCl(aq) \rightarrow H^+(aq) + Cl^-(aq)$
       This has already been assumed to be complete in considering major species.
   b) $H_2O(\ell) \rightleftarrows H^+(aq) + OH^-(aq)$

3. Is there a dominant source of H^+ in the solution?
   The dissociated HCl produces 1.0 M H^+. The only other acid is H_2O. How important is H_2O as a source of H^+? In pure water, H_2O produces 1.0×10^{-7} M H^+. In this problem, because of the large amount of H^+ from the HCl, the water equilibrium

   $$H_2O \rightleftarrows H^+ + OH^-$$

will be shifted to the left so that the contribution to $[H^+]$ from the autoionization of H_2O will be much smaller than 1.0×10^{-7} M. Thus $[H^+]_{total} = 1.0$ M (from HCl) plus a very small contribution from H_2O, which means that, for all practical purposes,

$$[H^+] = 1.0 \ M$$

Note that this problem could be very complicated, but is greatly simplified because H_2O can be ignored as a source of H^+. *Remember:* Intelligent approximations are the key to solving acid-base problems.

Since $[H^+] = 1.0$ M,

$$pH = -\log[H^+] = -\log(1.0) = 0$$

The pH of 1.0 M HCl is 0. Note that a pH of zero does *not* mean that the $[H^+] = 0$.

TEST 2–3

A. Calculate the pH of 0.10 M HNO_3.
   1. List the materials used to prepare this solution and the major species in solution.
   2. Indicate the major and minor sources of H^+. (Write the reactions that produce H^+.)
   3. Indicate the approximations to be made.
   4. Calculate the pH.

B. Calculate the pH of 1.0×10^{-10} M HCl.
   1. List the species in solution.
   2. Indicate the sources of H^+. (Write reactions.)
   3. Choose the dominant source of H^+.
   4. Calculate the pH.

2.4   CALCULATING THE pH FOR SOLUTIONS CONTAINING WEAK ACIDS

Now consider a weak acid problem. This situation is more complicated than that for a strong acid. Since a weak acid is not completely dissociated, an equilibrium calculation must be performed to find the $[H^+]$. A weak acid can be recognized by its small K_a value.

Sample Problem 2–4

Calculate (a) the $[H^+]$ and the $[F^-]$, (b) the pH, and (c) the percentage dissociation in a 1.00 M solution of hydrofluoric acid, HF(aq). The K_a for HF(aq) is 7.2×10^{-4}.

Solution

This problem will be solved by using a series of steps that will be summarized at the end.

1. First list the major species: HF(aq) and H_2O.
    Note that the acid present is represented as HF rather than as H^+ and F^-. HF is a weak acid (small K_a) and will be present primarily as HF.
2. Determine which of the major species contribute to the $[H^+]$ and write the equations for the reactions that produce H^+.
    Both H_2O and and HF are acids:

$$H_2O \rightleftarrows H^+ + OH^- \qquad K_w = 1.0 \times 10^{-14}$$
$$HF \rightleftarrows H^+ + F^- \qquad K_a = 7.2 \times 10^{-4}$$

From the magnitudes of the equilibrium constants, it can be seen that although HF is a weak acid, it is much stronger than H_2O. Thus the dissociation of HF will make the dominant contribution to the $[H^+]$.

Use the size of the equilibrium constants to decide which acid is dominant.

3. Write the equilibrium expression for the dominant acid.

$$HF(aq) \rightleftarrows H^+(aq) + F^+(aq) \qquad K_a = \frac{[H^+][F^-]}{[HF]}$$

4. List the *initial concentrations* (the concentrations before any acid dissociation occurs) of all species in the dominant equilibrium:

$[HF]_0 = 1.00\ M$

$[F^-]_0 = 0$

$[H^+]_0 = 10^{-7}\ M$ from water, which we will assume can be ignored.

Thus assume $[H^+]_0 \approx 0$ ($\approx$ indicates an approximation)

5. Define x, the change needed to achieve equilibrium.
    Let x represent the HF which dissociates to bring the system to equilibrium (use units of mole/ℓ). Refer to the balanced equation in step 3, and note that x moles/ℓ of HF will produce x mole/ℓ of H^+ and x mole/ℓ of F^-.
6. Write the equilibrium concentrations in terms of the initial concentrations and x:

$$[HF] = [HF]_0 - x = 1.00 - x$$
$$[F^-] = [F^-]_0 + x = 0 + x = x$$
$$[H^+] = [H^+]_0 + x = 0 + x = x$$

7. Substitute the equilibrium concentrations into the equilibrium expression:

$$K_a = 7.2 \times 10^{-4} = \frac{[H^+][F^-]}{[HF]} = \frac{(x)(x)}{1.00 - x} = \frac{x^2}{1.00 - x}$$

8. Simplify the expression by neglecting x, if possible. Then solve for x.
For example, note that expansion of the equation in step 7 leads to a quadratic equation. To solve this equation exactly requires use of the quadratic formula. This process can be avoided by making an intelligent approximation. Notice that $K_a = 7.2 \times 10^{-4}$, which indicates that HF does not dissociate to a large extent. Thus x should be a small number. The term "$1.00 - x$" appears in the denominator. If x is very small compared to 1.00, then

$$1.00 - x \approx 1.00$$

This will greatly simplify the math:

$$7.2 \times 10^{-4} = \frac{x^2}{1.00 - x} \approx \frac{x^2}{1.00}$$
$$x^2 \approx (1.00)(7.2 \times 10^{-4})$$
$$x \approx \sqrt{7.2 \times 10^{-4}} = 2.7 \times 10^{-2}$$

9. Check the validity of the approximation made in step 8.
In step 8, the assumption was made that x is small compared to 1.00. Is this justified? From the above calculation,

$$x = 2.7 \times 10^{-2}.$$

Subtracting x from 1.00 gives

$$1.00 - x = 1.00 - 0.027 = 0.97$$

Thus, $1.00 - x$ is not very different from 1.00, so that

$$[HF] \approx [HF]_0$$

Usually it can be assumed that the equilibrium concentration, $[HA]$, of a weak acid (which dissociates only to a slight extent) is the same as the initial concentration, $[HA]_0$. That is,

$$[HA] = [HA]_0 - x \approx [HA]_0$$

The best way to decide if this approximation is valid in a given case is to do the problem the easy way (*assume* the approximation *is* valid) and then check to see how large the calculated value of x is, relative to $[HA]_0$. We will use the convention that if $\dfrac{x}{[HA]_0} \times 100$ *is less than 5%*, the approximation $[HA]_0 - x \approx [HA]_0$ will be considered valid. (A 5% error in the value of $[HA]$ produces approximately a 2–3% error in the calculated $[H^+]$.)

In the present problem,

$$\frac{x}{1.00} \times 100 = \frac{2.7 \times 10^{-2}}{1.00} \times 100 = 2.7\%$$

The error is less than 5%, so that the approximation is considered to be valid.
10. Calculate (a) the $[H^+]$ and $[F^-]$.
Note that $x = 2.7 \times 10^{-2}$ mole/ℓ. In step 4, the assumption was made that water makes a negligible contribution to the final $[H^+]$. Is this assumption valid? Yes. The $[H^+]$ from HF (2.7×10^{-2}) is more than 10^5 times the *maximum* that could be contributed by water $(10^{-7}$ mole/$\ell)$. Thus from the expression for the equilibrium concentration in step 6,

$$[H^+] = x = 2.7 \times 10^{-2} \text{ mole/}\ell$$

Also

$$[F^-] = x = 2.7 \times 10^{-2} \text{ mole/}\ell$$

11. Calculate (b) the pH.
From step 10,

$$[H^+] = 2.7 \times 10^{-2} \text{ mole/}\ell$$
$$pH = -\log[H^+] = -\log(2.7 \times 10^{-2}) = 1.57$$

12. Calculate (c) the percentage dissociation of the HF in this solution.
The *percentage dissociation* of a week acid is defined as follows:

$$\% \text{ dissociation} = \frac{\text{no. of moles/}\ell \text{ of HA dissociated}}{\text{no. of original moles/}\ell \text{ of HA}} \times 100$$

In this problem

$$x = \text{no. of moles/}\ell \text{ of HF dissociated} = 2.7 \times 10^{-2}$$

So % dissociation $= \dfrac{2.7 \times 10^{-2} \text{ moles/}\ell}{1.00 \text{ moles/}\ell} \times 100 = 2.7\%$

Summary of the Steps

To summarize the important steps in attacking a weak acid problem:

1. List the major species in solution, as they exist in solution. Strong acids are written as completely dissociated. Weak acids are written as HA.
2. Write the balanced reactions for major species that produce H^+, and determine the dominant source of H^+. This can be done in a typical case by looking at the values of the equilibrium constants. In almost every case, one acid will clearly be dominant.
3. Write the equilibrium expression for the dominant acid.
4. List the initial concentrations of all species involved in the dominant equilibrium.
5. Define x, the change required to reach equilibrium.
6. Write the equilibrium concentrations in terms of the initial concentrations and x.
7. Substitute the equilibrium concentrations in the expression for K_a.

8. Simplify the expression by neglecting x where possible. That is, assume that $[HA]$ $= [HA]_0 - x \approx [HA]_0$. Then solve for x.
9. Check the validity of the assumption made in step 8. (Use the 5% rule.)
10. Calculate the $[H^+]$ from the definition of $[H^+]$ in step 6.
11. Calculate the pH.

TEST 2–4

A. Consider a 0.100 M solution of hypochlorous acid (HOCl), which has a K_a of 3.5×10^{-8}.
   1. List the *major* species in this solution.
   2. Write balanced equations for dissociation of the acids. Decide which of these will be the dominant contributor to the $[H^+]$.
   3. Write the equilibrium constant expression for the dominant equilibrium.
   4. List the initial concentrations for the species in this equilibrium.
   5. Define x.
   6. Write the equilibrium concentrations in terms of x and the initial concentrations.
   7. Substitute the equilibrium concentrations into the K_a expression.
   8. Solve for x using the "easy method."
   9. Decide whether the assumption made in 8 is valid.
   10. Calculate the $[H^+]$ and the pH.
   11. Calculate the $[OCl^-]$ at equilibrium.
   12. Calculate the percent dissociation of HOCl in this solution.
   13. Calculate the $[OH^-]$ in this solution.

B. Calculate the pH of a 0.50 M solution of boric acid ($K_a = 5.8 \times 10^{-10}$). Use the formula H_3BO_3 to represent the formula of boric acid. Remember to be systematic. Follow the steps given above.

Sample Problem 2–5

0.050 mole of a weak acid (HA) is dissolved in enough water to make 1.0 ℓ of solution. The pH of this solution is found to be 3.50. What is the value of K_a for this weak acid?

Solution

This problem is different from those considered previously. In this case the pH is given (which will allow the calculation of the $[H^+]$) and the value of K_a is to be calculated.

One of the secrets to solving acid-base problems is always to use the same system to approach every problem. Thus, even though this problem appears to be quite different from previous problems, the procedure will use the same steps.

1. The major species in solution are:

$$HA, H_2O$$

2. These are both acids:

$$H_2O \rightleftharpoons H^+ + OH^-$$
$$HA \rightleftharpoons H^+ + A^-$$

Since the given pH is significantly less than 7, the weak acid, HA, must be more important than H_2O as a contributor to $[H^+]$.

3. The K_a expression for HA is

$$K_a = \frac{[H^+][A^-]}{[HA]}$$

4. The initial concentrations are:

$$[HA]_0 = 0.050 \ M$$
$$[A^-]_0 = 0$$
$$[H^+]_0 \approx 0 \quad \text{(ignoring the contribution of } H_2O)$$

5. Determine the change needed to reach equilibrium. The change required is usually called x. However, in this case the pH is given. Calculate the $[H^+]$ in this solution by taking the antilog (INV and then LOG on most calculators) of $-pH$.

$$[H^+] = \text{antilog}(-pH) = 10^{-pH}$$

In this case, the pH $= 3.50$. Take the antilog of -3.50.

$$[H^+] = 10^{-3.50} = 3.16 \times 10^{-4} \ M$$

This $[H^+]$ has resulted from dissociation of HA. Thus 3.16×10^{-4} mole/ℓ of HA must have dissociated for the system to reach equilibrium. The change to reach equilibrium is thus 3.16×10^{-4} mole/ℓ.

6. The equilibrium concentrations are:

$$[HA] = [HA]_0 \text{ plus change} = 0.050 - 3.16 \times 10^{-4} \approx 0.050$$
$$[A^-] = [A^-]_0 \text{ plus change} = 0 + 3.16 \times 10^{-4}$$
$$[H^+] = [H^+]_0 \text{ plus change} = 0 + 3.16 \times 10^{-4}$$

Our unknown in this case is the equilibrium constant. (Reread the question if necessary.)

7. Substitute the equilibrium concentrations into the K_a expression.

$$K_a = \frac{[H^+][A^-]}{[HA]} = \frac{(3.16 \times 10^{-4})(3.16 \times 10^{-4})}{0.050 - 3.16 \times 10^{-4}} \approx \frac{(3.16 \times 10^{-4})^2}{5.0 \times 10^{-2}} = 2.0 \times 10^{-6}$$

This is the value of K_a required by the problem.

2.5   CALCULATIONS FOR SOLUTIONS OF WEAK ACIDS CONTAINING A COMMON ION

This type of problem deals with a solution containing a weak acid and a soluble salt containing the anion (conjugate base) of the weak acid. The acid and salt thus have the same anion.

Sodium and potassium salts are usually quite soluble in water and are often used. It is important to recognize that when a sodium or potassium salt (ionic compound) dissolves in water, it can be assumed to be completely dissociated. Thus a $1.0\ M$ NaCl solution really contains $1.0\ M$ Na^+ and $1.0\ M$ Cl^-; $5.0\ M$ KF contains $5.0\ M$ K^+ and $5.0\ M$ F^-, etc. This is something you must remember. It will be important in solving many types of chemistry problems.

Sample Problem 2–6

Calculate the $[H^+]$ in a solution containing $1.00\ M$ hydrofluoric acid (HF, $K_a = 7.2 \times 10^{-4}$) and $0.50\ M$ sodium fluoride (NaF).

Solution

1. The major species in solution are:

    > HF
    > dissolved NaF (Na^+, F^-)
    > H_2O

2. Consider the acid-base properties of each component:
    1) HF is a weak acid (HF $\rightleftharpoons$ H^+ + F^-).
    2) F^- is the conjugate base of HF.
    3) Na^+ has no acid or base properties.
    4) H_2O is a much weaker acid than HF (K_a for HF $>> K_w$).

3. Thus the HF dissociation equilibrium will determine the $[H^+]$:

    $$\text{HF} \rightleftharpoons H^+ + F^- \qquad K_a = \frac{[H^+][F^-]}{[HF]} = 7.2 \times 10^{-4}$$

4. The initial concentrations are

    $[HF]_0 = 1.00\ M$ Assume no dissociation has yet occurred.
    $[F^-]_0 = 0.50\ M$ From the dissolved NaF.
    $[H^+]_0 \approx 0$ Ignore H_2O.

5. Let x be the number of moles/ℓ of HF that dissociate to reach equilibrium, producing x moles/ℓ H^+ and x moles/ℓ F^-.

6. The equilibrium concentrations are:

$$[HF] = 1.00 - x$$
$$[F^-] = 0.50 + x$$
$$[H^+] = x$$

7. Now put these quantities into the K_a expression for HF:

$$7.2 \times 10^{-4} = K_a = \frac{[H^+][F^-]}{[HF]} = \frac{(x)\,(0.50 + x)}{1.00 - x}$$

8. Simplify the expression by neglecting x where possible. The terms

$$1.00 - x \quad \text{and} \quad 0.50 + x$$

occur in step 7. Assume that x can be neglected in both terms. This gives the expression

$$K_a = 7.2 \times 10^{-4} \approx \frac{(x)\,(0.50)}{1.00}$$

Solving this expression for x gives

$$x = 1.4 \times 10^{-3}$$

9. Check the assumption in step 8.

$$\frac{1.4 \times 10^{-3}}{1.00} \times 100 = 1.4\%$$

$$\frac{1.4 \times 10^{-3}}{0.50} \times 100 = 2.8\%$$

In both caes, x can be neglected, since the "5% rule" is obeyed.

10. Calculate $[H^+]$.
    From the definition of $[H^+]$ in step 6:

$$[H^+] = x = 1.4 \times 10^{-3} \; M$$
$$pH = -\log[H^+] = -\log(1.4 \times 10^{-3}) = 2.85$$

Compare the $[H^+]$ from sample problem 2–6 with that obtained previously for 1.0 M HF (sample problem 2–4):

1.0 M HF	1.0 M HF, 0.50 M NaF
$[H^+] = 2.7 \times 10^{-2} \; M$	$[H^+] = 1.4 \times 10^{-3} \; M$
$pH = 1.57$	$pH = 2.85$

In the solution containing dissolved NaF, the $[H^+]$ is much smaller. This is exactly the result expected from LeChatelier's Principle. The equilibrium is

$$HF \rightleftarrows H^+ + F^-$$

and the presence of extra F^- should drive the position of the equilibrium to the left, lowering the $[H^+]$. This is the observed result.

This effect is sometimes called the *common ion effect:* When a solution contains a salt having an ion in common with one in the equilibrium, the position of the equilibrium is driven away from the side containing that ion.

TEST 2–5

A solution contains 0.050 M HA and 0.025 M NaA (Na^+, A^-) and has a pH of 4.0. Calculate the K_a value for HA. Remember to use the steps shown in sample problem 2–6.

2.6   CALCULATING THE pH FOR SOLUTIONS OF BASES

In the Brønsted-Lowry model, a base is defined as a proton acceptor. When a base dissolves in water, it reacts with some of the molecules of water, pulling off protons:

$$B(aq) + H_2O(\ell) \rightleftarrows BH^+(aq) + OH^-(aq)$$

Here "B" is used as a general symbol for a base other than OH^-. Note that the B molecules are competing with OH^- for protons.

It is useful to think of bases in two categories: (1) those that contain OH^- and (2) those, like B above, that do not contain OH^- but generate it by reaction with water.

A.   Bases That Contain OH^-

Typically, these bases are soluble metal hydroxides such as $NaOH(s)$, $KOH(s)$, and $Ca(OH)_2(s)$. When these compounds dissolve in water, they completely dissociate to produce metal cations and hydroxide ions. Consider, for example, $NaOH(s)$:

$$NaOH(s) \xrightarrow{\text{H}_2\text{O}} Na^+(aq) + OH^-(aq)$$

By analogy with completely dissociated acids, which are called "strong acids," these bases are called "strong bases."

Sample Problem 2–7

For a 1.0 M NaOH solution calculate:
A. $[OH^-]$
B. $[H^+]$
C.   pH

Solution

A. Since the NaOH is completely dissociated in solution, the solution contains H_2O, Na^+ (1.0 M) and OH^- (1.0 M). The $[OH^-]$ produced from autoionization of H_2O is very small and can be ignored. Therefore

$$[OH^-] = 1.0 \ M$$

B. What is the $[H^+]$?
To find the $[H^+]$, remember that water is in equilibrium with $H^+(aq)$ and $OH^-(aq)$:

$$H_2O(\ell) \rightleftharpoons H^+(aq) + OH^-(aq)$$
$$K_w = 1.0 \times 10^{-14} = [H^+][OH^-]$$

In part A, $[OH^-]$ was determined to be 1.0 M, so

$$[H^+][OH^-] = [H^+](1.0 \ M) = 1.0 \times 10^{-14}$$

Thus

$$[H^+] = 1.0 \times 10^{-14}$$

C. What is the pH?

$$pH = -\log(1.0 \times 10^{-14}) = -(-14.00) = 14.00$$

This is a basic solution:

The $[OH^-]$ is greater than the $[H^+]$.
The pH is greater than 7.

TEST 2–6

Calculate the pH of a 0.10 M KOH solution by answering the following questions to solve the problem:

A. What are the major species present in the solution?

B. Which component will determine the $[OH^-]$?

C. Calculate the $[OH^-]$.

D. Calculate the $[H^+]$.

E. Calculate the pH.

B.   Bases That Do Not Contain OH⁻.

These are typically molecules, such as NH_3, which have at least one pair of unshared electrons. This pair of electrons competes with a pair of electrons on the hydroxide ion for the proton:

$$H-\overset{\displaystyle H}{\underset{\displaystyle H}{N|}} \quad + \quad H-\bar{O}\underset{\displaystyle H}{|} \quad \rightarrow \quad H-\overset{\displaystyle H}{\underset{\displaystyle H}{N^+}}-H \quad + \quad (|\bar{O}-H)^-$$

or, in general

$$B(aq) + H_2O(\ell) \rightleftharpoons BH^+(aq) + OH^-(aq)$$

The equilibrium constant expression for this reaction is the definition of the **base dissociation constant**, K_b:

$$K_b = \frac{[BH^+][OH^-]}{[B]}$$

where $[H_2O(\ell)]$ is left out as usual.

Note the definition of K_b. It *always* refers to a reaction in which a base reacts with water to produce OH^- and the conjugate acid.

Bases of this type are often called **weak bases**. Since B is competing with OH^- for H^+ in this reaction, it is accurate to describe B as a weak base compared to OH^-.

Sample Problem 2–8

Calculate the $[OH^-]$ and the pH for a 15.0 *M* NH_3 solution. The K_b for NH_3 is 1.8×10^{-5}.

Solution

1. First, list the major species in solution: H_2O, NH_3.
   a. H_2O is both an acid and a base, and it produces small concentrations of both H^+ and OH^-.

   $$H_2O \rightleftharpoons H^+ + OH^- \qquad K_w = 10^{-14}$$

   b. Since the K_b is given for NH_3, it must be a base. It will therefore react with H_2O:

   $$NH_3 + H_2O \rightleftharpoons NH_4^+ + OH^- \qquad K_b = 1.8 \times 10^{-5}$$

2. Select the dominant equilibrium.
   Since the K_b is much larger than K_w, nearly all the OH^- in this solution at equilibrium results from the reaction of NH_3 with H_2O.

3. Write the equilibrium expression for the dominant equilibrium:

$$K_b = \frac{[NH_4^+][OH^-]}{[NH_3]} = 1.8 \times 10^{-5}$$

4. List the initial concentrations:

$[NH_3]_0 = 15.0 \; M$ No NH_3 has yet reacted.

$[NH_4^+]_0 = 0$

$[OH^-]_0 = 10^{-7} \approx 0$ Assume the contribution from the autoionization of H_2O is negligible.

5. Define x.

x moles/ℓ of NH_3 react with water to reach equilibrium.

6. Write the equilibrium concentrations of relevant species:

$$[NH_3] = [NH_3]_0 - x = 15.0 - x$$
$$[NH_4^+] = [NH_4^+]_0 + x = 0 + x = x$$
$$[OH^-] = [OH^-]_0 + x = 0 + x = x$$

7. Substitute into the equilibrium expression:

$$K_b = 1.8 \times 10^{-5} = \frac{[NH_4^+][OH^-]}{[NH_3]} = \frac{(x)(x)}{15.0 - x}$$

8. Simplify the expression by neglecting x where possible. Then solve for x.

$$\text{Assume } 15.0 - x \approx 15.0$$
$$K_b = 1.8 \times 10^{-5} \approx \frac{x^2}{15.0}$$
$$x \approx 1.6 \times 10^{-2} \; M$$

9. Check the assumption in step 8.

$$\frac{x}{[NH_3]_0} \times 100 = \frac{1.6 \times 10^{-2}}{15.0} \times 100 = 0.11\%$$

Thus the assumption that $15.0 - x = 15.0$ is valid, and the value of x calculated in step 8 is correct.

10. Calculate $[H^+]$.
From step 8, $[OH^-] = 1.6 \times 10^{-2} \; M$. Since we know that $K_w = [H^+][OH^-] = 1.0 \times 10^{-14}$ for H_2O, we can write

$$[H^+] = \frac{1.0 \times 10^{-14}}{[OH^-]} = \frac{1.0 \times 10^{-14}}{1.6 \times 10^{-2}} = 6.3 \times 10^{-13} \; M$$

11.   Calculate the pH.

$$pH = -\log[H^+] = -\log(6.3 \times 10^{-13})$$
$$= 12.20$$

Note that the $[NH_3]$ at equilibrium in 15.0 M NH_3 is

$$15.0 - 1.6 \times 10^{-2} = 15.0 \ M$$

to the correct number of significant figures. When NH_3 is dissolved in water, only a small percentage of the molecules react. In 15.0 M NH_3:

$$\text{percent } NH_3 \text{ reacting} = \frac{[NH_4^+]}{[NH_3]_0} \times 100 = \frac{1.6 \times 10^{-2}}{15.0} \times 100 = 0.11\%$$

Often a 15.0 M aqueous solution of NH_3 is labeled 15.0 M NH_4OH. From the above calculations, it can be seen that the latter is not a very accurate description of this solution, since it contains only small amounts of NH_4^+ and OH^-.

TEST 2–7

A.   To what reaction does K_b always refer?

B.   Define K_b in words.

C.   Does K_b for NH_3 equal $\dfrac{1}{K_a}$ for NH_4^+? Prove your answer.

D.   Consider a solution containing 1.0 M methylamine (CH_3NH_2), which has a K_b value of 4.38×10^{-4}.
   1.   List the major species in the solution.
   2.   Write the equation for the reaction of CH_3NH_2 with H_2O. Hint: Remember the definition of K_b. Even though CH_3NH_2 may be unfamiliar, you should be able to write the K_b reaction.
   3.   Will the autoionization of water or the reaction of CH_3NH_2 with water dominate in the production of OH^-?
   4.   Write the K_b equilibrium expression for CH_3NH_2.
   5.   List the initial concentrations for the species in the dominant equilibrium.
   6.   Define x.
   7.   Write the equilibrium concentrations in terms of x.
   8.   Substitute the equilibrium concentrations into the equilibrium expression and solve for x. Make the usual assumption and check its validity.
   9.   Calculate the pH.

E.   Calculate the pH of a 0.10 M solution of pyridine (C_5H_5N:), which has a K_b value of 1.4×10^{-9}. Be sure to use the usual steps.

2.7   BUFFERED SOLUTIONS

A **buffered solution** is a solution that resists a change in its pH when H^+ or OH^- is added. A very important buffered solution is blood: it can absorb the acids and bases produced in biological reactions without significantly changing pH. This is very important because cells can survive only in a very narrow pH range.

A solution can be buffered at acidic or basic pH. To buffer a solution at an acidic pH, a weak acid (HA) and its salt (usually a sodium salt, NaA, because of its high solubility) are used. To buffer a solution at a basic pH, a weak base (B) and its salt (such as BHCl, which contains BH^+ and Cl^- ions) are used. The way in which these solutions resist a pH change will be discussed in this section.

Acidic Buffers

Sample Problem 2–9

To explore the properties of acidic buffers, consider a solution that contains 0.10 M acetic acid, $HC_2H_3O_2$, often abbreviated as HOAc ($K_a = 1.8 \times 10^{-5}$), and 0.10 M sodium acetate, $NaC_2H_3O_2$ (abbreviated as NaOAc).

A. What is the pH of this solution? (This is identical to the type of problems solved in section 2–5.)
1. Remember, the first thing that should *always* be done is to write down the major species in the solution, in this case: HOAc, Na^+, OAc^-, H_2O. Remember that when a salt, such as NaOAc, dissolves, it dissociates into its ions.
2. What equilibrium will be dominant in this solution? To answer this question, go through the list of species:
    (1) HOAc   Weak acid, $K_a = 1.8 \times 10^{-5}$
    (2) Na^+ Neither an acid nor a base
    (3) OAc^- Conjugate base of HOAc
    (4) H_2O Weaker acid than HOAc   (K_w is much less than K_a)
    Note that the HOAc dissociation reaction

$$HOAc \rightleftharpoons H^+ + OAc^-$$

involves both HOAc and OAc^- and is the dominant equilibrium.
3. Following normal procedures for a weak acid problem, write the equilibrium expression for the dominant equilibrium:

$$K_a = \frac{[H^+][OAc^-]}{[HOAc]} = 1.8 \times 10^{-5}$$

4–6. *Initial Concentrations*

$[HOAc]_0 = 0.10\ M$

$[OAc^-]_0 = 0.10\ M$

(why is $[OAc^-]_0 \neq 0$?)

$[H^+]_0 \approx 0$

Let x moles/ℓ
——HOAc——→
dissociate

Equilibrium Concentrations

$[HOAc] = 0.10 - x$

$[OAc^-] = 0.10 + x$

$[H^+] = x$

Note that the three steps (initial concentrations, definition of x, and the equilibrium concentrations) have been represented in a condensed form.

7–8. Now substitute into K_a, simplify, and solve for x:

$$1.8 \times 10^{-5} = \frac{[H^+][OAc^-]}{[HOAc]} = \frac{(x)(0.10 + x)}{(0.10 - x)} \approx \frac{(x)(0.10)}{0.10}$$

$$x \approx 1.8 \times 10^{-5} \ M$$

9. Checking the assumptions shows them to be valid (they pass the 5% rule), so we go onward.

10. $[H^+] = x = 1.8 \times 10^{-5} \ M$

11. $pH = -\log[H^+] = 4.74$

B. What happens to the pH of this solution if 0.010 mole of NaOH(s) is added to 1.0 ℓ of this buffered solution?

First, write down the major species in the solution (before any reaction occurs): HOAc, OAc^-, Na^+, OH^-, H_2O.

Note that the solution contains relatively large quantities of OH^-, which is a strong base. It will be looking for the best source of H^+ with which to react. The weak acid, HOAc, can furnish H^+ according to the following reaction:

$$HOAc + OH^- \rightarrow H_2O + OAc^-$$

Assume this reaction goes to completion. (OH^- is a much stronger base than OAc^-.) In dealing with a solution where a reaction goes to completion, it is always best to consider the reaction first, then do the equilibrium problem. A situation like this really involves two problems: (1) a stoichiometry problem and (2) an equilibrium problem. First consider the stoichiometry problem involved when OH^- reacts to completion with HOAc.

1. The Stoichiometry Problem
     0.010 mole of NaOH(s) has been added to 1.0 ℓ of a solution containing 0.10 M HOAc and 0.10 M NaOAc.
     The reaction is

	OH^-	$+$	HOAc	$\rightarrow$	H_2O	$+$	OAc^-
Before the reaction:	0.01 mole		$(1.0 \ \ell \times 0.10 \ M)$ $= 0.10$ mole				$1.0 \ \ell \times 0.10 \ M$ $= 0.10$ mole
After the reaction:	0		$0.10 - 0.01$ $= 0.09$ mole				$0.10 + 0.01$ $= 0.11$ mole

2. The Equilibrium Problem
     After the reaction, the solution contains Na^+, OAc^-, HOAc, H_2O. As before, use the weak acid dissociation reaction:

$$HOAc \rightleftarrows H^+ + OAc^-$$

Initial Concentrations

$$[HOAc]_0 = \frac{0.09 \text{ mole}}{1.0 \ \ell}$$

$$= 0.09 \ M$$

$$[OAc^-]_0 = \frac{0.11 \text{ mole}}{1.0 \ \ell}$$

$$= 0.11 \ M$$

$$[H^+]_0 \approx 0$$

Let x
moles/ℓ of
————HOAc————→
dissociate

Equilibrium Concentrations

$$[HOAc] = 0.09 - x$$

$$[OAc^-] = 0.11 + x$$

$$[H^+] = x$$

$$1.8 \times 10^{-5} = K_a = \frac{[H^+][OAc^-]}{[HOAc]} = \frac{(x)(0.11 + x)}{(0.09 - x)} \approx \frac{(x)(0.11)}{0.09}$$

$$x \approx \frac{0.09}{0.11}(1.8 \times 10^{-5}) = 1.5 \times 10^{-5} \ M$$

Note that the assumptions are valid. Thus $[H^+] = 1.5 \times 10^{-5} \ M$, and

$$pH = -\log(1.5 \times 10^{-5}) = 4.82$$

The pH of the solution (containing 0.10 M HOAc and 0.10 M NaOAc) before addition of NaOH was 4.74. After the addition of 0.01 mole of NaOH(s), the pH is 4.82. The increase is only 0.08 pH unit. Contrast this pH change with the one that occurs when 0.010 mole of NaOH(s) is added to 1.0 ℓ of water; in that case, the pH changes from 7 to 12, as we will show.

1. Pure water has pH = 7.0.
2. Addition of 0.01 mole NaOH(s) to 1.0 ℓ of water produces a 0.01 M solution of NaOH. This is a strong base (completely dissociated) so that

$$[OH^-] = 0.010 \ M$$
$$1.0 \times 10^{-14} = K_w = [H^+][OH^-] = [H^+](0.010 \ M)$$
$$[H^+] = \frac{1.0 \times 10^{-14}}{1.0 \times 10^{-2}} = 1.0 \times 10^{-12}$$
$$pH = -\log(1.0 \times 10^{-12}) = 12.00$$

The pH increases from 7.0 (pure water) to 12.0 (0.01 M NaOH solution), which is an increase of 5 pH units. Thus, adding a given quantity of OH^- to 1.0 ℓ of water produces a much greater change in pH than adding the same quantity of OH^- to 1.0 ℓ of a buffered solution. Why is this true? How is buffering accomplished?

Remember that an acidic buffer contains large quantities of HA and A^-. The pH is governed by the dissociation equilibrium

$$HA \rightleftarrows H^+ + A^-$$

where

$$K_a = \frac{[H^+][A^-]}{[HA]}$$

Rearranging the K_a expression:

$$[H^+] = K_a \frac{[HA]}{[A^-]}$$

Notice from this form of the K_a expression that the $[H^+]$ depends on the $[HA]/[A^-]$ ratio. The $[H^+]$ changes to the extent that this ratio changes.

When OH^- is added to a buffered solution, the reaction

$$OH^- + HA \rightarrow A^- + H_2O$$

occurs; *i.e.*, HA is changed to A^-. Now if $[HA]$ and $[A^-]$ are both large compared to the amount of OH^- added, the percentage change in the $[HA]/[A^-]$ ratio will be small, and thus the change in $[H^+]$ will be small.

On the other hand, if either $[HA]$ or $[A^-]$ is small, a much larger percentage change in $[HA]/[A^-]$ will occur and $[H^+]$ will change more significantly. Thus, buffers are best prepared by using nearly equal amounts of HA and A^-.

When a strong acid is added to a buffered solution containing HA and A^-, the reaction

$$H^+ + A^- \rightarrow HA$$

can be assumed to go to completion. In this case, A^- is changed to HA.

TEST 2–8

Consider a solution containing 0.20 M HOAc ($K_a = 1.8 \times 10^{-5}$) and 0.10 M NaOAc.

1. Calculate the pH of this solution.

2. Calculate the pH of the solution after 0.020 mole of HCl(g) is dissolved in 1.0 ℓ of this solution.

3. How much does the pH of the original buffer change upon addition of 0.020 mole of NaOH(s) to 1.0 ℓ of this solution?

Choosing a Buffering System

A buffer is effective in maintaining a particular pH only to the extent that the ratio $[HA]/[A^-]$ is insensitive to added H^+ or OH^-. The ratio $[HA]/[A^-]$ is most insensitive to change when $[HA] = [A^-]$. This is an important point to remember in choosing the buffering system.

Sample Problem 2–10

A chemist wishes to prepare a solution buffered at pH = 4.0. He can choose among the following acids:

Weak Acid	K_a
HA	1.0×10^{-2}
HB	1.0×10^{-4}
HC	1.0×10^{-6}

Which acid (along with its conjugate base) should the chemist choose?

Solution

The solution is to be buffered at pH $= 4.0$. This means that $[H^+] = 1.0 \times 10^{-4} \; M$. Rearrange the K_a expression:

$$[H^+] = K_a \frac{[acid]}{[anion]} = 1.0 \times 10^{-4}$$

The most effective buffering will occur when $[acid]/[anion] = 1.0$. Thus

$$[H^+] = 1.0 \times 10^{-4} = K_a(1.0)$$

Therefore the acid (HB) with $K_a = 1.0 \times 10^{-4}$ should be chosen, and a comparable amount of B^- added to make the buffer.

The Capacity of a Buffer

The **capacity** of a buffer reflects its ability to absorb H^+ or OH^- without significantly changing pH. The more buffering material present in the solution, the greater the capacity of the buffer.

TEST 2–9

Consider two solutions:

I. 1.0 M HA ($K_a = 1.0 \times 10^{-5}$), 1.0 M NaA
II. 0.10 M HA ($K_a = 1.0 \times 10^{-5}$), 0.10 M NaA

1. Calculate the pH of each solution.

2. Which buffered solution has the greater capacity?

3. Support your answer to (2) by calculating the change in pH that occurs when 0.050 mole of OH^- is added to 1.0 ℓ of each solution.

Basic Buffers

To buffer a solution at a basic pH requires a weak base and its salt. For example, one might use NH_3 ($K_b = 1.8 \times 10^{-5}$) and NH_4Cl.

Sample Problem 2–11

Consider a solution containing 0.30 M NH_3 and 0.20 M NH_4Cl.
A. Calculate the pH of this solution.

Solution

The solution contains the major species: NH_3, NH_4^-, Cl^-, H_2O.
1. NH_3 is a base:

$$NH_3 + H_2O \rightleftharpoons NH_4^+ + OH^-$$

2. NH_4^+ is the conjugate acid of NH_3.
3. Cl^- is a very weak base (it is the anion of HCl) and will not affect the pH.
4. H_2O is a weak acid and base:

$$H_2O \rightleftharpoons H^+ + OH^-$$

The dominant equilibrium involves NH_3 and NH_4^+:

$$NH_3 + H_2O \rightleftharpoons NH_4^+ + OH^-$$

$$K_b = \frac{[NH_4^+][OH^-]}{[NH_3]} = 1.8 \times 10^{-5}$$

Initial Concentrations
$[NH_3]_0 = 0.30\ M$
$[NH_4^+]_0 = 0.20\ M$
$[OH^-]_0 \approx 0$ (ignore water)

Let x moles/ℓ
$\xrightarrow{\quad NH_3 \quad}$
react with H_2O

Equilibrium Concentrations
$[NH_3] = 0.30 - x$
$[NH_4^+] = 0.20 + x$
$[OH^-] = x$

$$K_b = 1.8 \times 10^{-5} = \frac{[NH_4^+][OH^-]}{[NH_3]} = \frac{(0.20 + x)\,(x)}{0.30 - x}$$

Neglect x compared to 0.30 and 0.20:

$$1.8 \times 10^{-5} \approx \frac{(0.20)\,(x)}{0.30}$$
$$x \approx 2.7 \times 10^{-5}$$

Application of the "5% rule" shows the approximations to be valid. Thus

$$[OH^-] = x = 2.7 \times 10^{-5}$$

From the water equilibrium

$$[H^+] = \frac{K_w}{[OH^-]} = \frac{1.0 \times 10^{-14}}{2.7 \times 10^{-5}} = 3.7 \times 10^{-10}$$
$$pH = 9.43$$

B. Calculate the pH after 0.050 mole of HCl is added to this solution.

Solution

After the HCl has been added, but before any reaction occurs, the solution contains:

$$H^+, Cl^-, NH_4^+, NH_3, H_2O$$

Note that the solution contains large quantities of H^+ and NH_3. The reaction between them will go essentially to completion.

Do the stoichiometry problem first.

	H^+	$+$	NH_3	$\rightarrow$	NH_4^+
Before the reaction:	0.050 mole		0.30 mole		0.20 mole
After the reaction:	0		0.30 − 0.050 = 0.25 mole		0.20 + 0.050 = 0.25 mole

Now do the equilibrium problem: After the reaction, the major species are

$$NH_4^+, Cl^-, NH_3, H_2O$$

The dominant equilibrium is

$$NH_3 + H_2O \rightleftarrows NH_4^+ + OH^-$$

$$K_b = \frac{[NH_4^+][OH^-]}{[NH_3]}$$

Initial Concentrations
$[NH_3]_0 = 0.25\ M$
$[NH_4^+]_0 = 0.25\ M$
$[OH^-]_0 \approx 0$ (ignore H_2O)

Let x moles/ℓ
———NH_3———→
react with H_2O

Equilibrium Concentrations
$[NH_3] = 0.25 - x$
$[NH_4^+] = 0.25 + x$
$[OH^+] = x$

$$K_b = 1.8 \times 10^{-5} = \frac{(0.25 + x)\,(x)}{0.25 - x} \approx \frac{(0.25)\,(x)}{0.25}$$

$$x \approx 1.8 \times 10^{-5}$$

The "5% rule" shows the assumptions to be valid. Thus

$$[OH^-] = x = 1.8 \times 10^{-5}\ M$$

From the H_2O equilibrium,

$$[H^+] = \frac{K_w}{[OH^-]} = \frac{1.0 \times 10^{-14}}{1.8 \times 10^{-5}} = 5.6 \times 10^{-10}\ M$$

$$pH = 9.25$$

C. Calculate the pH after 0.030 mole of NaOH(s) is added to the original solution.

Solution

After the NaOH is added, but before any reaction occurs, the solution contains Na^+, OH^-, NH_4^+, NH_3, H_2O. The OH^- is a very strong base and will react essentially completely with the NH_4^+.

1. The stoichiometry problem.
   Assume that the reaction goes to completion:

	OH^-	+	NH_4^+	→	NH_3	+	H_2O
Before the reaction:	0.030 mole		0.20 mole		0.30 mole		
After the reaction:	0		0.20 − 0.03 = 0.17 mole		0.30 + 0.03 = 0.33 mole		

2. The equilibrium problem.

$$K_b = \frac{[NH_4^+][OH^-]}{[NH_3]}$$

Initial Concentrations
$[NH_3]_0 = 0.33\ M$
$[NH_4^+]_0 = 0.17\ M$
$[OH^-]_0 \approx 0$ (ignore H_2O)

Let x moles/ℓ
—NH_3—→
react with H_2O

Equilibrium Concentrations
$[NH_3] = 0.33 - x$
$[NH_4^+] = 0.17 + x$
$[OH^-] = x$

$$K_b = 1.8 \times 10^{-5} = \frac{(0.17 + x)(x)}{0.33 - x} \approx \frac{(0.17)(x)}{0.33}$$

$$x \approx 3.5 \times 10^{-5}$$

The "5% rule" shows the approximations to be valid. Thus

$$[OH^-] = x = 3.5 \times 10^{-5}\ M$$

From the H_2O equilibrium

$$[H^+] = \frac{K_w}{[OH^-]} = \frac{1.0 \times 10^{-14}}{3.5 \times 10^{-5}} = 2.9 \times 10^{-10}$$

$$pH = 9.54$$

TEST 2–10

A. Consider a solution containing 0.50 M HA ($K_a = 1.0 \times 10^{-6}$) and 0.50 M NaA.
   1. Calculate the pH of this solution.

2. Calculate the pH of the solution after 0.10 mole of NaOH(s) is added to 1.0 ℓ of this solution.
3. Calculate the pH of the solution after 0.10 mole of HCl(g) is added to 1.0 ℓ of this solution.

B. Consider the following two solutions:

   I.   0.50 M HF (K_a = 7.2 × 10^{-4}) and 0.50 M NaF
   II. 5.0 M HF and 5.0 M NaF

   1. Calculate the pH of each solution.
   2. Which buffered solution has the largest capacity?
   3. Support your answer to (2) by calculating the change in pH when 0.05 mole of HCl(g) is added to 1.0 ℓ of each solution.

C. What concentration of NaNO$_2$ is necessary to buffer 0.050 M HNO$_2$ (K_a = 4.0 × 10^{-4}) at pH = 3.00?

D. What is the pH of a solution formed by mixing 50.0 mℓ of 0.05 M HCl with 100.0 mℓ of 0.10 M NaOAc? The K_a for HOAc is 1.8 × 10^{-5}.

E. A solution is prepared by adding 0.100 mole of NaOH(s) to 1.0 ℓ of 0.500 M NH$_4$Cl. Calculate the pH. The K_b for NH$_3$ is 1.8 × 10^{-5}.

2.8   ACID-BASE REACTIONS THAT OCCUR WHEN SALTS ARE DISSOLVED IN WATER*

"Salt" is simply another name for an ionic compound. When a typical salt is dissolved in water, it breaks up into its ions which, in dilute solution, move about independently. Some salts, when dissolved in water, form an acidic solution; others form a basic solution, and still others are neutral in water.

Ions may behave as weak acids. For example, when NH$_4$Cl is dissolved in water, NH$_4{}^+$ and Cl$^-$ are produced. The NH$_4{}^+$ is a weak acid:

$$H_2O(\ell) + NH_4{}^+(aq) \rightleftarrows NH_3(aq) + H_3O^+(aq)$$

Here NH$_3$ and H$_2$O compete for the proton.

Note that NH$_4{}^+$ is the conjugate acid of the base, NH$_3$. There are many similar salts in which the *cation is the conjugate acid of a base;* such salts produce acidic solutions when dissolved in water.

A second kind of salt involves ions that produce an acidic solution but that are not in themselves Brønsted-Lowry acids. These ions gain their acidic character from waters of hydration. All ions are hydrated when they are placed in water. In many cases, these ions have no effect on the acidity of the water molecules. However, when *small, highly charged ions* are hydrated, the tendency for the hydrating water molecules to give up H$^+$ is much

---

*Called hydrolysis in most textbooks.

greater than for unattached water molecules. For example, when $AlCl_3$ is dissolved in water:

$$AlCl_3(s) \xrightarrow{\text{H}_2\text{O}} Al^{3+}(aq) + 3Cl^-(aq)$$

the Al^{3+} ion is hydrated by six water molecules to form $Al(OH_2)_6^{3+}$:

This hydrated ion undergoes the reaction

$$Al(OH_2)_6^{3+} + H_2O \rightleftharpoons Al(OH)(OH_2)_5^{2+} + H_3O^+$$

The charge on the metal ion causes the attached water molecules to be more acidic than free H_2O.

A third case involves salts in which the anion behaves as a base. For example, a solution of NaCN contains Na^+ and CN^- ions. The CN^- ion has a high affinity for H^+ (we know this because HCN, $K_a = 6.2 \times 10^{-10}$, is a very weak acid) and thus produces a basic solution via the reaction

$$CN^- + H_2O \rightleftharpoons HCN + OH^-$$

This behavior is characteristic of the anion of any weak acid.

In summary, there are these important cases to consider:
1. Acid solutions result when the following are dissolved:
    a. Salts that contain the conjugate acid of a base.
    b. Salts that contain small, highly charged cations.
2. A basic solution results when a salt containing the anion of a weak acid is dissolved.
    Each of these will now be considered in more detail.

Acidic Solutions: Case 1

First we consider salts containing the conjugate acid of a base. To illustrate this case, consider NH_4Cl dissolved in water to produce NH_4^+ and Cl^-. The NH_4^+ behaves as a weak acid:

$$NH_4^+ + H_2O \rightleftharpoons NH_3 + H_3O^+$$

which is more commonly represented as a simple dissociation:

$$NH_4^+ \rightleftharpoons NH_3 + H^+ \qquad K_a = \frac{[NH_3][H^+]}{[NH_4^+]}$$

Solutions of NH_4^+ can be treated in the same way as those of any weak acid. The only difference is that the K_a for NH_4^+ is not usually listed in tables of acid-base equilibrium constants. Rather, K_b for NH_3 is given.

How can the K_b for NH_3 be used to calculate the K_a for NH_4^+? Remember the following important definitions:

$$K_b(NH_3) = \frac{[NH_4^+][OH^-]}{[NH_3]} = 1.8 \times 10^{-5}$$

$$K_a(NH_4^+) = \frac{[NH_3][H^+]}{[NH_4^+]} = ?$$

$$K_w(H_2O) = [H^+][OH^-] = 1.00 \times 10^{-14}$$

Note that

$$\frac{[NH_3][H^+]}{[NH_4^+]} \times \frac{[NH_4^+][OH]}{[NH_3]} = [H^+][OH^-]$$

$$\uparrow \qquad\qquad \uparrow \qquad\qquad \uparrow$$
$$K_a(NH_4^+) \qquad K_b(NH_3) \qquad K_w(H_2O)$$

Thus

$$K_a \times K_b = K_w$$

This is true for
1. any base, B, and its conjugate acid, BH^+.
2. any acid, HX, and its conjugate base, X^-.

This relationship is very useful, as can be seen in the solution of the problems in this section.

Sample Problem 2–13

Calculate the pH of a solution prepared by dissolving 0.010 mole of $NH_4Cl(s)$ in enough water to make 1.0 ℓ of solution. The K_b for NH_3 is 1.8×10^{-5}.

Solution

To solve this problem, recognize that $NH_4Cl(s)$ is an ionic solid, containing NH_4^+ and Cl^-, which breaks up into its ions when it dissolves:

$$NH_4Cl(s) \xrightarrow{\text{H}_2\text{O}} NH_4^+(aq) + Cl^-(aq)$$

so that the major species in solution are

$$H_2O, \ NH_4^+, \ Cl^-$$

To decide which of the reactions is dominant, consider the acid or base properties of each major component:

1. H_2O acid or base—very weak
2. NH_4^+ weak acid (it can lose a proton to form NH_3)
3. Cl^- extremely weak base (we know this because HCl is a very strong acid)

Will H_2O or NH_4^+ be the dominant acid?

To answer this question, find the acid dissociation constant for each. K_w is 10^{-14}. What is K_a for NH_4^+? K_b for NH_3 is given in the problem as 1.8×10^{-5}. Thus

$$K_b(NH_3) \times K_a(NH_4^+) = K_w$$
$$K_a(NH_4^+) = \frac{K_w}{K_b(NH_3)} = \frac{10^{-14}}{1.8 \times 10^{-5}} = 5.6 \times 10^{-10}$$

Thus NH_4^+ is a stronger acid than H_2O and will dominate in the production of H^+, making the reaction of interest

$$NH_4^+ \rightleftarrows NH_3 + H^+ \qquad K_a = \frac{[NH_3][H^+]}{[NH_4^+]} = 5.6 \times 10^{-10}$$

Note the following:

1.   Just because K_b for NH_3 is given in this problem does not mean that the K_b reaction should be used. Let the solution components tell you what reaction to use. This solution contains NH_4^+, not NH_3. Thus NH_4^+ is the reactant, not NH_3.
2.   This is a typical weak acid problem. The only differences between this case and previous weak acid problems are that the acid in this problem is ionic and the K_a for the acid is not given, but must be calculated from K_b and K_w.

The problem may now be solved in the normal way:

Initial Concentrations
$[NH_4^+]_0 = 0.010 \ M$
$[H^+]_0 \approx 0$
$[NH_3]_0 = 0$

Let x moles/ℓ
of NH_4^+
——dissociate to——▶
come to
equilibrium

Equilibrium Concentrations
$[NH_4^+] = 0.010 - x$
$[H^+] = x$
$[NH_3] = x$

$$K_a = 5.6 \times 10^{-10} = \frac{[NH_3][H^+]}{[NH_4^+]} = \frac{(x)\,(x)}{0.010 - x} \approx \frac{x^2}{0.010}$$

$$x^2 \approx 5.6 \times 10^{-12}$$
$$x = 2.4 \times 10^{-6}$$

Noting that the assumption is valid,

$$[H^+] = x = 2.4 \times 10^{-6}$$

and

$$pH = 5.62$$

Acidic Solutions: Case 2

Now we consider solutions containing highly charged cations. Recall that when small, highly charged cations are placed in water, the resulting hydrated ion may be acidic. For example, when Co^{3+} is placed in water, $Co(OH_2)_6^{3+}$ is formed, which undergoes acid dissociation:

$$Co(OH_2)_6^{3+} \rightleftharpoons Co(OH)(OH_2)_5^{2+} + H^+$$

where $K_a = 1.02 \times 10^{-5}$.

Sample Problem 2–14

A solution is prepared by dissolving 0.050 mole of $CoCl_3(s)$ in enough water to make 1.00 ℓ of solution. Calculate the pH of this solution. (K_a for $Co(OH_2)_6^{3+}$ is 1.02×10^{-5}.)

Solution

Since $CoCl_3(s)$ is an ionic compound, the solution will contain the major species:

$$Co^{3+}(aq), Cl^-(aq), H_2O$$

where $Co^{3+}(aq)$ is $Co(OH_2)_6^{3+}$. Consider the acid-base properties of each major component:

1. $Co(OH_2)_6^{3+}$ weak acid (K_a given)
2. Cl^- extremely weak base (no effect on pH)
3. H_2O acid or base (very weak)

Clearly $Co(OH_2)_6^{3+}$ is the dominant weak acid (K_a for $Co(OH_2)_6^{3+}$ is much greater than K_w).

$$Co(OH_2)_6^{3+} \rightleftharpoons Co(OH)(OH_2)_5^{2+} + H^+$$

$$K_a = \frac{[Co(OH)(OH_2)_5^{2+}][H^+]}{[Co(OH_2)_6^{3+}]} = 1.02 \times 10^{-5}$$

Now go through the usual steps:
1. Define the initial concentrations.
2. Define x.
3. Write down equilibrium concentrations.

Initial Concentrations		Equilibrium Concentrations
$[Co(OH_2)_6^{3+}]_0 = 0.050\ M$	Let x moles/ℓ	$[Co(OH_2)_6^{3+}] = 0.050 - x$
$[Co(OH)(OH_2)_5^{2+}]_0 = 0$	$\longrightarrow Co(OH_2)_6^{3+} \longrightarrow$	$[Co(OH)(OH_2)_5^{2+}] = x$
$[H^+]_0 \approx 0$	dissociate	$[H^+] = x$

$$1.02 \times 10^{-5} = K_a = \frac{[\text{Co(OH)}(\text{OH}_2)_5{}^{2+}][\text{H}^+]}{[\text{Co(OH}_2)_6{}^{3+}]} = \frac{(x)(x)}{0.050 - x} \approx \frac{x^2}{0.050}$$

$$x^2 \approx (0.050)(1.02 \times 10^{-5}) = 5.10 \times 10^{-7}$$
$$x \approx 7.1 \times 10^{-4}$$

Since

$$\frac{x}{[\text{HA}]_0} \times 100 = \frac{7.10 \times 10^{-4}}{5.0 \times 10^{-2}} \times 100 = 1.4\%$$

the assumption is valid, so

$$[\text{H}^+] = 7.1 \times 10^{-4}$$
$$\text{pH} = 3.15$$

Note that the solution is quite acidic.

TEST 2–11

A. Calculate the pH of a 0.10 M solution of $C_6H_5NH_3Cl$. The K_b for $C_6H_5NH_2$ is 3.8×10^{-10}.
   1. What are the major species in solution? (Hint: $C_6H_5NH_3Cl$ is a salt.)
   2. What is the value of K_a for $C_6H_5NH_3{}^+$?
   3. What reaction will dominate in determining the pH?
   4. Set up the equilibrium expression for (3).
   5. List the initial concentrations.
   6. Define x.
   7. Write the equilibrium concentrations in terms of x.
   8. Solve for x. (Check assumptions.)
   9. Calculate the pH.

B. Calculate the pH of a 0.20 M solution of $CrCl_3$. ($Cr(OH_2)_6{}^{3+}$ has $K_a = 1.5 \times 10^{-4}$.)

Summary

Certain positive ions can behave as acids. In general there are two classes:
1. Positive ions that are conjugate acids of bases (that is, protonated bases).
2. Hydrated metal ions.

Basic Solutions

When some salts are dissolved in water, a basic solution results. For example, consider what happens when sodium acetate is dissolved in water:

$$\text{NaOAc(s)} \xrightarrow{\text{H}_2\text{O}} \text{Na}^+(\text{aq}) + \text{OAc}^-(\text{aq})$$

What are the acid or base properties of these ions?
   1. Na^+ is neither an acid nor a base.

2. OAc^- is a base. Acetate ion is the conjugate base of acetic acid (a weak acid), which means that acetate ion has a significant affinity for H^+.

Sample Problem 2–15

Calculate the pH of a 1.0 M solution of sodium acetate. The K_a for acetic acid is 1.8×10^{-5}.

Solution

The major species are: Na^+, OAc^-, H_2O.
1. Na^+ neither an acid nor a base.
2. OAc^- a base (HOAc is a weak acid)
3. H_2O weak acid or base

When OAc^- is placed in water, what reaction will occur? Acetate ion is a base, which means it will combine with a proton. Where will the proton come from? Water is the only source. Thus the reaction must be

$$OAc^- + H_2O \rightleftarrows HOAc + OH^- \qquad K_b = \frac{[HOAc]\,[OH^-]}{[OAc^-]}$$

What is the value of K_b? We know that

$$K_a\,(HOAc) \times K_b\,(OAc^-) = K_w$$

thus

$$(1.8 \times 10^{-5})\,K_b = 1.0 \times 10^{-14}$$
$$K_b\,(OAc^-) = \frac{1.0 \times 10^{-14}}{1.8 \times 10^{-5}} = 5.6 \times 10^{-10}$$

Note that this is a very small equilibrium constant. OAc^- does not compete well against OH^- for H^+. However,

$$K_b\,(OAc^-) \gg K_w$$

so that this reaction is much more important in producing OH^- than is the simple dissociation of water. Thus the dominant reaction in this solution is the K_b reaction of OAc^-:

$$OAc^- + H_2O \rightleftarrows HOAc + OH^- \qquad K_b = \frac{[HOAc]\,[OH^-]}{[OAc^-]} = 5.6 \times 10^{-10}$$

Intial Concentrations
$[OAc^-]$ = 1.0 M
$[OH^-]_0$ ≈ 0
$[HOAc]_0$ = 0

Let x moles/ℓ
OAc^-
react with H_2O

Equilibrium Concentrations
$[OAc^-]$ = 1.0 $- x$
$[OH^-]$ = x
$[HOAc]$ = x

$$5.6 \times 10^{-10} = K_b = \frac{[OH^-][HOAc]}{[OAc^-]} = \frac{(x)(x)}{1.0 - x} \approx \frac{x^2}{1.0}$$

$$x^2 \approx (1.0)(5.6 \times 10^{-10})$$
$$x \approx 2.4 \times 10^{-5} \; M$$

Note that $1.0 \ggg 2.4 \times 10^{-5} \; M$; so the assumption is valid. Then

$$x = [OH^-] = 2.4 \times 10^{-5} \; M$$

To find the pH, use K_w:

$$K_w = 1.0 \times 10^{-14} = [H^+][OH^-] = [H^+](2.4 \times 10^{-5})$$
$$[H^+] = \frac{1.0 \times 10^{-14}}{2.4 \times 10^{-5}} = 4.2 \times 10^{-10}$$
$$pH = 9.38$$

Thus a 1.0 M sodium acetate solution is quite basic.

Summary

When salts are dissolved in water, acid-base reactions may occur. Consider the following cases:

A. A basic solution will result if the anion of the salt is the conjugate base of a *weak acid*. The K_b for the anion can be calculated from the K_a value of the parent acid ($K_a \cdot K_b = K_w$). Anions of strong acids (*e.g.*, Cl^-, NO_3^-, ClO_4^-, HSO_4^-) have very low affinities for H^+ and thus do not affect the pH. (A solution of NaCl or KNO_3 has pH = 7.)

B. An acidic solution will result when:
    1. The cation is the conjugate acid of a weak base. The cation is a weak acid whose K_a can be calculated from K_b for the parent base ($K_a \cdot K_b = K_w$).
    2. The cation is a hydrated metal ion (usually with a charge of $+3$ or greater), which behaves as a weak acid. The K_a value for this type of weak acid will be given.

TEST 2–12

A. Consider an aqueous solution of each of the following salts. For each salt state whether the solution will be neutral, acidic, or basic, and write the reaction for the latter two cases.
    1. NaCl
    2. NH_4NO_3
    3. $Al(NO_3)_3$
    4. NaCN   (K_a for HCN is 6.2×10^{-10})
    5. $(CH_3)_3NHCl$ (K_b for $(CH_3)_3N$ is 5.3×10^{-5})

B. Since acetic acid (HOAc) is a weak acid, we say that acetate ion (OAc⁻) must be a strong base. However, the K_b for OAc⁻ is only 5.6×10^{-10}. Explain this apparent discrepancy. (Hint: compare the K_a reaction for HOAc and the K_b reaction for OAc⁻. In both reactions OAc⁻ competes for H⁺. Does it compete with the same base in both reactions?)

2.9   HENDERSON-HASSELBALCH EQUATION (optional)

For the dissociation of a weak acid,

$$HA \rightleftharpoons H^+ + A^-$$

$$K_a = \frac{[H^+][A^-]}{[HA]} = [H^+]\frac{[A^-]}{[HA]}$$

Now take the log of both sides

$$\log K_a = \log[H^+] + \log\frac{[A^-]}{[HA]}$$

(remembering that the log of a product is the sum of the logs, $i.e.$, $\log xy = \log x + \log y$). Multiply both sides of the equation by -1:

$$-\log K_a = -\log[H^+] - \log\frac{[A^-]}{[HA]}$$

$$pK_a = pH - \log\frac{[A^-]}{[HA]}$$

or

$$pH = pK_a + \log\frac{[A^-]}{[HA]}$$

This "log form" of the K_a expression is called the **Henderson-Hasselbalch equation.** This equation is useful in situations where the [HA] and [A⁻] are known.

Sample Problem 2–12

The acid HOCl has a pK_a value of 7.50. Calculate the pH of a solution containing 0.25 M HOCl and 0.75 M NaOCl.

Solution

$$pH = pK_a + \log \frac{[A^-]}{[HA]}$$

$$= 7.50 + \log\left(\frac{0.75}{0.25}\right) = 7.50 + \log(3.0)$$

$$= 7.50 + 0.48 = 7.98$$

2.10   REVIEW OF PROCEDURES

Remember: The most important part of doing an acid-base problem is the analysis you do at the beginning of the problem:

Does a reaction occur?

What is it?

What equilibrium dominates?

The best way to answer these questions successfully is to *write down the major species in solution*. Then ask the question: Does a reaction occur that goes to completion? The situations to look for are:

Has OH$^-$ been added to a solution containing an acid?

Has H$^+$ been added to a solution containing a base?

In both of these situations, the reaction that occurs can be assumed to go to completion. After the reaction has been allowed to go to completion, again *write down the major species*. Now check each one for acid or base properties and select the dominant equilibrium by looking at the values of the various equilibrium constants. In almost every case, one equilibrium will dominate and can be used to solve for the [H$^+$] or [OH$^-$].

When faced with an acid-base problem, the best strategy is to assume that it is not exactly like any other problem you may have done. One small change can cause a problem that looks very similar to one you have done before to be quite different.

When starting an acid-base problem, the **wrong** question to ask is: How can I use a problem whose solution I have memorized to solve this problem? The **correct** question is: What species are in solution and what do they do? (Think Chemistry!) *Let the problem guide you*.

The steps to follow are:

1. Write down the major species in solution before any reactions take place.
2. Look for any reactions taking place that can be assumed to go to completion.
    Examples: OH$^-$ with acid (strong or weak)
    H$^+$ with base (strong or weak)
3. If a reaction occurs that can be assumed complete:
    a. Do the stoichiometry problem.
    b. Write down the major species in solution after the reaction.
4. Look at each major component of the solution and decide which are acids or bases.
5. Pick the equilibrium that will control the [H$^+$]. Use the K's for the various species to help decide.
6. Do the equilibrium calculation.
    a. Write the equation for the reaction and the equilibrium expression.
    b. Compute the initial concentrations (assuming the equilibrium of interest has not yet occurred, *i.e.*, no acid dissociation, etc.).

 c. Define x.
 d. Compute the equilibrium concentrations in terms of x.
 e. Substitute in the equilibrium expression and solve for x, making approximations to simplify the math if possible.
 f. Check the validity of the approximations.
 g. Calculate the pH.

Exercises

1. For each of the following solutions, list the major species in solution and select
  the equilibrium that will control the pH.
 a) $1.00\ M\ HNO_2\ (K_a = 4.0 \times 10^{-4})$
 b) $0.010\ M\ HNO_3$
 c) $1.0\ M\ C_5H_5N\ (K_b = 1.4 \times 10^{-9})$
 d) $0.10\ M\ NaCN\ (K_a\ \text{for HCN} = 6.2 \times 10^{-10})$
 e) $0.050\ M\ HCHO_2$ (formic acid, $K_a = 1.8 \times 10^{-4}$) and
   $0.025\ M\ NaCHO_2$ (sodium formate)
 f) $1.0\ M\ NaOH$
 g) $1.0 \times 10^{-2}\ M\ Pu(NO_3)_3\ (K_a\ \text{for Pu(OH}_2)_6^{3+} = 1.1 \times 10^{-7})$
 h) $1.00\ M\ HOCl\ (K_a = 3.5 \times 10^{-8})$
 i) $1.00\ M\ (CH_3)_3N\ (K_b = 5.3 \times 10^{-5})$
 j) $0.100\ M\ HCl$
 k) $1.0 \times 10^{-3}\ M\ KOH$
 l) $0.100\ M\ HNO_2\ (K_a = 4.0 \times 10^{-4})$
   $0.050\ M\ NaNO_2$
 m) $1.00\ M\ HF\ (K_a = 7.2 \times 10^{-4})$
   $2.50\ M\ NaF$
 n) $0.500\ M\ CH_3NH_2\ (K_b = 4.4 \times 10^{-4})$
 o) $1.00 \times 10^{-2}\ M\ Al(NO_3)_3\ (K_a\ \text{for Al(OH}_2)_6^{3+} = 1.4 \times 10^{-5})$

2. Calculate the pH for each solution in problem 1.

3. A solution is to be buffered at pH $= 7.0$. Which of the following acid-salt
  pairs would be the best choice for buffering this solution?.
 a) HCl, NaCl
 b) $HOCl\ (K_a = 3.5 \times 10^{-8})$, NaOCl
 c) $HCN\ (K_a = 6.2 \times 10^{-10})$, NaCN
 d) $HF\ (K_a = 7.2 \times 10^{-4})$, NaF

4. To buffer a solution at pH $= 7.0$, what is the ideal K_a value for the acid to
  be used?

5. A solution contains $0.50\ M$ propionic acid ($HC_3H_5O_2$, $K_a = 1.3 \times 10^{-3}$) and
  $0.20\ M$ sodium propionate ($NaC_3H_5O_2$).
 a) Calculate the pH of this solution.
 b) Calculate the pH after 0.10 mole of HCl(g) has been added to 1.0 ℓ of
   this solution.
 c) Calculate the pH after 0.050 mole of NaOH(s) has been added to 1.0 ℓ
   of the original solution.

6. Calculate the pH of a 0.10 M solution of NaOCN. The K_a for HOCN is 1.3×10^{-4}.

7. Calculate the pH of a solution formed by mixing 500.0 mℓ of 0.100 M NH$_3$ and 500.0 mℓ of 0.0500 M HCl. (K_b for NH$_3$ is 1.8×10^{-5}.)

8. Consider a solution containing 0.500 M C$_6$H$_5$NH$_2$ ($K_b = 3.8 \times 10^{-10}$) and 0.200 M C$_6H_5NH_3$Cl.
   a) Calculate the pH.
   b) Calculate the pH after 0.100 mole of HCl(g) is dissolved in 1.0 ℓ of this solution.

Verbalizing General Concepts

Answer the following in your own words:

9. What is an acid?

10. What does "acid strength" mean?

11. What is a base?

12. What do strong and weak acids have in common? How are they different?

13. What is a buffered solution?

14. When a salt is dissolved in water, what property of the anion causes the solution to be basic?

15. When a salt is dissolved in water, what properties of the salt might cause the solution to be acidic?

Name_____ Section_____ Date_____

Multiple Choice Questions

16. The pH of a 10^{-3} M NaCl solution is closest to
    a)   3.0   b)   6.0   c)   7.0   d)   8.0

17. The acid HX has an ionization constant of 1×10^{-4}. A solution is 0.1 M in HX and 1 M in the salt Na^+X^-. What is a close approximation of the hydrogen ion concentration?
    a) 10^{-3} M b) 2×10^{-5} M c) 10^{-5} M d) 10^{-8} M

18. A 0.20 M solution of the hypothetical weak acid HZ is found to have a pH of exactly 3.0. The ionization constant, K_a, of the acid HZ is
    a)   0.6   b) 1.0×10^{-3} c) 2.0×10^{-4} d) 5.0×10^{-6}

19. A buffer solution is formed by adding 0.500 mole of sodium acetate and 0.500 mole of acetic acid to 1.00 ℓ H_2O. What is the pH of the solution at equilibrium? ($K_a = 1.80 \times 10^{-5}$)
    a)   5.05   b)   4.74   c)   4.44   d)   2.38   e)   none of these

20. 0.10 mole HCl is added to the solution in problem 19. Now what is the concentration of H^+?
    a) 2.7×10^{-5} M d) 1.2×10^{-5} M
    b) 4.5×10^{-5} M e)   none of these
    c) 3.0×10^{-5} M

21. The approximate pH of 10^{-3} M HCl at 25°C is
    a) 10^{-3} d) 10^3
    b) -3 e)   11
    c)   3

22. The OH^- concentration in 10^{-3} M HCl at 25°C is
    a) 10^{-3} M d) 10^{-11} M
    b) 10^{-6} M e) 5×10^{-10} M
    c) 2×10^{-6} M

23. (a)   If K_b for the reaction

$$NH_3 + H_2O \rightleftarrows NH_4^+ + OH^-$$

is 1.8×10^{-5}, what concentration of ammonium ion would have to be present at equilibrium in a 0.15 M solution of NH_3 to make the OH^- concentration 1.4×10^{-4} M?
    a)   0.15 M d) 1.4×10^{-4} M
    b) 1.8×10^{-5} M e)   15 M
    c) 1.9×10^{-2} M

(b)   How would you make the solution in (a) from aqueous ammonia and hydrochloric acid?

  a) 1.0 ℓ of 0.169 M NH_3 and 1.0 ℓ of 0.019 M HCl.
  b) 100.0 mℓ of 0.30 M NH_3 and 100.0 mℓ of 0.019 M HCl.
  c) 1.0 ℓ of 0.15 M NH_3 and 1.0 ℓ of 0.019 M HCl.
  d) 500.0 mℓ of 0.038 M HCl and 500.0 mℓ of 0.338 M NH_3.

24. Which species is *most* likely to function *both* as an acid and as a base?
  a) Cl^- b) NH_4^+ c) H_2O d) H_3O^+

25. Under conditions of equal molar concentration in water, which metal ion probably produces the most acidic solution?
  a) Al^{3+} b) Ba^{2+} c) K^+ d) Zn^{2+}

26. Which statement is a logical consequence of the fact that a 0.10 molar solution of potassium acetate, $KC_2H_3O_2$, is less basic than a 0.10 molar solution of potassium cyanide, KCN?
  a) Hydrocyanic acid (HCN) is a weaker acid than acetic acid.
  b) Hydrocyanic acid is less soluble in water than acetic acid.
  c) Cyanides are less soluble than acetates.
  d) Acetic acid is a weaker acid than hydrocyanic acid.

27. How many moles of pure NaOH must be used to prepare 10 liters of a solution that has a pH of 13.00?
  a) 1.0   b) 0.10   c) 0.010   d) 0.0010

28. What is the pH of a solution that has an OH^- concentration of 4.0×10^{-9} M?
  a) 8.40   b) 5.60   c) 9.40   d) 4.60   e) none of these

29. What is the H^+ concentration of a solution produced from 80.0 g of NaOH added to 0.50 ℓ of H_2O (assume no volume increase on addition of NaOH)?
  a) 2.5×10^{-15} M d) 4.0×10^{-14} M
  b) 5.0×10^{-15} M e) none of these
  c) 1.0×10^{-14} M

30. Calculate the OH^- concentration in a 0.0100 M solution of aniline, $C_6H_5NH_2$:

$$C_6H_5NH_2(aq) + H_2O(\ell) \rightleftarrows C_6H_5NH_3^+(aq) + OH^-(aq)$$

  ($K_b = 3.8 \times 10^{-10}$)
  a) 3.0×10^{-7} M d) 5.1×10^{-9} M
  b) 3.8×10^{-12} M e) none of these
  c) 3.8×10^{-6} M

31. In the reaction

$$HCN(aq) + HCO_3^-(aq) \rightleftarrows CN^-(aq) + H_2CO_3(aq)$$

  $K < 1$ (K is the equilibrium constant). What is the strongest base in this system?
  a) HCN   b) HCO_3^- c) CN^- d) H_2CO_3

32. Consider the reaction

$$CH_3NH_2(aq) + H_2O(\ell) \rightleftarrows CH_3NH_3{}^+(aq) + OH^-(aq)$$

where $K_b = 4.4 \times 10^{-4}$. To a solution formed from the addition of 2.0 moles CH_3NH_2 to 1.0 ℓ of H_2O is added 1.0 mole of KOH (assume no volume change on addition of solutes). What is the concentration of $CH_3NH_3{}^+$ at equilibrium?
a) 3.2×10^{-2} M d) 8.8×10^{-4} M
b) 2.2×10^{-4} M e) none of these
c) 2.0×10^{-3} M

33. The Henderson-Hasselbalch equation applied to a solution of an acid, HIn, is

$$pH = pK_a + \log\frac{[In^-]}{[HIn]}$$

You wish to calculate the pH of a solution using the above equation. You know pK_a, [HIn], and [In$^-$]. However, you accidentally use twice the concentration of In$^-$ in the calculation. What effect will this have on the calculated pH?
a) No effect.
b) Make it too large.
c) Make it too small.
d) The pH would be too small or too large depending on the concentration of In$^-$ used in the calculation.

34. Which of the following reactions is associated with the normal definition of K_b?
a) $Al(OH_2)_6{}^{3+} \rightleftarrows [Al(OH_2)_5OH]^{2+} + H^+$
b) $CN^- + H^+ \rightleftarrows HCN$
c) $F^- + H_2O \rightleftarrows HF + OH^-$
d) $Cr^{3+} + 6H_2O \rightleftarrows Cr(OH_2)_6{}^{3+}$

35. What is the pH of a 1.0 M solution of aniline? ($K_b = 4 \times 10^{-10}$)
a) 4.7   b) 9.3   c) 9.4   d) none of these

36. A solution has a pOH of 5.5. What is the [H$^+$]?
a) 8.5 M b) $10^{-5.5}$ M c) $10^{-8.5}$ M d) 5.5×10^{-14} M

37. The pH of a 1.0 M solution of sodium propionate ($NaC_3H_5O_2$) is 8.3. The pK_a for propionic acid ($HC_3H_5O_2$) is
a) 8.3   b) 5.7   c) 11.4   d) 2.6   e) none of these

38. Calculate the [H$^+$] in a solution prepared by adding 0.050 mole of nitrous acid (HNO_2) to 0.100 mole of sodium nitrite ($NaNO_2$) to form 1.00 ℓ of solution. The K_a for HNO_2 is 4.0×10^{-4}.
a) 2.0×10^{-4} M d) 6.3×10^{-3} M
b) 4.0×10^{-4} M e) none of these
c) 8.0×10^{-4} M

39. What is the $[H^+]$ after 0.025 mole of $HCl(g)$ is added to the solution described in question 38?
    a) $2.0 \times 10^{-4} M$
    b) $4.0 \times 10^{-4} M$
    c) $8.0 \times 10^{-4} M$
    d) $2.5 \times 10^{-2} M$
    e) none of these

40. The $[H^+]$ in a 1.0 M solution of HA ($K_a = 4.0 \times 10^{-8}$) is
    a) 1.0 M b) $4.0 \times 10^{-8} M$ c) $2.0 \times 10^{-8} M$ d) none of these

41. What is the pH of a 1.0 M solution of HCl?
    a) 10   b) 1.0   c) 0   d) -1.0

42. The pH of a 5.0 M solution of HNO_3 is
    a) 5.0   b) -0.30 c) -0.70 d) 0.70

43. If the pK_a of the acid HX is 8.0, the K_b for X^- is
    a) 10^8 b) 10^{-8} c) 10^{-6} d) 10^6 e) none of these

44. The fact that acetic acid ($HC_2H_3O_2$) is a stronger acid than HCN implies that
    a) the acetate ion ($C_2H_3O_2^-$) is a stronger base than CN^-.
    b) CN^- is a stronger base than $C_2H_3O_2^-$.
    c) a 0.1 M solution of $HC_2H_3O_2$ has a higher pH than 0.1 M HCN.
    d) a 0.1 M solution of $NaC_2H_3O_2$ has a higher pH than 0.1 M NaCN.

45. Which of the following is a base-conjugate acid pair?
    a) $C_6H_5NH_2$, $C_6H_5NH_3^+$
    b) Cl^-, NH_4^+
    c) NH_3, $HC_2H_3O_2$
    d) $HC_2H_3O_2$, H_2O

46. A solution is $1.25 \times 10^{-2} M$ in benzoic acid (HA) and $8.50 \times 10^{-3} M$ in sodium benzoate. If the K_a of benzoic acid is 6.50×10^{-5}, the $[H^+]$ of this solution is
    a) $1.26 \times 10^{-2} M$
    b) $4.47 \times 10^{-4} M$
    c) $9.56 \times 10^{-5}M$
    d) $4.42 \times 10^{-5} M$
    e) none of these

47. A 0.625 M solution of a weak acid (HA) has an $[H^+]$ of 4.20×10^{-3}. What is the K_a of this weak acid?
    a) 2.82×10^{-5}
    b) 6.72×10^{-3}
    c) 1.76×10^{-5}
    d) 3.55×10^{-4}
    e) none of these

48. When 1.0000 gram of sodium acetate (MW = 82.0) is added to 150. mℓ of 0.0500 molar acetic acid (MW = 60.0), the pOH of the resulting solution is (K_a for acetic acid is 1.80×10^{-5})
    a) 1.06   b) 4.97   c) 9.04   d) 12.9   e) none of these

49. The amount (in grams) of sodium acetate (MW = 82.0) to be added to 500 mℓ of 0.200 molar acetic acid ($K_a = 1.80 \times 10^{-5}$) in order to make a buffer with pH = 5.00 is
    a) 369   b) 0.180   c) 14.8   d) 29.5   e) none of these

50. A solution is $0.120\ M$ in acetic acid and $0.0900\ M$ in sodium acetate. Calculate the $[H^+]$ at equilibrium. (K_a of acetic acid is 1.80×10^{-5})
    a) $4.87\ M$
    b) $2.40 \times 10^{-5}\ M$
    c) $1.35 \times 10^{-5}\ M$
    d) $4.62\ M$
    e) $6.00 \times 10^{-6}\ M$

51. A $0.30\ M$ solution of a weak acid (HA) has an $[H^+]$ of $1.66 \times 10^{-4}\ M$. What is the K_a of this weak acid?
    a) 4.8×10^1
    b) 5.5×10^{-4}
    c) 1.2×10^8
    d) 9.2×10^{-8}
    e) the K_a cannot be calculated without additional information

52. What volumes of $0.500\ M$ HNO_2 ($K_a = 4.0 \times 10^{-4}$) and $0.500\ M$ $NaNO_2$ must be mixed to prepare $1.0\ \ell$ of a solution buffered at pH 3.55?
    a) 500 mℓ of each solution
    b) 703 mℓ $0.500\ M$ HNO_2, 297 mℓ $0.500\ M$ $NaNO_2$
    c) 413 mℓ $0.500\ M$ HNO_2, 587 mℓ $0.500\ M$ $NaNO_2$
    d) 297 mℓ $0.500\ M$ HNO_2, 703 mℓ $0.500\ M$ $NaNO_2$
    e) 587 mℓ $0.500\ M$ HNO_2, 413 mℓ $0.500\ M$ $NaNO_2$

3

ACID-BASE TITRATIONS AND INDICATORS

Chapter Objectives

1. Define titration, millimole, indicator, equivalence (stoichiometric) point, end-point.

2. Calculate the pH of a solution during the titration of a strong acid with a sodium hydroxide solution.

3. Calculate the pH of a solution during the titration of a weak acid with a sodium hydroxide solution.

4. Know the differences between the titration curves for the titration of a strong acid with a strong base and that of a weak acid with a strong base.

5. Calculate pH when strong or weak bases are titrated with solutions of strong acids.

6. Know the mechanism for indicator color changes.

7. Know the principles involved in choosing an appropriate indicator.

3.1   INTRODUCTION

An acid-base titration involves a quantitative study of the reaction occurring when a solution containing a base is mixed with a solution containing an acid. The calculations involved in a titration depend on concepts already covered, but their application may not be completely straightforward. Thus it is especially important to attack these problems in a systematic way.

A titration problem always involves a stoichiometry problem, and may also involve an equilibrium problem. The two problems must be treated separately.

The simplest case, the titration involving a strong acid and a strong base, will be treated first.

3.2   STRONG ACID-STRONG BASE TITRATIONS

This case involves only a stoichiometry problem. No equilibrium calculations are necessary.

Sample Problem 3–1

Consider the titration of 100.0 mℓ of 1.00 M HCl with 0.500 M NaOH. Calculate the [H^+] in the solution after 50.0 mℓ of 0.50 M NaOH have been added.

Solution

A titration always involves a chemical reaction. To determine what reaction will occur, consider the major species existing in the mixed solution before any reaction occurs:

$$H^+, Cl^-, Na^+, OH^-, H_2O$$

Note that the solution contains large quantities of H^+ and OH^-. These ions readily react to form H_2O:

$$H^+ + OH^- \rightleftarrows H_2O$$

Since this equilibrium lies far to the right $\left(K = \dfrac{1}{K_w} = 10^{14}\right)$, assume the reaction that occurs upon mixing goes to completion (that is, the reaction proceeds until it "runs out" of the limiting reagent).

Now do a stoichiometry problem:

How much H^+ was originally present in the solution? 100.0 mℓ of 1.00 M HCl gives

$$100.0 \text{ mℓ} \times \frac{1.0 \text{ ℓ}}{1000 \text{ mℓ}} \times 1.0 \frac{\text{mole}}{\text{ℓ}} = 0.100 \text{ mole HCl}$$
$$= 0.100 \text{ mole } H^+$$

since the HCl (a strong acid) is completely dissociated.

How much NaOH was added? 50.0 mℓ of 0.50 M NaOH was added, and

$$50.0 \text{ mℓ} \times \frac{1.0 \text{ ℓ}}{1000 \text{ mℓ}} \times 0.50 \frac{\text{mole}}{\text{ℓ}} = 0.025 \text{ mole NaOH}$$
$$= 0.025 \text{ mole } OH^-$$

since the NaOH (a strong base) is completely dissociated.

The reaction is

	H^+	+	OH^+	$\rightarrow$	H_2O
Before the reaction	0.100 mole		0.025 mole		large and essentially constant

After the reaction goes to completion	$0.100 - 0.025$ $= 0.075$ mole	$0.025 - 0.025$ $= 0$	large and essentially constant

After the reaction is complete, the major species present in the solution are:

$$H^+, Cl^-, Na^+, H_2O$$

The $[H^+]$ will be determined by the excess H^+ remaining:

$$[H^+] = \frac{moles}{volume(\ell)} = \frac{0.075 \text{ mole}}{0.100 \; \ell + 0.050 \; \ell} = \frac{0.075 \text{ mole}}{0.150 \; \ell}$$

↗   ↗   ↗
volume of   volume   total
HCl solution   of NaOH   volume
            solution   of the mixture

$$[H^+] = 0.50 \; M$$
$$pH = -\log(0.50) = 0.30$$

Titration problems typically involve volumes of 100 mℓ or less. Having to change the units on these volumes to liters is a hassle and a source of "silly errors." This problem can be avoided by using the units milliliters and millimoles. A millimole (mmole) is one one-thousandth of a mole $\left(\dfrac{mole}{1000} \text{ or } 10^{-3} \text{ mole} \right)$.

$$Molarity = \frac{moles}{\ell} = \frac{\dfrac{moles}{1000}}{\dfrac{\ell}{1000}} = \frac{mmoles}{m\ell}$$

Thus molarity can be expressed as either moles/ℓ or mmoles/mℓ. The volume in mℓ times the molarity gives the number of millimoles. For example,

$$100.0 \text{ m}\ell \text{ of } 1.00 \; M \text{ HCl contains}$$
$$100.0 \text{ m}\ell \times 1.00 \frac{mmole \; HCl}{m\ell} = 100 \text{ mmoles HCl}$$
$$50.0 \text{ m}\ell \times \frac{0.50 \text{ mmole}}{m\ell} = 25 \text{ mmoles NaOH}$$

Now do the calculations for Sample Problem 3–1 using millimoles:

$$H^+ \quad + \quad OH^- \quad \rightarrow \quad H_2O$$

Before the reaction	100 mmoles	25 mmoles	

After the reaction goes to completion	75 mmoles	0

$$[H^+] = \frac{\text{mmoles } H^+}{\text{m}\ell \text{ of solution}} = \frac{75 \text{ mmoles}}{(100+50) \text{ m}\ell} = \frac{75 \text{ mmoles}}{150 \text{ m}\ell}$$

$$= 0.50 \frac{\text{mmoles}}{\text{m}\ell}$$

$$\frac{0.50 \text{ mmole}}{\text{m}\ell} = \frac{0.50 \text{ mole}}{\ell} = 0.50 \text{ } M$$

The advantage in using mmoles to do titration problems is that it eliminates the need to change the volume to liters, which can lead to math errors.

Remember: mmoles $= \text{m}\ell \times$ Molarity
and
moles $= \ell \times$ Molarity

Learn to use mmoles when the volumes are given in mℓ. Use moles when the volumes are given in liters.

Sample Problem 3–2

Consider the titration of 50.0 mℓ of 0.200 M HNO$_3$ with 0.100 M NaOH. Calculate the pH at the following points in the titration:

Total volume of 0.100 M NaOH added (mℓ)
A)   0
B)   10.0
C)   20.0
D)   50.0
E)   100.0
F)   150.0
G)   200.0

Solution

A. 0 mℓ of NaOH added.
    The solution contains: HNO$_3$, H$_2$O
    HNO$_3$ is a strong acid and thus is completely dissociated:

$$HNO_3 \longrightarrow H^+ + NO_3^-$$

0.20 M HNO$_3$ produces 0.20 M H$^+$, so [H$^+$] = 0.20 M, and

$$pH = -\log(0.20) = 0.70$$

B.   10.0 ml of NaOH added.
     Before the reaction, the mixed solution contains:

$$HNO_3, \ NaOH, \ H_2O$$

Since both the HNO_3 and NaOH are completely dissociated, the solution would contain:

$$H^+, \ NO_3^-, \ Na^+, \ OH^-, \ H_2O$$

Note that large quantites of both H^+ and OH^- are present. These ions will immediately react to form water:

	H^+	+	OH^-	→	H_2O
Before the reaction	50.0 ml × 0.200 M = 10.0 mmoles		10.0 ml × 0.10 M = 1.0 mmole		large and constant
After the reaction	10.0 − 1.0 = 9.0 mmoles		1.0 − 1.0 = 0		large and constant

After the reaction, the solution contains:

$$H^+, \ NO_3^-, \ Na^+, \ H_2O \ \text{(the } OH^- \text{ has been consumed)}$$

$$[H^+] = \frac{\text{no. of mmoles } H^+}{\text{volume of solution (ml)}} = \frac{9.0}{50.0 + 10.0} = 0.15 \ M$$

volume of acid solution ↗   ↖ volume of NaOH added

$$pH = -\log(0.15) = 0.82$$

C.   20.0 ml (total) has been added.
     Consider this problem as 20.0 ml of NaOH added to the original solution rather than as 10.0 ml of NaOH added to the solution we have just dealt with in B. The problem can be done either way, but it is best to go back to the original solution each time so that a mistake made in an earlier part does not invalidate each succeeding calculation. As before, the added OH^- will react with the H^+:

	H^+	+	OH^-	→	H_2O
Before the reaction	50.0 ml × 0.200 M = 10.0 mmoles		20.0 ml × 0.10 M = 2.0 mmoles		
After the reaction	10.0 − 2.0 = 8.0 mmoles		2.0 − 2.0 = 0 mmoles		

After the reaction, $[H^+] = \dfrac{8.0 \text{ mmoles } H^+}{50.0 + 20.0 \text{ ml}} = 0.11 \ M$

$$pH = -\log(0.11) = 0.94$$

D. 50.0 mℓ (total) of NaOH added.
    Do this one to test what you have learned. (Answer: pH = 1.30.)
E. 100.0 mℓ (total) NaOH added.
    At this point the amount of NaOH added is

$$100.0 \text{ mℓ} \times 0.100 \ M = 10.0 \text{ mmoles}$$

The original amount of nitric acid was

$$50.0 \text{ mℓ} \times 0.200 \ M = 10.0 \text{ mmoles}$$

Enough OH^- has been added to react exactly with the H^+ from the nitric acid. This is the **stoichiometric point** or the **equivalence point** of the titration. At this point, the main species in solution are: Na^+, NO_3^-, H_2O. Since neither Na^+ nor NO_3^- is an acid or a base (NO_3^- is the anion of the strong acid HNO_3 and thus is a *very* weak base), the solution is neutral; the pH is 7.0.

F. 150.0 mℓ (total) of NaOH added.
    Now the OH^- added is in excess. The reaction is

	H^+	$+$	OH^-	$\rightarrow$	H_2O
Before the reaction	50.0 mℓ × 0.200 M = 10.0 mmoles		150.0 mℓ × 0.100 M = 15.0 mmoles		
After the reaction	10.0 − 10.0 = 0		15.0 − 10.0 = 5.0 mmoles		

The OH^- is in excess, and it will determine the pH.

$$[OH^-] = \frac{\text{no. of mmoles } OH^-}{\text{volume (mℓ)}} = \frac{5.0 \text{ mmoles}}{50.0 + 150.0 \text{ mℓ}} = \frac{5.0 \text{ mmoles}}{200 \text{ mℓ}} = 0.025 \ M$$

The $[H^+]$ can be found by substituting into the water equilibrium:

$$[H^+][OH^-] = [H^+](0.025 \ M) = 1.0 \times 10^{-14}$$
$$[H^+] = \frac{1.0 \times 10^{-14}}{2.5 \times 10^{-2}} = 4.0 \times 10^{-13} \ M$$
$$pH = -\log(4.0 \times 10^{-13}) = 12.40$$

G. 200.0 mℓ of NaOH added to the original solution.
    Do this one to test your understanding. (Answer: pH = 12.60.)

A graph of a titration where pH is plotted against the volume of titrant added is called a **pH curve**. The pH curve for the titration considered above is shown in Figure 3–1.

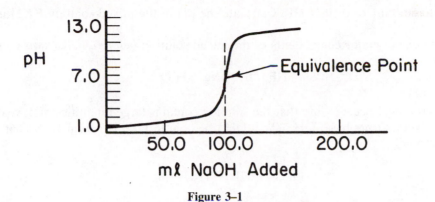

Figure 3–1

This pH curve is typical of the titration of a strong acid with a sodium hydroxide solution.

Summary

The following are characteristics of the calculations involved in the titration of a strong acid with a strong base (OH^-):

1. Before the stoichiometric point, calculate the number of mmoles of acid left and divide by the total volume of the solution to obtain the $[H^+]$.
2. At the stoichiometric (equivalence) point, the pH = 7.0.
3. After the stoichiometric point, calculate the number of mmoles of OH^- in excess and divide by the total volume of the solution to obtain the $[OH^-]$. Then use K_w to obtain the $[H^+]$.

The titration of a strong base with a strong acid is just the opposite of the case just considered.

TEST 3–1

Consider the titration of 100.0 mℓ of 0.50 M NaOH with 1.0 M HCl. Calculate the pH at the following total volumes of added HCl:

A)   0.0 mℓ
B)   25.0 mℓ
C)   50.0 mℓ
D)   75.0 mℓ

3.3   WEAK ACID–STRONG BASE TITRATIONS

Titrations considered so far have involved strong acids and strong bases. Now titrations involving weak acids and strong bases will be discussed. In these cases, two problems will have to be solved:

1. a stoichiometry problem, and
2. an equilibrium problem.

IT IS ESSENTIAL TO DO THESE PROBLEMS SEPARATELY.

As an illustration, consider the following situation: 30.0 mℓ of 0.10 M NaOH solution is added to 50.0 mℓ of 0.10 M HF. Calculate the pH in the mixed solution. (K_a for HF is 7.2 × 10^{-4}.)

Consider the major components of the mixed solution *before any reaction occurs:*

$$HF, OH^-, Na^+, H_2O$$

What reaction will occur? Note that the solution contains large quantities of a weak acid, HF, and a very strong base, OH$^-$. Will OH$^-$ be able to take H$^+$ from HF? That is, will the reaction

$$OH^- + HF \rightarrow H_2O + F^-$$

occur?

The answer is a definite "yes." OH$^-$ is a much stronger base than F$^-$. The equilibrium constant for the above reaction is 7.2 × 10^{10}, which is a very large number. For all practical purposes one may make the assumption that the reaction between HF and OH$^-$ goes to completion (until one of them runs out). This is typical of weak acids: *OH$^-$ can be assumed to react completely with all common weak acids.*

The first step in a titration problem is to do the stoichiometry calculations. In this case, the following questions must be answered:

1. What major species are present in solution before any reaction occurs?
2. What reaction occurs?
3. How much HF was originally present?
4. How much OH$^-$ was added?
5. How much HF is consumed?
6. How much F$^-$ is formed?

Consider these questions one at a time:

1. The solution (before any reaction) contains: HF, Na$^+$, OH$^-$, H$_2$O.

2. The OH$^-$ will react to completion with the HF:

$$OH^- + HF \rightarrow H_2O + F^-$$

3. The amount of HF originally present is

$$50.0 \text{ m}\ell \times 0.10 \ M = 5.0 \text{ mmoles}$$

4. The amount of OH$^-$ added is

$$30.0 \text{ m}\ell \times 0.10 \ M = 3.0 \text{ mmoles}$$

5. The OH$^-$ will consume 3.0 mmoles of HF.

6. 3.0 mmoles of F$^-$ will be formed.

All of this can be summarized as follows:

	HF	+	OH$^-$	→	F$^-$	+	H$_2$O
Before the reaction	5.0 mmoles		3.0 mmoles		0		
After the reaction	5.0 − 3.0 = 2.0 mmoles		3.0 − 3.0 = 0		3.0 mmoles formed		

After the reaction goes to completion, the solution contains the major species:

$$HF, F^-, Na^+, H_2O$$

To calculate the pH, an equilibrium problem must now be done. Which equilibrium makes the dominant contribution to the [H$^+$]? Looking at the above collection of species, it is clear that the HF dissociation (which involves both HF and F$^-$) will control the pH. Do the equilibrium problem in the usual way:

$$HF \rightleftharpoons H^+ + F^-$$
$$K_a = \frac{[H^+][F^-]}{[HF]} = 7.2 \times 10^{-4}$$

The volume of the solution is 50.0 + 30.0 = 80.0 mℓ. Remember that the *total volume* of the mixed solutions must be used in carrying out the equilibrium calculations.

Initial Concentrations (before any dissociation)

$$[HF]_0 = \frac{2.0 \text{ mmoles HF left}}{(50.0 + 30.0) \text{ m}\ell}$$

$$[F^-]_0 = \frac{3.0 \text{ mmoles F}^- \text{ formed}}{(50.0 + 30.0) \text{ m}\ell}$$

$$[H^+]_0 = 0$$

Let x moles/ℓ of HF dissociate →

Formed in the reaction of OH$^-$ with HF

Equilibrium Concentrations

$$[HF] = \frac{2.0}{80.0} - x$$

$$[F^-] = \frac{3.0}{80.0} + x$$

$$[H^+] = x$$

Note that this is really a "common ion problem." The common ion is the F$^-$ formed in the initial, complete reaction of OH$^-$ with HF.

Now substitute into the equilibrium expression and solve for x:

$$7.2 \times 10^{-4} = K_a = \frac{[H^+][F^-]}{[HF]} = \frac{(x)\left(\frac{3.0}{80.0} + x\right)}{\left(\frac{2.0}{80.0} - x\right)} \approx \frac{(x)\left(\frac{3.0}{80.0}\right)}{\left(\frac{2.0}{80.0}\right)}$$

$$x \approx \frac{(7.2 \times 10^{-4})\left(\frac{2.0}{80.0}\right)}{\left(\frac{3.0}{80.0}\right)} = 4.8 \times 10^{-4} \, M$$

Since $\dfrac{2.0}{80.0} = 2.5 \times 10^{-2}$ and $x = 4.8 \times 10^{-4}$, the assumptions that $\dfrac{2.0}{80.0} - x \approx$ $\dfrac{2.0}{80.0}$ and $\dfrac{3.0}{80.0} + x \approx \dfrac{3.0}{80.0}$ are valid.

$$x = [H^+] = 4.8 \times 10^{-4}$$
$$pH = -\log[H^+] = -\log(4.8 \times 10^{-4}) = 3.32$$

For the titration of a weak acid with a strong base, the following steps are necessary:
1. Calculate the amount (in mmoles) of weak acid (HA) originally in solution.
2. Calculate the number of millimoles of OH^- added.
3. Run the reaction between OH^- and the weak acid to completion

$$HA + OH^- \rightarrow H_2O + A^-$$

4. Calculate the amounts (mmoles) of HA left and of A^- formed.
5. Do the weak acid equilibrium problem as usual. (Do not forget to account for the A^- formed in the reaction with OH^- when computing the initial concentrations.)

Sample Problem 3–3

Consider the titration of 50.0 mℓ of 0.10 M acetic acid (HOAc) with 0.10 M NaOH. (K_a for HOAc is 1.8×10^{-5}.) Calculate the pH at each of the following total added volumes of NaOH:
A. 0 mℓ
    This is a standard weak acid calculation. Do it for practice. (Answer: pH = 2.87.)
B. 10.0 mℓ of 0.10 M NaOH added.
    Consider the major species in the mixed solution before any reaction takes place. (*Always* do this. The hardest things about acid-base problems are to decide what reaction takes place and what equilibrium dominates. Writing the major species is the key to making the correct decisions. The importance of doing this cannot be overemphasized.)
    In solution, the major species are: HOAc, OH^-, Na^+, H_2O. The strong base, OH^-, will react with the strongest proton donor, which in this solution is HOAc. As always, do the stoichiometry problem first.

	OH^-	+	HOAc	$\rightarrow$	OAc^-	+ H_2O
Before the reaction	10.0 mℓ × 0.10 M = 1.0 mmole		50.0 mℓ × 0.10 M = 5.0 mmole		0	
After the reaction	0		5.0 − 1.0 = 4.0 mmole		1.0 mmole	

Now, to decide what equilibrium to use, examine the major components left in the solution after the reaction:

$$HOAc, OAc^-, Na^+, H_2O$$

1. HOAc   weak acid
2. OAc⁻   conjugate base of HOAc
3. Na⁺   no effect on pH
4. H₂O   very weak acid/base

The pH will be determined by the acetic acid equilibrium:

$$HOAc \rightleftarrows H^+ + OAc^-$$

which involves HOAc and OAc⁻ and thus reflects the effects of each of these components on the pH of the solution. Now follow the usual steps to complete the equilibrium calculations:

Initial Concentrations

$$[HOAc]_0 = \frac{4.0 \text{ mmole}}{(50.0 + 10.0)m\ell} = \frac{4.0}{60.0}$$

$$[OAc^-]_0 = \frac{1.0 \text{ mmole}}{(50.0 + 10.0)m\ell} = \frac{1.0}{60.0}$$

$$[H^+]_0 \approx 0$$

Let x moles/ℓ of HOAc dissociate ⟶

Equilibrium Concentrations

$$[HOAc] = \frac{4.0}{60.0} - x$$

$$[OAc^-] = \frac{1.0}{60.0} + x$$

$$[H^+] = x$$

$$1.8 \times 10^{-5} = K_a = \frac{[H^+][OAc^-]}{[HOAc]} = \frac{(x)\left(\dfrac{1.0}{60.0} + x\right)}{\left(\dfrac{4.0}{60.0} - x\right)} \approx \frac{x\left(\dfrac{1.0}{\cancel{60.0}}\right)}{\dfrac{4.0}{\cancel{60.0}}}$$

$$x = \left(\frac{4.0}{1.0}\right)(1.8 \times 10^{-5}) = 7.2 \times 10^{-5} = [H^+]$$

$$pH = -\log(7.2 \times 10^{-5}) = 4.14$$

The next step in the titration will be done in the format of a test.

TEST 3–2

C. 25.0 mℓ of 0.10 M NaOH has been added to the original solution.
1. List the major species before any reaction occurs.
2. Decide what reaction occurs.
3. Do the stoichiometry problem.
    a. How much HOAc remains after the reaction is complete?
    b. How much OAc⁻ is formed by the reaction?
4. Do the equilibrium problem.
    a. List the major species after the reaction of question 2 occurs.
    b. Decide which equilibrium will dominate.
    c. Write down the initial concentrations (after the reaction of question 2 goes to completion but before any HOAc dissociation occurs).
    d. Define x.
    e. Write the equilibrium concentrations in terms of x.
    f. Solve for x.
    g. Calculate the pH.

This point in the titration is a special one. It is halfway to the equivalence point. The original solution consisted of 50.0 mℓ of 0.10 M HOAc, which contains 5.0 mmoles of HOAc.

What amount of OH$^-$ is required to reach the equivalence point? Remember that the equivalence point occurs when the amount of OH$^-$ added is equal to the total amount of acid. (Thus, in this problem, 5.0 mmoles of OH$^-$ are required.) Since

$$50.0 \text{ m}\ell \times 0.100 \ M = 5.0 \text{ mmoles of OH}^-,$$

50.0 mℓ of NaOH are required to reach the stoichiometric point. Thus 25.0 mℓ of added base represents the halfway point (half of the original HA has been converted to A$^-$) where [HA] $\approx$ [A$^-$]. This leads to the conclusion that [H$^+$] = K_a, which can be shown as follows:

$$1.8 \times 10^{-5} \frac{[\text{H}^+][\text{OAc}^-]}{[\text{HOAc}]} = \frac{(x)\left(\dfrac{2.5}{75.0} + x\right)}{\dfrac{2.5}{75.0} - x} \approx \frac{(x)\dfrac{2.5}{75.0}}{\dfrac{2.5}{75.0}}$$

$$x = 1.8 \times 10^{-5} = K_a$$

This is an important result. *At the point half-way to the equivalence point,*

$$[\text{H}^+] = K_a$$

or

$$-\log [\text{H}^+] = -\log K_a$$
$$\text{pH} = \text{p}K_a$$

D. 40.0 mℓ (total) of NaOH added.
    Do this one to test yourself. (Answer: pH = 5.35.)
E. 50.0 mℓ (total) of NaOH added.
    This is the equivalence point of the titration. 5.0 mmoles of OH$^-$ have been added, which will just react with the 5.0 mmoles of HOAc originally present. At this point (*after the* OH$^-$, HOAc *reaction is complete*) the solution contains:

$$\text{Na}^+, \text{OAc}^-, \text{H}_2\text{O}$$

How is the pH calculated? Note that the solution contains OAc$^-$, which is a base. Remember that a base will combine with a proton. The only source of protons in the solution is H$_2$O, so that the reaction which will occur is

$$\text{OAc}^- + \text{H}_2\text{O} \rightleftarrows \text{HOAc} + \text{OH}^-$$
$$K_b = \frac{[\text{HOAc}][\text{OH}^-]}{[\text{OAc}^-]} = \frac{K_w}{K_a} = \frac{1.0 \times 10^{-14}}{1.8 \times 10^{-5}} = 5.6 \times 10^{-10}$$

Initial Concentrations
(before any OAc$^-$ reacts)

$$[\text{OAc}^-]_0 = \frac{5.0 \text{ mmole}}{(50.0 + 50.0) \text{ m}\ell}$$

$$[\text{OH}^-]_0 \approx 0$$
$$[\text{HOAc}]_0 = 0$$

Let x moles/ℓ
OAc$^-$ react
with H$_2$O
$\xrightarrow{\hspace{1.5cm}}$

Equilibrium Concentrations

$$[\text{OAc}^-] = \frac{5.0}{100} - x$$

$$[\text{OH}^-] = x$$
$$[\text{HOAc}] = x$$

$$5.6 \times 10^{-10} = K_b = \frac{[HOAc][OH^-]}{[OAc^-]} = \frac{(x)(x)}{0.050 - x} \approx \frac{x^2}{0.050}$$
$$x^2 \approx (0.050)(5.6 \times 10^{-10}) = 2.8 \times 10^{-11}$$
$$x \approx 5.3 \times 10^{-6}$$

The assumption, $0.050 - x \approx 0.050$, is valid, so

$$[OH^-] = 5.3 \times 0^{-6} M$$
$$1.0 \times 10^{-14} = K_w [H^+][OH^-] = [H^+](5.3 \times 10^{-6} M)$$
$$[H^+] = 1.9 \times 10^{-9} M$$
$$pH = -\log(1.9 \times 10^{-9}) = 8.72$$

This is another important result: The pH at the stoichiometric point in the titration of a weak acid with a strong base is always greater than 7. This results because the anion of the acid, which remains in solution at the stoichiometric point, is a base.

Contrast this weak acid–strong base titration to the titration of a strong acid with a strong base, where the pH at the stoichiometric point is 7.0 because the anion remaining is not a good base.

F.   60.0 mℓ (total) of NaOH added.
At this point, excess OH^- has been added:

	OH^-	+	HOAc	$\rightarrow$	OAc^-	+	H_2O
Before the reaction	$60.0 \times 0.10 M$ = 6.0 mmole		50.0 m$\ell \times 0.10 M$ = 5.0 mmole		0		
After the reaction	$6.0 - 5.0$ = 1.0 mmole		$5.0 - 5.0 = 0$		5.0 mmole		

After the reaction, the solution contains Na^+, OAc^-, OH^-, and H_2O. The pH will be determined by the excess OH^-.

$$[OH^-] = \frac{\text{no. of mmoles } OH^-}{\text{volume (m}\ell)} = \frac{1.0 \text{ mmole}}{(50.0 + 60.0) \text{ m}\ell}$$
$$= 9.1 \times 10^{-3} M$$
$$1.0 \times 10^{-14} = [H^+][OH^-] = [H^+](9.1 \times 10^{-3})$$
$$[H^+] = \frac{1.0 \times 10^{-14}}{9.1 \times 10^{-3}} = 1.1 \times 10^{-12} M$$
$$pH = 11.96$$

G.   75.0 mℓ of NaOH added.
Do this one to test yourself. (Answer: pH = 12.30.)

The pH curve for the titration considered above is shown in Figure 3–2. This curve is typical of the titration of a weak acid with a strong base. Note the difference in shape between this curve and that for the titration of a strong acid (Figure 3–1). Near the beginning of the titration of a weak acid, the pH changes more rapidly than in the middle region of titration because of the buffering effect, which is greatest when [HA] = [A$^-$] at the halfway point (25 mℓ of NaOH). Note that the rate of change of pH is smallest in this region.

The other notable difference between the curves for strong and weak acids is the pH corresponding to the equivalence point. For the titration of a strong acid, the equivalence

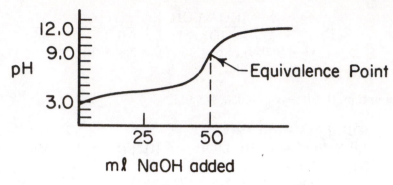

Figure 3–2

point occurs at pH 7. For a weak acid, on the other hand, the equivalence point occurs at a pH greater than 7 because of the basicity of the conjugate base of the weak acid.

Sample Problem 3–4

A 0.350 g sample of a solid weak acid (HA) is dissolved in 50.0 mℓ of water and titrated with 0.100 M NaOH.

A.   23.2 mℓ of 0.100 M NaOH is required to reach the equivalence point. What is the molecular weight of the acid?

Solution

The titration reaction is

$$HA + OH^- \rightarrow A^- + H_2O$$

23.2 mℓ × 0.100 M NaOH = 2.32 mmoles of OH^- have been added. This means that 2.32 mmoles of HA must have been dissolved in the solution originally. Thus

$$0.350 \text{ g of HA} = 2.32 \text{ mmoles HA} = 2.32 \times 10^{-3} \text{ mole HA}$$
$$\text{MW of HA} = \frac{0.350 \text{ g}}{2.32 \times 10^{-3} \text{ mole}} = 151 \text{ g/mole}$$

B.   After 10.0 mℓ of 0.100 M NaOH were added, the pH was measured and found to be 4.00. Calculate the K_a for the weak acid.

Solution

From part A, the solution originally contained 2.32 mmoles of HA. 10.0 mℓ of 0.100 M NaOH contains 10.0 mℓ × 0.10 M = 1.00 mmole of OH^-. The reaction is

	HA	+	OH$^-$	→	A$^-$	+	H$_2$O
Before the reaction	2.32 mmole		1.00 mmole		0		
After the reaction	2.32 − 1.00 = 1.32 mmole		1.00 − 1.00 = 0 mmole		1.00 mmole		

Now consider the dissociation of the HA that remains:

$$HA \rightleftarrows H^+ + A^- \qquad K_a = \frac{[H^+][A^-]}{[HA]}$$

Initial Concentrations
(before dissociation)

$$[HA]_0 = \frac{1.32 \text{ mmoles}}{(50.0 + 10.0)m\ell}$$

$$[A^-]_0 = \frac{1.00 \text{ mmole}}{(50.0 + 10.0)m\ell}$$

$$[H^+]_0 \approx 0$$

Let x moles/ℓ
————HA————→
dissociate

Equilibrium Concentrations

$$[HA] = \frac{1.32}{60.0} - x$$

$$[A^-] = \frac{1.00}{60.0} + x$$

$$[H^+] = x$$

In this problem, we know that the pH = 4.00. Since $[H^+] = 10^{-pH}$, the $[H^+]$ is 1.0×10^{-4} M.

$$K_a = \frac{[H^+][A^-]}{[HA]} = \frac{(1.0 \times 10^{-4})\left(\dfrac{1.00}{60.0} + 1.0 \times 10^{-4}\right)}{\dfrac{1.32}{60.0} - 1.0 \times 10^{-4}}$$

$$= \frac{(1.0 \times 10^{-4})(1.67 \times 10^{-2} + 1.0 \times 10^{-4})}{2.20 \times 10^{-2} - 1.0 \times 10^{-4}}$$

$$K_a \approx \frac{(1.0 \times 10^{-4})(1.67 \times 10^{-2})}{2.20 \times 10^{-2}} = 7.6 \times 10^{-5}$$

TEST 3–3

A. Consider 25. 0 mℓ of 0.30 M HNO$_2$ (K_a = 4.0 × 10^{-4}) that is titrated with 0.500 M NaOH.
    1. What volume of NaOH solution is required to reach the equivalence point?
    2. Calculate the pH of the solution after the following total volumes of base are added.
        a. 5.0 mℓ
        b. 7.5 mℓ
        c. 15.0 mℓ
        d. 20.0 mℓ

B. 0.200 g of an unknown solid acid (HA) is dissolved in 100.0 mℓ of water.
    1. 40.0 mℓ of 0.0500 M NaOH was required to reach the stoichiometric point. What is the molecular weight of the acid?
    2. The pH of the above solution after 20.0 mℓ of 0.0500 M NaOH has been added is 6.00. What is the K_a for this acid?
    3. Calculate the pH of the solution at the equivalence point for the titration of the original solution containing HA with 0.0500 M NaOH.

3.4   TITRATION OF WEAK BASES WITH STRONG ACIDS

Since all of the chemistry needed to handle this case has already been introduced, this section will encourage you to generalize your knowledge by doing a problem in the format of a test.

TEST 3–4

Consider the titration of 100.0 mℓ of 0.050 M NH_3 with 0.10 M HCl. The K_b for NH_3 is 1.8×10^{-5}.

Calculate the pH at the following total volumes of added HCl:

A. 0 mℓ added.

B. 10.0 mℓ has been added to the original solution. Before any reaction occurs, the solution contains NH_3, H^+, Cl^-, and H_2O. The reaction will be

$$NH_3 + H^+ \rightarrow NH_4^+$$

which can be assumed to go to completion.
1. Do the stoichiometry problem.
    a. How much NH_3 is consumed in the reaction?
    b. How much NH_3 remains after the reaction?
    c. How much NH_4^+ is formed in the reaction?
2. Do the equilibrium problem.
    a. What major species are present?
    b. What equilibrium will be dominant?
    c. List the initial concentrations.
    d. Define x.
    e. Write the equilibrium concentrations in terms of x.
    f. Solve for x.
    g. Calculate the pH.

C. 25.0 mℓ of HCl has been added to the original solution.

D. 50.0 mℓ of HCl has been added to the original solution. This is the stoichiometric point. After the titration is complete, the solution contains NH_4^+, Cl^-, and H_2O.
1. What equilibrium will be dominant?
2. Calculate the pH.

E. 60.0 mℓ of HCl has been added to the original solution. The solution now contains excess H^+. Calculate the $[H^+]$ and the pH.

3.5   INDICATORS

An acid-base indicator is a substance that indicates the endpoint of an acid-base titration by changing color. The most commonly used acid-base indicators are complex organic molecules that are weak acids, HIn. They exhibit one color when a proton is attached and a different color when the proton is absent. To see how these molecules function as indicators, consider the following weak acid equilibrium:

$$HIn \rightleftharpoons H^+ + In^- \qquad K_a = 1.0 \times 10^{-6}$$
$$\text{red} \qquad\qquad \text{blue}$$

If this indicator is introduced into a very acidic solution, the position of the above equilibrium will be far to the left and the solution will be red. For example, assume that pH = 1.0 ($[H^+] = 1.0 \times 10^{-1}$ M):

$$K_a = 1.0 \times 10^{-6} = \frac{[H^+][In^-]}{[HIn]}$$

Rearranging:

$$\frac{K_a}{[H^+]} = \frac{[In^-]}{[HIn]}$$

and

$$\frac{K_a}{[H^+]} = \frac{1.0 \times 10^{-6}}{1.0 \times 10^{-1}} = 10^{-5} = \frac{[In^-]}{[HIn]} = \frac{1}{100,000}$$

HIn is by far the predominant form of the indicator; the solution will be red.

If OH^- is added, the $[H^+]$ concentration decreases, and the equilibrium

$$HIn \rightleftharpoons H^+ + In^-$$

shifts to the right (HIn is changed to In^-). At some point enough In^- will be present in solution so that a bluish tinge will be noticeable. That is, a color change from red to reddish-purple will occur.

Another way to think about this process is that the stronger acid reacts with the OH^- first; when this acid is gone, the OH^- reacts with the indicator, changing it from HIn to In^-, producing the color change. This way of thinking about the process is somewhat oversimplified, but may be helpful.

At what pH will the color change be apparent? The normal assumption about indicators is that the color change will be visible when enough of the predominant form (HIn) is converted to the minor form (In^-) so that

$$\frac{[In^-]}{[HIn]} = \frac{1}{10}$$

Remember this assumption. Although the ratio is arbitrary, it serves well enough for most indicators and is important in almost all problems involving indicators.

Sample Problem 3–5

An indicator, HIn ($K_a = 1.0 \times 10^{-6}$) where HIn is red and In$^-$ is blue, is placed in a solution of strong acid. The solution is then titrated with a NaOH solution. At what pH will the indicator color change occur?

Solution

For the indicator

$$K_a = 1.0 \times 10^{-6} = \frac{[H^+][In^-]}{[HIn]}$$

Assume the color change is visible when $\dfrac{[In^-]}{[HIn]} = \dfrac{1}{10}$

$$K_a = 1.0 \times 10^{-6} = [H^+]\frac{1}{10}$$
$$[H^+] = 1.0 \times 10^{-5}$$
$$pH = 5.0$$

The color change occurs at pH = 5.0.

Note that the color change is not gradual but sharp. This is because the pH changes dramatically near the equivalence point of a titration (see the pH curves in Figures 3–1 and 3–2). Thus in a given titration the [HIn] may be much greater than the [In$^-$] at one point, but the next drop of OH$^-$ will change the pH so much that the [In$^-$] may be comparable to or greater than the [HIn]. This drop of OH$^-$ solution, then, will produce the color change. This phenomenon will be discussed more thoroughly in the next section.

TEST 3–5

Two drops of an indicator, HIn ($K_a = 1.0 \times 10^{-8}$) where HIn is yellow and In$^-$ is blue, are placed in 100.0 mℓ of 0.30 M HCl.
1. What color is the solution initially?
2. This solution is titrated with 0.20 M NaOH. At what pH will the color change (yellow to greenish-yellow) occur?
3. What color will the solution be after 300.0 mℓ of NaOH has been added?

3.6   SELECTION OF INDICATORS FOR PARTICULAR TITRATIONS (optional)

The purpose of a titration is usually to answer questions such as: What is the concentration of acid or base in a given solution? What is the molecular weight of an unknown acid? To answer questions of this type, one must know when the equivalence point of the titration is reached. There are two typical methods for determining the equivalence point:

1. Plotting a pH curve by using a pH meter to monitor the pH. The vertical region of the pH curve indicates the equivalence point.
2. Using an indicator. The point where the indicator changes color is called the *endpoint*. The goal of the person doing the titration is to have the endpoint and the equivalence point be identical (or at least within acceptable error limits). The task of choosing an indicator is made easier by the dramatic change of the pH near the equivalence point, as seen from the curves in Figure 3–3.

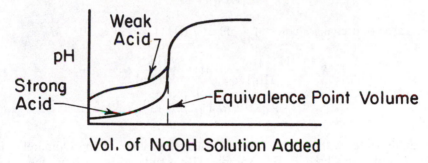

Figure 3–3

This dramatic change in pH near the equivalence point produces a sharp endpoint (the color change usually occurs with one drop of added titrant) and minimizes the error if the endpoint and the equivalence point are not identical.

Sample Problem 3–6

Consider the titration of 100.00 mℓ of 0.100 M HCl with 0.1000 M NaOH. What should be the K_a value of the indicator used for this titration?

Solution

The first question to be answered is: At what pH does the equivalence point occur?

Solutions containing Na^+, OH^-, H^+, and Cl^- are being mixed in this titration. The titration reaction will be

$$H^+ + OH^- \rightarrow H_2O$$

and at the equivalence point the solution will contain the major species:

$$Na^+, Cl^-, H_2O$$

Since neither Na^+ nor Cl^- is a significant acid or base, the solution will be neutral (pH = 7.00) at the equivalence point. Thus an indicator that changes color at pH 7 will be needed.

Recall the principles discussed in the previous section. The indicator (HIn) will be predominantly in the HIn form in the initially acidic solution. As OH^- is added, the pH will increase rather slowly at first and then will rise dramatically at the equivalence point. This will cause the indicator equilibrium

$$HIn \rightleftarrows H^+ + In^-$$

to shift suddenly to the right, producing enough In^- to cause a color change. The color change for a typical indicator can be seen when

$$\frac{[In^-]}{[HIn]} \approx \frac{1}{10}$$

For an indicator that changes color at a pH of 7 ($[H^+] = 1.0 \times 10^{-7} M$)

$$K_a = \frac{[H^+][In^-]}{[HIn]} = [H^+]\left(\frac{[In^-]}{[HIn]}\right)$$

$$K_a = (1.0 \times 10^{-7})\left(\frac{1}{10}\right) = 1.0 \times 10^{-8}$$

Thus an indicator with $K_a = 1.0 \times 10^{-8}$ will change color at approximately pH 7 when an acid is titrated with a base. If, for example, HIn is red and In^- is blue, the color change will be from red to reddish purple (red with a little blue mixed in).

Another significant question is: How much leeway is there in choosing an indicator? That is, how close do the endpoint of the indicator and the equivalence point of the titration have to be? Consider again the titration of Sample Problem 3–6. What is the pH of the solution after 99.99 mℓ of 0.1000 M NaOH have been added? (This is just before the equivalence point.)

$$\text{no. of mmoles } H^+ \text{ left} = 10.000 - 9.999 = 0.001 \text{ mmole } H^+$$

$$[H^+] = \frac{0.001 \text{ mmole}}{(100.00 + 99.99) \text{ m}\ell} = 5 \times 10^{-6} M$$

$$pH = 5.3$$

What is the pH of the solution after 100.01 mℓ of 0.1000 M NaOH has been added? (This is just after the equivalence point, and the OH^- is in excess.)

$$\text{no. of mmoles } OH^- \text{ in excess} = 10.001 - 10.000 = 0.001 \text{ mmole } OH^-$$

$$[OH^-] = \frac{0.001 \text{ mmole}}{(100.00 + 100.01)\text{m}\ell} = 5 \times 10^{-6} M$$

$$[H^+][OH^-] = 1.00 \times 10^{-14} = [H^+](5 \times 10^{-6})$$

$$[H^+] = 2 \times 10^{-9}$$

$$pH = 8.7$$

These calculations show that in going from 99.99 mℓ to 100.01 mℓ of added NaOH solution, the pH will change from 5.3 to 8.7. The difference between 99.99 mℓ and 100.01 mℓ is 0.02 mℓ, which is about half of an ordinary drop. Two important conclusions can be drawn from this phenomenon:

1. Indicator color changes will be sharp. The large change in pH around the equivalence point will cause an appropriate indicator to pass, with the additional of one drop of base, from a condition where the [HIn] is much greater than the [In$^-$] (the solution being colored by HIn) to a condition where the [In$^-$] is significant (the solution is now colored by both HIn and In$^-$). Thus the color change occurs with the addition of a single drop of titrant.
2. There is some leeway in choosing the indicator. Consider this titration to be carried out twice using two indicators:
    a. Indicator A—color change at a pH of 5.
    b. Indicator B—color change at a pH of 9.
    The results of these titrations would agree within one drop of titrant, which is acceptable error in a typical titration.

The point is that this titration could be done accurately using a wide range of indicators. This is typical of a strong acid-strong base titration.

TEST 3–6

What range of indicator K_a values could be used in the titration of 100.0 mℓ of 0.10 M HCl with 0.10 M NaOH (assuming that the color change must occur between pH 5 and pH 9)?

Now consider the case of a weak acid being titrated with a solution of NaOH. Note from Figure 3–3 that the vertical region around the equivalence point is much smaller for the titration of a weak acid than for a strong acid. This means that there is less leeway in choosing the indicator for the titration of a weak acid than for a strong acid.

Sample Problem 3–7

Consider the titration of 50.00 mℓ of 0.500 M HOCl ($K_a = 3.50 \times 10^{-8}$) with 0.100 M NaOH. What value of K_a should an indicator have to be used to mark the equivalence point of this titration?

Solution

The question that must be answered first is: What is the pH at the equivalence point? The titration reaction is

$$HOCl + OH^- \rightarrow H_2O + OCl^-$$

Initially the solution contains

$$(50.00 \text{ m}\ell) \ (0.500 \ M) = 25.0 \text{ mmoles of HOCl}$$

Thus 25.0 mmoles of OH^- must be added to reach the equivalence point. What volume of NaOH solution is required?

$$(x \text{ m}\ell) \ (0.100 \ M) = 25.0 \text{ mmoles}$$
$$x = \frac{25.0}{0.100} = 250. \text{ m}\ell$$

The total volume at the equivalence point is $50.0 \text{ m}\ell + 250.0 \text{ m}\ell = 300. \text{ m}\ell$. At the equivalence point the major species in solution are: Na^+, OCl^-, H_2O.

In considering these species, one concludes that OCl^- is a base (anion of the weak acid, HOCl) and will react with H_2O to produce a basic solution:

$$OCl^- + H_2O \rightleftarrows HOCl + HO^-$$
$$K_b = \frac{[HOCl] \ [OH^-]}{[OCl^-]} = \frac{K_w}{K_a} = \frac{1.00 \times 10^{-14}}{3.50 \times 10^{-8}} = 2.86 \times 10^{-7}$$

Initial Concentrations

$$[OCl^-]_0 = \frac{25.0 \text{ mmole}}{300.0 \text{ m}\ell}$$
$$= 8.33 \times 10^{-2} \ M$$
$$[HOCl]_0 = 0$$
$$[OH^-]_0 \approx 0$$

Let x moles/ℓ of OCl^- react with H_2O $\longrightarrow$

Equilibrium Concentrations

$$[OCl^-] = 8.33 \times 10^{-2} - x$$
$$[HOCl] = x$$
$$[OH^-] = x$$

$$2.86 \times 10^{-7} = K_b = \frac{[HOCl] \ [OH^-]}{[OCl^-]} = \frac{(x) \ (x)}{8.33 \times 10^{-2} - x} \approx \frac{x^2}{8.33 \times 10^{-2}}$$
$$x^2 \approx 2.38 \times 10^{-8}$$
$$x \approx 1.54 \times 10^{-4}$$

This simplification is valid so

$$x = 1.54 \times 10^{-4} = [OH^-]$$
$$[H^+] \ [OH^-] = 1.00 \times 10^{-14} = (1.54 \times 10^{-4}) \ [H^+]$$
$$[H^+] = 6.49 \times 10^{-11}$$
$$pH = 10.19$$

The pH at the equivalence point is 10.19, so an indicator that changes color near pH 10.19 must be chosen. As usual, the indicator will be a weak acid:

$$HIn \rightleftarrows H^+ + In^-$$

and the color change will be apparent when $\dfrac{[In^-]}{[HIn]} \approx \dfrac{1}{10}$, so

$$K_a = [H^-]\left(\frac{[In^-]}{[HIn]}\right)$$

$$K_a = (6.49 \times 10^{-11})\left(\frac{1}{10}\right) = 6.49 \times 10^{-12}$$

Thus an indicator with a K_a value in the range of 10^{-11} to 10^{-12} is needed to mark accurately the equivalence point of this titration.

TEST 3–7

What K_a value should the indicator have to mark the equivalence point of the titration of 100.0 ml of 0.100 M HCN ($K_a = 6.2 \times 10^{-10}$) with 0.100 M NaOH?

So far in the discussion of indicators, only the titrations of acids with NaOH have been considered. How is the situation different when a base is titrated with a strong acid?

Consider the titration of a base with a solution of HCl. The indicator is a weak acid:

$$HIn \rightleftarrows H^- + In^-$$
$$\text{red} \qquad\qquad \text{blue}$$

The initially basic solution will be blue, because the $[H^+]$ is very small. This means the equilibrium is shifted far right, and In^- is the predominant form of the indicator. As acid is added during the titration, the pH will decrease slowly until near the equivalence point, when it will decrease rapidly. This will cause a color change as the amount of HIn present increases dramatically. When will the color change be visible? As before, assume that the color change will be apparent when approximately one-tenth of the major (predominant) form is converted to the minor form. In this case, the predominant form is In^- since the solution is basic. Thus when $\frac{[In^-]}{[HIn]}$ is approximately $\frac{10}{1}$ the color change will be apparent. Note that the ratio $\frac{[In^-]}{[HIn]}$ for a color change is $\frac{1}{10}$ for titration of an acid and $\frac{10}{1}$ for titration of a base.

Sample Problem 3–8

An indicator, HIn, has a K_a value of 1.0×10^{-7}. Determine at what pH the color change occurs when the indicator is used to mark the equivalence point for
1. the titration of an acid.
2. the titration of a base.

Solution

1. The solution is initially acidic, so that HIn is the predominant form. The color change will occur when

$$\frac{[In^-]}{[HIn]} = \frac{1}{10}$$

$$K_a = 1.0 \times 10^{-7} = \frac{[H^+][In^-]}{[HIn]} = [H^+]\frac{1}{10}$$

$$[H^+]_{color\ change} = (10)(1.0 \times 10^{-7}) = 1.0 \times 10^{-6}$$

$$pH = 6.0$$

2. The solution here is initially basic and In^- is predominant. The color change will occur when $\dfrac{[In^-]}{[HIn]} = \dfrac{10}{1}$.

$$K_a = 1.0 \times 10^{-7} = \frac{[H^+][In^-]}{[HIn]} = [H^+]\left(\frac{10}{1}\right)$$

$$[H^+]_{color\ change} = \frac{1.0 \times 10^{-7}}{10} = 1.0 \times 10^{-8}$$

$$pH = 8.0$$

To summarize, consider the following hypothetical indicator:

$$HIn \rightleftarrows H^+\ In^- \qquad K_a = 1.0 \times 10^{-7}$$
$$red \qquad\qquad blue$$

$$K_a = \frac{[H^+][In^-]}{[HIn]} = [H^+]\left(\frac{[In^-]}{[HIn]}\right) = 1.0 \times 10^{-7}$$

Titration	Color change	Ratio where color change occurs	$[H^+]$ where color change occurs	pH where color change occurs
Acid with a base	red→reddish purple	$\dfrac{[In^-]}{[HIn]} \approx \dfrac{1}{10}$	1.0×10^{-6}	6.0
Base with an acid	blue→bluish purple	$\dfrac{[In^-]}{[HIn]} \approx \dfrac{10}{1}$	1.0×10^{-8}	8.0

Note that when this indicator is used in the titration of a base by an acid, the color change (blue–bluish purple) occurs at pH 8, whereas when this indicator is used in the titration of an acid with a base, the color change (red–reddish purple) occurs at pH 6.

TEST 3–8

The titration of ammonia with a solution of hydrochloric acid produces a pH of about 5 at the equivalence point. What K_a should an indicator have to mark the equivalence point accurately?

Exercises

1. In each of the following cases:
   1) Write down the major species before any reaction occurs.
   2) Write the equation for the reaction that occurs.
   3) Write down the major species in solution after the reaction.
   4) Determine what equilibrium will control the $[H^+]$.
   a) 500.0 mℓ of 0.10 M HCl is mixed with 500.0 mℓ of 0.20 M NaOH.
   b) 250.0 mℓ of 0.50 M NaOH is added to 300.0 mℓ of 1.0 M HOAc. (K_a = 1.8 × 10^{-5})
   c) 0.010 mole of HCl(g) is dissolved in 1.0 ℓ of 0.05 M NH$_3$. (K_b = 1.8 × 10^{-5}) Assume no volume change.
   d) 500.0 mℓ of 0.10 M HCl is added to 500.0 mℓ of 0.20 M NaCN. (The K_a for HCN is 6.2 × 10^{-10}.)
   e) 200.0 mℓ of 0.30 M NaOH is added to 800.0 mℓ of 0.10 M HCHO$_2$ (formic acid, K_a = 1.8 × 10^{-4}).
   f) 500.0 mℓ of 1.0 M NaOH is added to 500.0 mℓ of 0.10 M benzoic acid (C$_6$H$_5$ COOH, K_a = 6.3 × 10^{-5}).
   g) 0.010 mole of HNO$_3$ is added to 1.0 ℓ of 0.10 M C$_5$H$_5$N (pyridine, K_b = 1.4 × 10^{-9}). Assume no volume change.
   h) A solution is formed by mixing 500.0 mℓ of 0.20 M NH$_3$ (K_b = 1.8 × 10^{-5}) and 500.0 mℓ of 0.10 M HCl.

2. Calculate the pH of each solution in problem 1.

3. Consider the titration of 75.0 mℓ of 0.20 M HCl with 0.10 M NaOH. Calculate the pH after the following total volumes of NaOH solution have been added:
   a) 0.0 mℓ
   b) 50.0 mℓ
   c) 75.0 mℓ
   d) 150.0 mℓ
   e) 300.0 mℓ

4. Consider the titration of 25.0 mℓ of 0.10 M Ba(OH)$_2$ with 0.05 M HNO$_3$. Calculate the pH of the solution after the following total volumes of HNO$_3$ have been added:
   a) 0.0 mℓ
   b) 10.0 mℓ
   c) 25.0 mℓ
   d) 50.0 mℓ
   e) 100.0 mℓ
   f) 200.0 mℓ

5. Consider the titration of 75.0 mℓ of 0.20 M HCN (K_a = 6.2 × 10^{-10}) with 0.10 M NaOH.
   A. Calculate the pH after the following total volumes of 0.10 M NaOH have been added:

1) 0.0 mℓ   4) 150.0 mℓ
2) 50.0 mℓ   5) 300.0 mℓ
3) 75.0 mℓ

B. What K_a should an indicator have to mark correctly the equivalence point of this titration?

6. An indicator HIn has a K_a value of 5.0×10^{-5}. The equilibrium is

$$HIn \rightleftarrows H^+ + In^-$$
$$\text{yellow} \qquad\qquad \text{red}$$

a) Assume this indicator is used to mark the equivalence point for an acid titrated with a base.
   1) What color will the solution be at the beginning of the titration?
   2) At what pH will the color change (endpoint) be apparent?
   3) What is the color change at the endpoint?
b) Assume this indicator is used to mark the equivalence point of the titration of a base with a strong acid.
   1) What is the color of the solution at the beginning of the titration?
   2) At what pH does the endpoint occur?
   3) What is the color change at the endpoint?
c) At what pH will this indicator appear medium orange?

7. Consider the titration of 25.0 mℓ of 0.20 M NH_3 ($K_b = 1.8 \times 10^{-5}$) with 0.050 M HNO_3. Calculate the pH of the solution after the following total volumes of HNO_3 have been added:
   a) 0.0 mℓ   d) 50.0 mℓ
   b) 10.0 mℓ   e) 100.0 mℓ
   c) 25.0 mℓ   f) 200.0 mℓ

Verbalizing General Concepts

Answer the following in your own words:

8. Define titration, equivalence or stoichiometric point, and endpoint.

9. Describe the differences between the pH curves for the titration of a strong acid with a sodium hydroxide solution and a weak acid with a sodium hydroxide solution.

10. In the titration of a weak acid with sodium hydroxide, why is the pH at the equivalence point greater than 7?

11. Explain how an indicator works.

12. Why does one have to be more selective in choosing an indicator for the titration of a weak acid than for the titration of a strong acid?

Multiple Choice Questions

13. A 50.0 mℓ solution of 1.50 M NaOH is being titrated with a 2.00 M HCl solution. What will the pH be after the addition of 35.0 mℓ of HCl?
    a) 1.23   b) 11.7   c) 12.8   d) 2.30   e) 10.5

14. In question 13, what will be the final volume of solution when the NaOH has been completely neutralized by the HCl?
    a) 87.5 mℓ   b) 100. mℓ   c) 90.0 mℓ   d) 97.5 mℓ   e) 89.0 mℓ

15. Given:

Indicator	Acid color	pH range of color change	Base color
thymol blue	yellow	8.0–9.6	blue
thymol yellow	red	1.2–2.8	yellow
phenolphthalein	colorless	8.3–10.0	red
bromcresol green	yellow	3.8–5.5	blue

You are given an unknown solution and asked to determine its basicity or acidity. On adding thymol yellow to half of the solution, it turns yellow, while the other half remains colorless on addition of phenolphthalein. The possible pH range of the unknown is:
    a) 2.8–8.3   b) 0.0–8.3   c) 2.8–9.6   d) 8.0–8.3   e) 2.8–5.5

For exercises 16 and 17 consider the titration of 100. mℓ of a 0.5000 M HCl solution with 0.2500 M KOH solution.

16. What will the pH be after the addition of 150. mℓ of the KOH solution?
    a) 1.08   b) 1.30   c) 5.70   d) 12.7   e) none of these

17. What will the final volume of solution be when the HCl solution has been completely neutralized by the KOH solution?
    a) 150. mℓ   b) 200. mℓ   c) 250. mℓ   d) 300. mℓ   e) 400. mℓ

18. What is the pH of a 5.00×10^{-3} M aqueous solution of a soluble compound with formula $M(OH)_2$, assuming complete dissociation?
    a) 11.7   b) 2.30   c) 7.00   d) 2.00   e) 12.0

19. When 20.0 mℓ of 0.200 M NaOH are added to 100. mℓ of 0.050 M acetic acid ($HC_2H_3O_2$, $K_a = 1.8 \times 10^{-5}$), the pH of the resulting solution is
    a) 10.7   b) 5.35   c) 4.14   d) 8.32   e) none of these

20. The pH of a solution that results from the addition of 26.0 mℓ of 0.200 M NaOH to 50.0 mℓ of 0.100 M HCl is
    a) 2.58   b) 11.4   c) 3.42   d) 10.6   e) none of these

21. When 100.0 mℓ of 0.500 M NaOH is added to 150. mℓ of a solution of 0.300 M acetic acid ($K_a = 1.8 \times 10^{-5}$), the pH of the resulting solution at equilibrium is
    a) 2.30   b) 11.7   c) 12.7   d) 12.3   e) 1.70

For exercises 22–24, consider the titration of 200.0 mℓ of a 0.5000 M HCl solution with 1.000 M NaOH solution.

22. What will the pH be after the addition of 75.00 mℓ of the NaOH solution?
    a) 0.477   b) 0.903 c) 1.04   d) 1.60   e) none of these

23. What will the final volume of solution be when the HCl solution has been completely neutralized by the NaOH solution?
    a) 100.0 mℓ b) 275.0 mℓ c) 300.0 mℓ d) 400.0 mℓ
    e) 600.0 mℓ

24. What will the pH of the solution be after the addition of 125.0 mℓ of the NaOH solution?
    a) 1.11   b) 8.11   c) 12.9   d) 13.1   e) none of these

25. A strong acid is being titrated with a 0.500 M NaOH solution. Which statement is true for this titration?
    a)   The pH at the equivalence point cannot be determined without knowing the identity of the acid.
    b)   The pH at the equivalence point cannot be determined unless the concentration of the acid is known.
    c)   The pH at the equivalence point will be less than 7.0, since an acid is being titrated.
    d)   The pH at the equivalence point will be 7.0.
    e)   The pH at the equivalence point will be greater than 7.0, since a strong base is being used.

For exercises 26–28, consider the titration of 100.0 mℓ of 0.500 M NH$_3$ with 0.500 M HCl. The K_b for NH$_3$ is 1.8×10^{-5}.

26. After 50.0 mℓ of HCl has been added, the [H$^+$] of the solution is
    a) 1.8×10^{-5} M d) 1.0×10^{-7} M
    b) 5.6×10^{-10} M e) none of these
    c) 1.2×10^{-5} M

27. How many mℓ of 0.500 M HCl are required to reach the stoichiometric point of this reaction?
    a) 25.0 mℓ b) 50.0 mℓ c) 100.0 mℓ d) 200.0 mℓ e) none
    of these

28. At the stoichiometric point of this titration, the $[H^+]$ is
    a) $1.0 \times 10^{-7} \, M$ d) $5.6 \times 10^{-10} \, M$
    b) $1.8 \times 10^{-5} \, M$ e) none of these
    c) $1.2 \times 10^{-5} \, M$

29. 50.0 mℓ of 0.10 M HNO_2 ($K_a = 4.0 \times 10^{-4}$) is being titrated with 0.10 M NaOH. The pH after 25.0 mℓ of NaOH has been added is
    a) 7.0   b) 1.0   c) 12.5   d) 3.4   e) none of these

30. In the titration of a weak acid, HA, with 0.100 M NaOH, the stoichiometric point is known to occur at a pH value of approximately 10. Which of the following indicator acids would be best to use to mark the endpoint of this titration?
    a) Indicator A, $K_a = 10^{-14}$ d) Indicator D, $K_a = 10^{-6}$
    b) Indicator B, $K_a = 10^{-11}$ e) none of these will work well
    c) Indicator C, $K_a = 10^{-8}$

31. Consider the titration of 100.0 mℓ of 0.100 M NaOH with 1.00 M HCl. How much 1.00 M HCl must be added to reach a pH of 12.0?
    a) 10.0 mℓ   b) 9.52 mℓ   c) 10.5 mℓ   d) 8.91 mℓ   e) none of these

For exercises 32–39 consider the titration of 60.0 mℓ of 0.250 M formic acid ($HCHO_2$, $K_a = 1.8 \times 10^{-4}$) with 0.200 M NaOH.

32. The pH before any NaOH is added is
    a) 4.35   b) 2.17   c) 0.60   d) 3.74   e) none of these

33. The pH after 15.0 mℓ of 0.200 M NaOH has been added is
    a) 4.34   b) 3.74   c) 0.80   d) 3.14   e) none of these

34. The pH after 25.0 mℓ of 0.200 M NaOH has been added is
    a) 3.44   b) 4.05   c) 3.74   d) 0.88   e) none of these

35. The pH after 37.5 mℓ of 0.200 M NaOH has been added is
    a) 1.11   b) 1.87   c) 3.74   d) 7.0   e) none of these

36. The pH after 60.0 mℓ of 0.200 M NaOH has been added is
    a) 4.35   b) 3.14   c) 1.60   d) 3.74   e) none of these

37. The pH after 75.0 mℓ of 0.200 M NaOH has been added is
    a) 7.00   b) 5.60   c) 8.40   d) 9.46   e) none of these

38. The pH after 100.0 mℓ of 0.200 M NaOH has been added is
    a) 1.51   b) 13.10   c) 14.00   d) 12.49   e) none of these

39. The indicator most appropriate to mark the equivalence point of this titration would have a K_a value of
    a) 4×10^{-10} d) 4×10^{-8}
    b) 4×10^{-5} e) none of these
    c) 4×10^{-13}

40. A 50.0 mℓ solution of 1.50 M NaOH is being titrated with a 3.00 M HCl solution. What will the pH be after the addition of 35.0 mℓ of HCl?
    a) 1.23   b) 11.7   c) 0.45 d) 2.30   e) 10.5

41. In exercise 40, what will be the final volume of solution when the NaOH has been completely neutralized by the HCl?
    a) 75.0 mℓ b) 100.0 mℓ c) 90.0 mℓ d) 97.5 mℓ e) 89.0 mℓ

42. What volume of 0.0100 M NaOH must be added to 1.00 ℓ of 0.0500 M HA ($K_a = 4.0 \times 10^{-8}$) to achieve a pH of 8.00?
    a) 1.00 ℓ b) 5.00 ℓ c) 1.00 ℓ d) 4.00 ℓ e) none of these

43. What is the [OH$^-$] after 50.00 mℓ of 0.100 M HNO$_3$ and 50.10 mℓ of 0.100 M NaOH have been mixed?
    a) 1.0 $\times$ 10^{-4} M d) 5.0 $\times$ 10^{-3} M
    b) 2.0 $\times$ 10^{-12} M e) none of these
    c) 1.0 $\times$ 10^{-10} M

For exercises 44–51, consider the titration of 100.0 mℓ of 0.100 M methylamine (CH$_3$NH$_2$, $K_b = 4.4 \times 10^{-4}$) with 0.100 M HCℓ.

44. Calculate the pH before any HCl has been added.
    a) 2.18   b) 11.82   c) 13.00   d) 10.64   e) none of these

45. Calculate the pH after 10.0 mℓ of 0.100 M HCl has been added.
    a) 11.60   b) 2.40   c) 4.31   d) 9.69   e) none of these

46. Calculate the pH after 25.0 mℓ of 0.100 M HCl has been added.
    a) 2.88 b) 11.12   c) 3.83   d) 10.17 e) none of these

47. Calculate the pH after 50.0 mℓ of 0.100 M HCl has been added.
    a) 7.00   b) 1.48   c) 3.36   d) 10.64   e) none of these

48. Calculate the pH after 75.0 mℓ of 0.100 M HCl has been added.
    a) 2.88   b) 11.12   c) 3.83   d) 10.17   e) none of these

49. Calculate the pH after 100.0 mℓ of 0.100 M HCl has been added.
    a) 9.03   b) 5.97   c) 7.00   d) 3.36   e) none of these

50. Calculate the pH after 200.0 mℓ of 0.100 M HCl has been added.
    a) 0.30   b) 1.00   c) 0.18   d) 1.48   e) none of these

51. The indicator most appropriate to mark the equivalence point of this titration would have the K_a value
    a) 1 $\times$ 10^{-5} d) 1 $\times$ 10^{-10}
    b) 1 $\times$ 10^{-7} e) none of these
    c) 1 $\times$ 10^{-3}

For exercises 52 and 53, consider the titration of 100.0 mℓ of 0.250 M aniline with 0.500 M HCl. The K_b for aniline is 3.8×10^{-10}.

52. What is the pH of the solution at the stoichiometric point?
    a) -0.78 b) 5.10   c) 2.68   d) 11.32   e) none of these

53. In the calculation of the volume of HCl required to reach a pH of 8.0, which of the following expressions is correct? (x = volume of HCl (in mℓ) required to reach a pH of 8.0.)
    a) $\dfrac{0.5x - (100)(0.25)}{100 + x} = $ [aniline]   d) $\dfrac{25 - 0.5x}{100 + x} - 10^{-6} = $ [aniline]
    b) $[H^+] = x$ e) none of these
    c) $\dfrac{0.5x}{100 + x} = $ [aniline]

54. 0.0100 mole of a weak acid (HA) was dissolved in 100.0 mℓ of distilled water, and a pH titration was performed using 0.100 M NaOH. After 40.00 mℓ of 0.100 M NaOH were added, the pH of the solution was observed to be 4.0. The K_a value for HA is:
    a) 1.0×10^{-4} d) 1.0×10^{-10}
    b) 6.7×10^{-5} e) none of these
    c) 1.5×10^{-4}

4

SOLUBILITY EQUILIBRIA

Chapter Objectives

1. Define solubility, solubility product constant, solubility product expression, ion product, and precipitation.

2. Calculate the K_{sp} value for a solid, given the solubility of the solid.

3. Calculate the solubility of a solid in pure water, given the K_{sp} of the solid.

4. Calculate the solubility of a solid (given its K_{sp}) in a solution containing a common ion.

5. Know the principles involved in predicting relative solubilities of solids, given their K_{sp} values.

6. Know the principles involved in predicting whether precipitation will occur when two solutions are mixed.

7. Know the principles involved in the separation of cations by selective precipitation.

4.1   INTRODUCTION

When a typical ionic solid is dissolved in water, the dissolved material can be assumed to be present as separate hydrated anions and cations. For example, consider $CaF_2(s)$ dissolving in water. The process can be represented as

$$CaF_2(s) \xrightarrow{H_2O} Ca^{2+}(aq) + 2F^-(aq)$$

The solubility of a substance is defined in terms of the amount of material which will dissolve in a given amount of solvent (for example, grams of solute per 100 mℓ of solvent) or the amount of material which will dissolve to produce a certain volume of the resulting solution (for example, moles of solute per liter of solution). The latter system will be used here to define solubility.

Consider the process that occurs as $CaF_2(s)$ is added to water. Initially the water

115

contains no Ca^{2+} or F^- ions, but as the solid dissolves the concentrations of Ca^{2+} and F^- build up in solution. As the concentrations of Ca^{2+} and F^- increase, it becomes more and more likely that these ions will collide and reform the solid phase. Thus, competing processes are occurring:

$$CaF_2(s) \rightarrow Ca^{2+} + 2F^- \tag{1}$$

and the reverse reaction

$$Ca^{2+} + 2F^- \rightarrow CaF_2(s) \tag{2}$$

At first, the dissolving process (1) dominates and solid disappears. As the concentrations of Ca^{2+} and F^- build up, however, the rate of the reverse process, (2), increases until it equals the rate of dissolving. At this point, dynamic equilibrium is reached: the solid is dissolving and reforming at the same rate, and no net change occurs in the amount of remaining undissolved solid. The combined process can be represented as

$$CaF_2(s) \rightleftarrows Ca^{2+} + 2F^-$$

and an equilibrium expression constructed according to the Law of Mass Action:

$$K_{sp} = [Ca^{2+}][F^-]^2$$

$CaF_2(s)$ is not included since pure condensed phases (solids and liquids) are never included in the equilibrium expression. This means that the amount of excess solid does not affect the position of the solubility equilibrium and thus does not affect the solubility of that solid.

This observation might seem strange at first. One might think that the more solid present and thus the more surface area exposed to the solvent (water), the greater the solubility. However, when the ions in solution reform the solid, they do so at the surface of the solid. Doubling the surface area of the solid not only doubles the rate of dissolving, but also doubles the rate of reformation of the solid, so that the amount of excess solid present has no effect on the equilibrium position.

Similarly, while grinding up the solid (to increase the surface area) or stirring the solution speeds up the attainment of equilibrium, neither procedure changes the *amount* of solid dissolved at equilibrium.

In summary, note the following points:
1. The equilibrium constant is given a special symbol (K_{sp}) and is called the *solubility product constant* ($K_{solubility\ product}$).
2. Solubility is an *equilibrium position*. The solubility of a substance and the solubility constant for a substance are *not* the same thing.
3. The solid itself is not included in the equilibrium expression.

4.2   SOLVING TYPICAL SOLUBILITY EQUILIBRIUM PROBLEMS

The most common solubility problems fall into two categories:
1. Calculation of the value of K_{sp} from the solubility of a solid.
2. Calculation of the solubility of a solid, given the K_{sp} value.
Both of these situations will be considered in sample problems.

Sample Problem 4–1

The solubility of CuBr(s) is 2.0×10^{-4} moles/ℓ at 25°C. Calculate the value of the K_{sp} for CuBr(s) at 25°C.

Solution

When CuBr(s) is placed in water, it dissolves by producing Cu^+ and Br^- ions according to the following equilibrium:

$$CuBr(s) \rightleftarrows Cu^+ + Br^-$$
$$K_{sp} = [Cu^+][Br^-]$$

Now follow the procedure of defining initial and equilibrium concentrations as in acid-base problems:

Initial Concentrations
(before the equilibrium of interest occurs)
$[Cu^+]_0 = 0$
$[Br^-]_0 = 0$

Now let the system come to equilibrium by dissolving CuBr(s). Let x = no. of moles/ℓ of CuBr(s) which dissolve when the system comes to equilibrium. That is: x moles/ℓ CuBr(s) dissolve to produce x moles/ℓ Cu^+ plus x moles/ℓ Br^- in solution. At equilibrium:

$$[Cu^+] = x$$
$$[Br^-] = x$$

The solubility has been given: Solubility = 2.0×10^{-4} moles/ℓ, which means that 2.0×10^{-4} mole of CuBr(s) dissolves to produce 2.0×10^{-4} mole of Cu^+ and 2.0×10^{-4} mole of Br^- per liter of the resulting solution.

$$K_{sp} = [Cu^+][Br^-] = (x)(x) = (2.0 \times 10^{-4})(2.0 \times 10^{-4})$$
$$= 4.0 \times 10^{-8} \, (mole/\ell)^2$$

This equilibrium constant is characteristic of CuBr(s) in water at 25°C. When excess CuBr(s) is placed in contact with an aqueous solution of CuBr(s) at 25°C, the product of $[Cu^+]$ and $[Br^-]$ must always be equal to $4.0 \times 10^{-8} \, (mole/\ell)^2$.

Note the following points:
1. When a K_{sp} value is given, the units are usually deleted.
2. In calculating the K_{sp} value for CuBr(s) from the measured solubility, it has been assumed that all of the CuBr(s) which dissolves does so to form separate Cu^+ and Br^- ions. Although some of the ions may exist as ion pairs ($Cu^+ \ldots Br^-$) in solution, this complication will be ignored.
3. If the solubility is given in units of g/100 mℓ, it must be changed to moles/ℓ before doing equilibrium calculations.

TEST 4–1

The solubility of silver iodide (AgI) is 1.2×10^{-8} moles/ℓ at 25°C. Calculate the K_{sp} for AgI(s) at 25°C.

A. What equilibrium occurs when AgI(s) is placed in water?

B. Write the K_{sp} expression for AgI(s).

C. Determine the initial concentrations.

D. Define x.

E. Write the equilibrium concentrations in terms of x.

F. Determine the value of x.

G. Calculate the K_{sp} value.

Sample Problem 4–2

The solubility of $CaF_2(s)$ is 2.15×10^{-4} moles/ℓ at 25°C. Calculate the K_{sp} for $CaF_2(s)$ at 25°C.

Solution

The usual steps will be done, but will be represented in condensed form. The equilibrium of interest is

$$CaF_2(s) \rightleftarrows Ca^{2+} + 2F^-$$
$$K_{sp} = [Ca^{2+}][F^-]^2$$

Initial Concentrations
$[Ca^{2+}]_0 = 0$
$[F^-]_0 = 0$

$\xrightarrow[\text{of } CaF_2(s)\text{---}]{\text{Let } x \text{ moles/}\ell}$
dissolve

Equilibrium Concentrations
$[Ca^{2+}] = x$
$[F^-] = 2x$

note that:
$$xCaF_2 \rightarrow xCa^{2+} + 2xF^-$$

Solubility $= x = 2.15 \times 10^{-4}$ moles/ℓ

$[Ca^{2+}] = x = 2.15 \times 10^{-4}$ moles/ℓ
$[F^-] = 2x = 2(2.15 \times 10^{-4} \text{ moles/}\ell) = 4.30 \times 10^{-4}$ moles/ℓ
$K_{sp} = [Ca^{2+}][F^-]^2 = (2.15 \times 10^{-4})(4.30 \times 10^{-4})^2$
$K_{sp} = 3.98 \times 10^{-11}$

Sample Problem 4-3

The K_{sp} for $Cu(IO_3)_2(s)$ is 1.4×10^{-7} at 25°C. Calculate the solubility of $Cu(IO_3)_2(s)$ at 25°C.

Solution

The solubility equilibrium is

$$Cu(IO_3)_2(s) \rightleftarrows Cu^{2+}(aq) + 2IO_3^-(aq)$$
$$K_{sp} = [Cu^{2+}][IO_3^-]^2$$

Initial Concentrations
(before any $Cu(IO_3)_2(s)$ dissolves)

Equilibrium Concentrations

$$[Cu^{2+}]_0 = 0 \qquad \xrightarrow[\substack{-Cu(IO_3)_2(s)-\\ \text{dissolve}}]{\text{Let } x \text{ moles}/\ell} \qquad [Cu^{2+}] = x$$

$$[IO_3^-]_0 = 0 \qquad\qquad\qquad [IO_3^-] = 2x$$

$$(xCu(IO_3)_2(s) \rightarrow xCu^{2+} + 2xIO_3^-)$$

$$1.4 \times 10^{-7} = K_{sp} = [Cu^{2+}][IO_3^-]^2 = (x)(2x)^2 = 4x^3$$
$$\frac{1.4 \times 10^{-7}}{4} = 3.5 \times 10^{-8} = x^3$$
$$x = \sqrt[3]{3.5 \times 10^{-8}} = \sqrt[3]{35} \times 10^{-3} = 3.3 \times 10^{-3} \text{ mole}/\ell$$
$$x = \text{no. of moles}/\ell \text{ of } Cu(IO_3)_2 \text{ which dissolves} = \text{solubility}$$
$$\text{solubility} = 3.3 \times 10^{-3} \text{ mole}/\ell$$

TEST 4-2

The solubility of $Bi_2S_3(s)$ is 1.0×10^{-15} moles$/\ell$ at 25°C. Calculate the K_{sp} for Bi_2S_3 at 25°C. Remember to go through the steps described above.

In the preceding problems, the K_{sp} value has been calculated from known solubility. In the following problems solubility will be calculated from the K_{sp}.

Sample Problem 4-4

The K_{sp} value for $AgBr(s)$ is 7.7×10^{-13} at 25°C. Calculate the solubility of $AgBr(s)$ in water at 25°C.

Solution

The equilibrium is

$$AgBr(s) \rightleftarrows Ag^+ + Br^-$$

and the equilibrium expression is

$$K_{sp} = [Ag^+][Br^-] = 7.7 \times 10^{-13}$$

Initial Concentrations
(before any AgBr(s) dissolves)
$[Ag^+]_0 = 0$
$[Br^-]_0 = 0$

Let x moles/ℓ
————of AgBr(s)————→
dissolve

Equilibrium Concentrations

$[Ag^+] = x$
$[Br^-] = x$

Note: $xAgBr(s) \rightarrow xAg^+ + xBr^-$
$7.7 \times 10^{-13} = K_{sp} = [Ag^+][Br^-] = (x)(x)$
$x^2 = 7.7 \times 10^{-13}$
$x = 8.8 \times 10^{-7}$ moles/ℓ = solubility

TEST 4–3

The K_{sp} for silver chromate (Ag_2CrO_4) is 9.0×10^{-12} at 25°C. Calculate the solubility of Ag_2CrO_4 at 25°C.

A. Write the solubility equilibrium.

B. Write the K_{sp} expression.

C. Write down the initial concentrations.

D. Define x.

E. Write the equilibrium concentrations in terms of x.

F. Substitute the equilibrium concentrations into the K_{sp} expression.

G. Calculate x.

H. Find the solubility.

Sample Problem 4–5

Rank the following solids in order of decreasing solubility.

A. AgI(s) ($K_{sp} = 1.5 \times 10^{-16}$), AgBr(s) ($K_{sp} = 7.7 \times 10^{-13}$),
AgCl(s) ($K_{sp} = 1.6 \times 10^{-10}$), SrSO$_4$ ($K_{sp} = 2.9 \times 10^{-7}$),
CuI(s) ($K_{sp} = 5.0 \times 10^{-12}$), and CaSO$_4$(s) ($K_{sp} = 6.1 \times 10^{-5}$)

Solution

Each of these solids dissolves to produce two ions

$$MA(s) \rightleftharpoons M^{n+} + A^{n-}$$

where

$$K_{sp} = [M^{n+}][A^{n-}]$$

If x = solubility, then in each case at equilibrium

$$[M^{n+}] = x$$
$$[A^{n-}] = x$$
$$K_{sp} = [M^{n+}][A^{n-}] = (x)(x)$$
$$x^2 = K_{sp}$$
$$x = \sqrt{K_{sp}} = \text{solubility}$$

Thus the order of solubility for these solids can be determined by ordering the K_{sp} values: the solid with the largest K_{sp} has the highest solubility. The order is

$$CaSO_4(s) > SrSO_4(s) > AgCl(s) > CuI(s) > AgBr(s) > AgI(s)$$

most soluble   least soluble

B. CuS(s) ($K_{sp} = 8.5 \times 10^{-45}$), Ag$_2$S(s) ($K_{sp} = 1.6 \times 10^{-49}$), and Bi$_2S_3$(s) ($K_{sp} = 1.1 \times 10^{-73}$).

Solution

In this case, each solid produces a different number of ions so that the K_{sp} values *cannot* be compared directly to determine the relative solubilities. Calculate the solubility for each solid as a test of your knowledge (Test 4–4).

TEST 4–4

Solve Sample Problem 4–5B.

4.3   COMMON ION EFFECT

In the cases so far considered, the solid has been dissolved in pure water. Problems in which the solution contains an ion in common with the one in the salt will now be introduced.

Sample Problem 4-6

Calculate the solubility $Ag_2CrO_4(s)$ in a 0.100 M solution of $AgNO_3$. (K_{sp} for Ag_2CrO_4 is 9.0×10^{-12}.)

Solution

Before any Ag_2CrO_4 dissolves, the solution contains Ag^+, NO_3^-, and H_2O. The $Ag_2CrO_4(s)$ dissolves as follows:

$$Ag_2CrO_4(s) \rightleftarrows 2Ag^+(aq) + CrO_4^{2-}(aq)$$
$$K_{sp} = [Ag^+]^2[CrO_4^{2-}] = 9.0 \times 10^{-12}$$

Initial Concentrations (before any $Ag_2CrO_4(s)$ dissolves)
$[Ag^+]_0 = 0.100\ M$ from the dissolved $AgNO_3$
$[CrO_4^{2-}]_0 = 0$
Let x moles/ℓ of Ag_2CrO_4 dissolve. This produces $xCrO_4^{2-}$ and $2xAg^+$.

Equilibrium Concentrations
$[Ag^+] = 0.100 + 2x$
$[CrO_4^{2-}] = x$
$9.0 \times 10^{-12} = K_{sp} = [Ag^+]^2[CrO_4^{2-}] = (0.100 + 2x)^2(x)$

Since the K_{sp} for Ag_2CrO_4 is small (the position of the equilibrium lies far to the left), x is expected to be small compared to 0.100 M. Therefore, assume that $0.100 + 2x \approx 0.100$ and

$$9.0 \times 10^{-12} = (0.100 + 2x)^2\ x \approx (0.100)^2 x$$
$$x \approx \frac{9.0 \times 10^{-12}}{(0.100)^2} = 9.0 \times 10^{-10}\ \text{moles}/\ell$$

Note that x is much less than 0.100 M so that the assumption is valid.

$$\text{Solubility} = x = 9.0 \times 10^{-10}\ \text{mole}/\ell$$

The equilibrium concentrations are

$$[Ag^+] = 0.100 + 2(9.0 \times 10^{-10}) = 0.100\ M$$
$$[CrO_4^{2-}] = x = 9.0 \times 10^{-10}\ \text{mole}/\ell$$

Now compare the solubility of $Ag_2CrO_4(s)$ in pure water (calculated in Test 4–3) and in 0.100 M $AgNO_3$.

	Pure water	0.100 M $AgNO_3$
Solubility of Ag_2CrO_4	1.3×10^{-4} mole/ℓ	9.0×10^{-10} mole/ℓ

Notice that the solubility of $Ag_2CrO_4(s)$ is much less when the water contains Ag^+ from

$AgNO_3$. This is an example of the *common ion effect*: The presence in solution of ions in common with one or more of those in the solid being dissolved lowers the solubility of the solid.

TEST 4–5

Calculate the solubility of $Ag_3PO_4(s)$ ($K_{sp} = 1.8 \times 10^{-18}$) in pure water and in a 1.0 M Na_3PO_4 solution and compare the results.

4.4   PRECIPITATION CONDITIONS

When solutions are mixed, reactions often occur. Acid-base reactions were considered in Chapter 3. In this section, reactions which cause precipitation (formation of a solid) will be considered.

The *ion product*, another name for a reaction quotient, will be used to solve these problems. The ion product expression is identical to the equilibrium expression for a given solid except that *initial concentrations* are used. This differs from the K_{sp} expression, which involves *equilibrium concentrations* only. For example, for the compound $CaF_2(s)$, the ion product expression is

$$\text{ion product} = Q = [Ca^{2+}]_0[F^-]_0^2$$

When a solution containing Ca^{2+} is added to a solution containing F^-, precipitation (formation of $CaF_2(s)$) may or may not occur. Precipitation *will occur* if $Q > K_{sp}$.

To predict whether precipitation of a given solid will occur, calculate the ion product for the solid using the concentrations of the ions in solution. Then apply the following rules:

If $Q > K_{sp}$ precipitation occurs
If $Q \leqslant K_{sp}$ no precipitation occurs

Sample Problem 4–7

A solution is prepared by mixing 100.0 mℓ of 1.0×10^{-3} M $Ca(NO_3)_2$ and 100.0 mℓ of 1.0×10^{-3} M NaF. Does $CaF_2(s)$ precipitate from this solution? (K_{sp} for $CaF_2(s)$ is 4.0×10^{-11}.)

Solution

Since $Ca(NO_3)_2(s)$ and NaF(s) are soluble salts, the $Ca(NO_3)_2$ solution contains Ca^{2+} and NO_3^- and the NaF solution contains Na^+ and F^-. To see if CaF_2 forms, the first thing to do is to compute the concentrations of Ca^{2+} and F^- in the mixed solution (which has a volume of 200.0 mℓ):

$$[Ca^{2+}]_0 = \frac{\text{no. of mmoles } Ca^{2+}}{\text{m}\ell \text{ of solution}} = \frac{(100.0 \text{ m}\ell)(1.0 \times 10^{-3} M)}{200.0 \text{ m}\ell}$$

$$= 5.0 \times 10^{-4} M$$

$$[F^-]_0 = \frac{\text{no. of mmoles } F^-}{\text{m}\ell \text{ of solution}} = \frac{(100.0 \text{ m}\ell)(1.0 \times 10^{-3} M)}{200.0 \text{ m}\ell}$$

$$= 5.0 \times 10^{-4} M$$

When $CaF_2(s)$ dissolves, the reaction is

$$CaF_2(s) \rightleftarrows Ca^{2+} + 2F^-$$

and the ion product is

$$Q = [Ca^{2+}]_0[F^-]_0^2$$

In this case

$$Q = [Ca^{2+}]_0[F^-]_0^2 = (5.0 \times 10^{-4})(5.0 \times 10^{-4})^2 = 1.25 \times 10^{-10}$$
$$K_{sp} = 4.0 \times 10^{-11}$$

Thus $Q > K_{sp}$ and $CaF_2(s)$ will form.

TEST 4–6

A mixture is formed by adding 50.0 mℓ of $1.0 \times 10^{-2} M$ $CuNO_3$ to 200.0 mℓ of $1.0 \times 10^{-4} M$ NaCl. Does CuCl(s) ($K_{sp} = 1.8 \times 10^{-7}$) form?

4.5   SELECTIVE PRECIPITATION

Precipitation is sometimes used to separate the ions in a mixture. For example, consider a solution containing Ba^{2+}, Ag^+, and NO_3^-. The Ba^{2+} and the Ag^+ can be separated in at least two different ways by precipitating one of the ions while leaving the other in solution. If NaCl is added to the Ba^{2+}, Ag^+ mixture, AgCl(s) (a white solid) will precipitate. Since $BaCl_2$ is soluble, it will not form, and Ba^{2+} will be left in solution.

Another way to accomplish this separation is to add Na_2SO_4 to the Ag^+, Ba^{2+} mixture. $BaSO_4(s)$ will precipitate, leaving Ag^+ in solution ($Ag_2SO_4(s)$ is very soluble).

Separation of ions by precipitation is called *selective precipitation*.

Since metal sulfides differ dramatically in solubility, sulfide ion is often used to separate metal ions. This type of separation will be considered in the following example.

Sample Problem 4–8

A solution contains 1.0×10^{-3} M $Fe(NO_3)_2$ and 1.0×10^{-3} M $MnSO_4$. Both Fe^{2+} and Mn^{2+} form sulfide salts: FeS ($K_{sp} = 3.7 \times 10^{-19}$) and MnS ($K_{sp} = 1.4 \times 10^{-15}$). If sulfide ion is added to the solution containing 10^{-3} M Fe^{2+} and 10^{-3} M Mn^{2+}, which sulfide salt will precipitate first and at what $[S^{2-}]$ will precipitation occur?

Solution

The solution contains 1.0×10^{-3} M Fe^{2+} and 1.0×10^{-3} M Mn^{2+}. Precipitation of each sulfide will occur when the ion product is greater than the K_{sp} for that salt.

For FeS (FeS(s) $\rightleftarrows$ Fe^{2+} + S^{2-}), the ion product is

$$Q = [Fe^{2+}]_0[S^{2-}]_0$$

Since $[Fe^{2+}]_0 = 1.0 \times 10^{-3}$ M,

$$Q = (1.0 \times 10^{-3})[S^{2-}]_0$$

K_{sp} for FeS is 3.7×10^{-19}. If $Q = K_{sp}$, no precipitation occurs, but any added S^{2-} will cause precipitation.

Let $Q = K_{sp} = 3.7 \times 10^{-19} = (1.0 \times 10^{-3})[S^{2-}]_0$. Then

$$[S^{2-}]_0 = \frac{3.7 \times 10^{-19}}{1.0 \times 10^{-3}} = 3.7 \times 10^{-16} \ M$$

Thus when $[S^{2-}] = 3.7 \times 10^{-16}$ M, no precipitation of FeS(s) will occur, but if $[S^{2-}] > 3.7 \times 10^{-16}$ M in this solution, FeS(s) will form.

Now do the same calculation for MnS:

$$Q = [Mn^{2+}]_0[S^{2-}]_0$$
$$[Mn^{2+}]_0 = 1.0 \times 10^{-3} \ M$$

Let $Q = K_{sp} = 1.4 \times 10^{-15} = (1.0 \times 10^{-3})[S^{2-}]_0$

$$[S^{2-}]_0 = \frac{1.4 \times 10^{-15}}{1.0 \times 10^{-3}} = 1.4 \times 10^{-12} \ M$$

If $[S^{2-}]_0 > 1.4 \times 10^{-12}$ M, MnS(s) will precipitate.

The questions posed above can now be answered. As S^{2-} is added to the solution containing 10^{-3} M Fe^{2+} and 10^{-3} M Mn^{2+}, the FeS(s) will precipitate first (when $[S^{2-}] > 3.7 \times 10^{-16}$ M) and the MnS(s) will precipitate when $[S^{2-}] > 1.4 \times 10^{-12}$ M.

TEST 4–7

A solution contains a mixture of 1.0×10^{-2} M $Pb(NO_3)_2$ and 1.0×10^{-4} M $AgNO_3$. The K_{sp} values for $PbCl_2$ and $AgCl$ are 1.0×10^{-4} and 1.6×10^{-10}, respectively. As Cl^- is added to this solution, which salt will precipitate first and at what concentration of Cl^-?

4.6   SELECTIVE PRECIPITATION OF SULFIDES (optional)

Sulfide forms many salts with widely varying solubilities. These salts are often used to precipitate metal ions selectively from solution in qualitative analysis schemes.

The key to the selective precipitation of sulfide salts is the basicity of S^{2-}, which allows its concentration to be controlled by controlling the pH of the solution.

Sulfide forms the acid H_2S, for which the following equilibrium expression can be written:

$$\frac{[H^+]^2[S^{2-}]}{[H_2S]} = K = 1.32 \times 10^{-20}$$

To form sulfide precipitates, the solution is saturated with H_2S, which produces a 0.10 M concentration of H_2S. Thus, for a saturated solution, the equilibrium expression can be written

$$\frac{[H^+]^2[S^{2-}]}{[H_2S]} = \frac{[H^+][S^{2-}]}{(0.10)} = 1.32 \times 10^{-20}$$

or

$$[H^+]^2[S^{2-}] = (0.10)(1.32 \times 10^{-20}) = 1.3 \times 10^{-21}$$

Note from this expression that the concentration of S^{2-} can be regulated by controlling the $[H^+]$. A large $[H^+]$ means a small $[S^{2-}]$ and vice versa.

Sample Problem 4–9

Calculate the $[S^{2-}]$ in a solution saturated with H_2S where the pH is 1.00.

Solution

The pH $= 1.00$. To find the $[H^+]$, take the antilog of pH:

$$[H^+] = 10^{-pH} = 1.00 \times 10^{-1} M$$

The equilibrium expression for H_2S in a saturated solution is

$$[H^+]^2[S^{2-}] = 1.3 \times 10^{-21}$$

or

$$[S^{2-}] = \frac{1.3 \times 10^{-21}}{[H^+]^2} = \frac{1.3 \times 10^{-21}}{(1.00 \times 10^{-1})^2}$$

$$[S^{2-}] = 1.3 \times 10^{-19} \ M$$

TEST 4–8

Calculate the $[S^{2-}]$ in a solution saturated with H_2S where the pH is 9.00.

The results of Sample Problem 4–9 and Test 4–8 show that the $[S^{2-}]$ can be varied over many orders of magnitude by varying the pH. This allows metal sulfide salts to be precipitated selectively, as will be shown in the following example.

Sample Problem 4–10

Consider a solution which contains $1.0 \times 10^{-3} \ M \ Mn^{2+}$ and $1.0 \times 10^{-3} \ M \ Cu^{2+}$, is saturated with H_2S, and has a pH of 2.00. Under these conditions, does either $CuS(s)$ ($K_{sp} = 8.5 \times 10^{-45}$) or $MnS(s)$ ($K_{sp} = 1.4 \times 10^{-15}$) form?

Solution

The solution is saturated with H_2S, so the relationship

$$[H^+]^2[S^{2-}] = 1.3 \times 10^{-21}$$

can be used. The pH = 2.00, which means that $[H^+]$ is obtained from the antilog of pH:

$$[H^+] = 10^{-pH} = 1.00 \times 10^{-2} \ M$$
$$[S^{2-}] = \frac{1.3 \times 10^{-21}}{[H^+]^2} = \frac{1.3 \times 10^{-21}}{(1.00 \times 10^{-2})^2} = 1.3 \times 10^{-17} \ M$$

Now compute Q for each salt to see if precipitation occurs.

For MnS: $Q = [Mn^{2+}]_0[S^{2-}]_0 = (1.0 \times 10^{-3})(1.3 \times 10^{-17}) = 1.3 \times 10^{-20}$
$K_{sp} = 1.4 \times 10^{-15}$
$Q < K_{sp}$
No MnS(s) forms.

For CuS: $Q = [Cu^{2+}]_0[S^{2-}]_0 = (1.0 \times 10^{-3})(1.3 \times 10^{-17}) = 1.3 \times 10^{-20}$
$K_{sp} = 8.5 \times 10^{-45}$
$Q > K_{sp}$
CuS(s) forms.

Under these conditions, Cu^{2+} precipitates as $CuS(s)$ while Mn^{2+} remains in solution. Thus a separation of Cu^{2-} from Mn^{2+} has been achieved. At pH 2 the $[S^{2-}]$ is large enough to precipitate $CuS(s)$ but not the more soluble $MnS(s)$.

TEST 4–9

Consider a solution which contains 1.0×10^{-2} M Fe^{2+} and 1.0×10^{-2} M Ni^{2+}. The solution is saturated with H_2S and has a pH of 1.00.

Under these conditions, will $NiS(s)$ ($K_{sp} = 1.4 \times 10^{-24}$) or $FeS(s)$ ($K_{sp} = 3.7 \times 10^{-19}$) precipitate?

Exercises

1. The solubility of $CuI(s)$ in water is 2.3×10^{-6} moles/ℓ. Calculate the K_{sp} for $CuI(s)$.

2. The solubility of $PbI_2(s)$ is 1.2×10^{-3} moles/ℓ. Calculate the K_{sp} for $PbI_2(s)$.

3. The K_{sp} for $ZnC_2O_4(s)$ is 1.5×10^{-9}. Calculate the solubility of $ZnC_2O_4(s)$.

4. The K_{sp} for $SrF_2(s)$ is 2.8×10^{-9}. Calculate the solubility of $SrF_2(s)$.

5. The solubility of $Ca_3(PO_4)_2(s)$ is 6.3×10^{-7} mole/ℓ. Calculate the K_{sp} value for $Ca_3(PO_4)_2(s)$.

6. The K_{sp} for $AgBr(s)$ is 7.7×10^{-13}. Calculate the solubility of $AgBr(s)$ in
   a) Pure water.
   b) 1.0×10^{-2} M $NaBr$ solution.

7. A solution is saturated with $BaSO_4(s)$ (solid is added until an excess remains). The $[Ba^{2+}]$ in this solution is 1.0×10^{-5} M. Calculate the value of the K_{sp} for $BaSO_4(s)$.

8. The K_{sp} for $Pb_3(PO_4)_2(s)$ is 1.0×10^{-42}. Calculate the solubility of $Pb_3(PO_4)_2(s)$ in
   a) Pure water.
   b) 0.100 M $Pb(NO_3)_2$.

9. Calculate the solubility of $Co(OH)_2(s)$ ($K_{sp} = 5.2 \times 10^{-15}$) in a solution with a pH of 11.00.

10. For each of the following pairs of solids, determine which solid is least soluble.
    a) $CaF_2(s)$ ($K_{sp} = 4.0 \times 10^{-11}$) or $BaF_2(s)$ ($K_{sp} = 1.1 \times 10^{-6}$)
    b) $Ca_3(PO_4)_2(s)$ ($K_{sp} = 1.0 \times 10^{-29}$) or $FePO_4$ ($K_{sp} = 1.0 \times 10^{-22}$).

11. A solution contains 1.0×10^{-5} M Ag^+ and 2.0×10^{-6} M CN^-. Will $AgCN(s)$ precipitate? (K_{sp} for $AgCN(s)$ is 2.2×10^{-12}.)

12. A solution contains 2.0×10^{-3} M Ce^{3+} and 1.0×10^{-2} M IO_3^-. Will $Ce(IO_3)_3(s)$ precipitate? (The K_{sp} for $Ce(IO_3)_3$ is 3.2×10^{-10}.)

13. A solution contains 1.0×10^{-8} M Co^{2+}. At what $[S^{2-}]$ will precipitation of $CoS(s)$ $(K_{sp} = 7.0 \times 10^{-23})$ begin?

14. A solution is prepared by mixing 50.0 mℓ of 1.0×10^{-3} M $Ca(NO_3)_2$ and 50.0 mℓ of 1.0×10^{-2} M Na_2SO_4. Will $CaSO_4(s)$ $(K_{sp} = 6.1 \times 10^{-5})$ precipitate?

15. A solution is prepared by mixing 75.0 mℓ of 1.0×10^{-3} M $CuNO_3$ and 150.0 mℓ of 1.0×10^{-3} M $NaCl$. Will $CuCl(s)$ $(K_{sp} = 1.8 \times 10^{-7})$ precipitate?

16. A solution is prepared by mixing 100.0 mℓ of 1.0×10^{-2} M $Pb(NO_3)_2$ and 100.0 mℓ of 1.0×10^{-3} M NaF. Will $PbF_2(s)$ $(K_{sp} = 3.7 \times 10^{-8})$ precipitate?

17. A solution contains 1.0×10^{-5} M PO_4^{3-}. What is the minimum concentration of Ag^+ which would cause precipitation of $Ag_3PO_4(s)$ $(K_{sp} = 1.8 \times 10^{-18})$?

18. The solubility of $Pb(IO_3)_2(s)$ in a 0.10 M KIO_3 solution is 2.6×10^{-11} moles/ℓ. Calculate the K_{sp} for $Pb(IO_3)_2(s)$.

Verbalizing General Concepts

Answer the following in your own words:

19. Define solubility (in two types of units), K_{sp}, ion product, selective precipitation, and the common ion effect.

20. Discuss the fact that solubility is an equilibrium position.

21. Under what conditions can K_{sp} values be compared directly to determine the relative solubilities of salts?

22. How can one determine whether a precipitate will form when two solutions are mixed?

Multiple Choice Questions

23. The $[IO_3^-]$ in a solution in equilibrium with $Ce(IO_3)_3(s)$ is 5.55×10^{-3} M. Calculate the K_{sp} for $Ce(IO_3)_3(s)$.
    a) 3.16×10^{-10}
    b) 1.03×10^{-5}
    c) 2.56×10^{-8}
    d) 3.51×10^{-11}
    e) none of these

24. A solution is 1×10^{-4} M in each of F^-, S^{2-}, and PO_4^{3-}. What would be the order of precipitation as Pb^{2+} is added?

    $K_{sp}(PbF_2) = 4 \times 10^{-8}$, $\qquad K_{sp}(PbS) = 3 \times 10^{-28}$,
    $K_{sp}(Pb_3(PO_4)_2) = 1 \times 10^{-42}$)

    a) PbF_2 before PbS before $Pb_3(PO_4)_2$.
    b) $Pb_3(PO_4)_2$ before PbS before PbF_2.
    c) PbS before PbF_2 before $Pb_3(PO_4)_2$.
    d) $Pb_3(PO_4)_2$ before PbF_2 before PbS.
    e) PbS before $Pb_3(PO_4)_2$ before PbF_2.

25. The concentration of Ag^+ in a saturated solution of $Ag_2C_2O_4(s)$ is 2.2×10^{-4} M. The K_{sp} of $Ag_2C_2O_4(s)$ is
    a) 5.3×10^{-12}
    b) 4.8×10^{-8}
    c) 1.1×10^{-11}
    d) 2.2×10^{-4}
    e) none of these

26. The K_{sp} of a metal sulfide, $MS(s)$, is 2.0×10^{-17}. The sulfide ion concentration of a solution containing $MS(s)$ at equilibrium is
    a) 4.5×10^{-9} M
    b) 1.0×10^{-17} M
    c) 2.0×10^{-17} M
    d) 2.3×10^{-9} M
    e) none of these

27. How many moles of CaF_2 will dissolve in 1.0 liter of a 0.025 M NaF solution? (K_{sp} for $CaF_2 = 4.0 \times 10^{-11}$)
    a) 6.4×10^{-8}
    b) 1.6×10^{-9}
    c) 4.0×10^{-11}
    d) 2.5×10^{-14}
    e) none of these

28. 0.005 mole Na_2SO_4 is added to 500. mℓ of each of two solutions, one containing $1.5 \times 10^{-3} M$ $BaCl_2$, the other $1.5 \times 10^{-3} M$ $CaCl_2$. Given that K_{sp} for $BaSO_4$ = 1.0×10^{-10} and K_{sp} for $CaSO_4$ = 6.1×10^{-5},
    a) $BaSO_4$ would precipitate, but $CaSO_4$ would not.
    b) $CaSO_4$ would precipitate, but $BaSO_4$ would not.
    c) Both $BaSO_4$ and $CaSO_4$ would precipitate.
    d) Neither $BaSO_4$ nor $CaSO_4$ would precipitate.
    e) Not enough information is given to determine if precipitation would occur.

29. The solubility of $Mg(OH)_2$ (MW = 58.3) is 8.34×10^{-5} g/10.0 mℓ at 25°C. The value of K_{sp} for $Mg(OH)_2$ at 25°C is
    a) 4.09×10^{-8} d) 16.7×10^{-12}
    b) 5.84×10^{-12} e) none of these
    c) 11.7×10^{-12}

30. The solubility of $CaF_2(s)$ (K_{sp} = 4.0×10^{-11}) in 1.0 ℓ of a $1.0 \times 10^{-2} M$ solution of NaF is
    a) 4.0×10^{-9} moles   d) 4.0×10^{-7} moles
    b) 1.0×10^{-7} moles   e) none of these
    c) 7.0×10^{-4} moles

31. Which of the following salts shows the smallest solubility in water?
    a) Bi_2S_3 (K_{sp} = 1×10^{-73})   d) HgS (K_{sp} = 1×10^{-52})
    b) Ag_2S (K_{sp} = 2×10^{-49})   e) $Mg(OH)_2$ (K_{sp} = 1×10^{-11})
    c) MnS (K_{sp} = 1×10^{-15})

32. In a solution prepared by adding excess $PbI_2(s)$ (K_{sp} = 6.9×10^{-9}) to water, the $[I^-]$ is
    a) 1.5×10^{-3} moles/ℓ d) 8.4×10^{-5} moles/ℓ
    b) 2.4×10^{-3} moles/ℓ e) none of these
    c) 1.2×10^{-3} moles/ℓ

33. The K_{sp} for $CuI(s)$ is 5.3×10^{-12}. The number of moles of $CuI(s)$ which will dissolve in 1.0 ℓ of $1.0 \times 10^{-2} M$ KI is
    a) 2.3×10^{-6} d) 5.3×10^{-10}
    b) 5.3×10^{-12} e) none of these
    c) 5.3×10^{-8}

34. A solution contains $1.0 \times 10^{-4} M$ Zn^{2+}, $1.0 \times 10^{-5} M$ Ag^+, $1.0 M$ H^+, and is saturated with H_2S ($0.10 M$). Using the following data,

$$ZnS(s) \qquad K_{sp} = 1 \times 10^{-23}$$
$$Ag_2S(s) \qquad K_{sp} = 2 \times 10^{-49}$$
$$1.3 \times 10^{-20} = \frac{[H^+]^2[S^{2-}]}{[H_2S]}$$

    determine which statement is correct.
    a) $ZnS(s)$ will form but not $Ag_2S(s)$.
    b) $Ag_2S(s)$ will form but not $ZnS(s)$.
    c) Both $ZnS(s)$ and $Ag_2S(s)$ will form.
    d) Neither $ZnS(s)$ nor $Ag_2(S)$ will form.

35. Consider a solution containing 10^{-3} M Bi^{3+}, 10^{-3} M Co^{2+}, and 0.1 M H_2S. Which of the following values for $[H^+]$ would allow precipitation of one of these ions as its sulfide salt while leaving the other ion in solution? The K_{sp} for $Bi_2S_3(s)$ is 1.1×10^{-73}, and the K_{sp} for $CoS(s)$ is 7.0×10^{-23}.

$$K = \frac{[H^+]^2[S^{2-}]}{[H_2S]} = 1.3 \times 10^{-20}.$$

a) 4.0 M b) 15.0 M c) 1.0 × 10^{-2} M
d) 1.0 × 10^{-1} M e) none of these

5

MORE INVOLVED EQUILIBRIUM PROBLEMS (optional)

5.1 INTRODUCTION

In this chapter some systems will be explored that require more elaborate treatment than those dealt with in the earlier chapters. Equilibrium calculations for the following cases will be considered:

1. Acid-base problems in which the quadratic formula must be used.
2. Acid-base problems in which water makes a significant contribution to the $[H^+]$.
3. Polyprotic acids.
4. Precipitation reactions.
5. Complex ions.
6. Solids dissolving in solutions in which secondary reactions occur.

5.2 USE OF THE QUADRATIC FORMULA

The following is an acid-base problem that requires use of the quadratic formula.

Sample Problem 5–1

Calculate the pH of a 0.10 M solution of HIO_3 ($K_a = 1.7 \times 10^{-1}$).

Solution

Go through the steps as usual:

A.   In solution are: HIO_3, H_2O.
B.   Both HIO_3 and H_2O are acids, but HIO_3 is much stronger (K_a is much greater than K_w) and it will dominate in the production of H^+.
C.   The equilibrium of interest is

$$HIO_3 \rightleftarrows H^+ + IO_3^-$$
$$K_a = \frac{[H^+][IO_3^-]}{[HIO_3]}$$

D.   Initial concentrations:

$$[HIO_3]_0 = 0.10 \ M$$
$$[IO_3^-]_0 = 0$$
$$[H^+]_0 \approx 0 \ (\text{ignore the contribution from } H_2O)$$

E.   Let x = no. of moles/ℓ of HIO_3 that dissociate.
F.   Equilibrium concentrations:

$$[HIO_3] = 0.10 - x$$
$$[IO_3^-] = x$$
$$[H^+] = x$$

G.   Substitute into the K_a expression:

$$1.7 \times 10^{-1} = K_a = \frac{[H^+][IO_3^-]}{[HIO_3]} = \frac{(x)(x)}{0.10 - x} \approx \frac{(x)(x)}{0.10}$$

Try this approximation as usual.

$$x^2 \approx (0.10)(1.7 \times 10^{-1}) = 1.7 \times 10^{-2}$$
$$x \approx 1.3 \times 10^{-1}$$

Note that x is larger than 0.10. This is clearly impossible. Thus the approximation is invalid. In order to solve the quadratic equation obtained above, either the quadratic formula or trial and error must be used.

For a general quadratic equation of the form

$$ax^2 + bx + c = 0,$$

the solution is given by

$$x = \frac{-b \pm \sqrt{b^2 - 4ac}}{2a}$$

In the present problem,

$$K_a = 1.7 \times 10^{-1} = \frac{x^2}{0.10 - x}$$

Now rearrange this expression so that it is written in the general form for a quadratic equation:

$$(1.7 \times 10^{-1})(0.10 - x) = x^2$$
$$(1.7 \times 10^{-2}) - (1.7 \times 10^{-1})x = x^2$$
$$x^2 + (1.7 \times 10^{-1})x - (1.7 \times 10^{-2}) = 0$$

where $a = 1$
        $b = 1.7 \times 10^{-1}$
        $c = -1.7 \times 10^{-2}$

Thus

$$x = \frac{(-1.7 \times 10^{-1}) \pm \sqrt{(1.7 \times 10^{-1})^2 - (4)(1)(-1.7 \times 10^{-2})}}{2(1)}$$

$$= \frac{-1.7 \times 10^{-1} \pm \sqrt{(2.9 \times 10^{-2}) + (6.8 \times 10^{-2})}}{2}$$

$$= \frac{-1.7 \times 10^{-1} \pm \sqrt{9.7 \times 10^{-2}}}{2} = \frac{-1.7 \times 10^{-1} \pm 3.1 \times 10^{-1}}{2}$$

$$= -2.4 \times 10^{-1}, +7.0 \times 10^{-2}$$

Since $x = [H^+]$, the negative root is physically impossible. Thus

$$x = 7.0 \times 10^{-2} \text{ mole}/\ell = [H^+]$$
$$pH = -\log(7.0 \times 10^{-2}) = 1.15$$

Sample Problem 5–2

A solution is prepared by dissolving 0.050 mole of $Fe(NO_3)_3(s)$ in enough water to make a total volume of 1.0 ℓ. The K_a for $Fe(OH_2)_6^{3+}$ is 6.0×10^{-3}. Calculate the pH of this solution.

Solution

Since $Fe(NO_3)_3(s)$ is an ionic compound, the major species are:

$$Fe^{3+}(aq), \ NO_3^-(aq), \ H_2O$$

where $Fe^{3+}(aq)$ is $Fe(OH_2)_6^{3+}$. (This information is conveyed in the description of the problem, since the K_a for $Fe(OH_2)_6^{3+}$ is given.)

Consider the acid-base properties of each component:

1) $Fe(OH_2)_6^{3+}$ weak acid (K_a given)
2) NO_3^- extremely weak base (conjugate base of strong acid, HNO_3)
3) H_2O very weak acid or base

Comparing the K_a for $Fe(OH_2)_6^{3+}$ with K_w indicates that $Fe(OH_2)_6^{3+}$ will be dominant. Remembering the definition of K_a:

$$Fe(OH_2)_6^{3+} \rightleftarrows Fe(OH)(OH_2)_5^{2+} + H^+$$

$$K_a = \frac{[Fe(OH)(OH_2)_5^{2+}][H^+]}{[Fe(OH_2)_6^{3+}]} = 6.0 \times 10^{-3}$$

Initial Concentrations   *Equilibrium Concentrations*

$[Fe(OH_2)_6^{3+}]_0 = 0.050\ M$ $[Fe(OH_2)_6^{3+}] = 0.050 - x$

$[H^+]_0 \approx 0$ (Neglect H^+ from   Let x moles/ℓ $[H^+] = x$

H_2O) $\xrightarrow{\ \ Fe(OH_2)_6^{3+}\ \ }$ $[Fe(OH)(OH_2)_5^{2+}] = x$

$[Fe(OH)(OH_2)_5^{2+}]_0 = 0$ dissociate

$$K_a = 6.0 \times 10^{-3} = \frac{(x)(x)}{0.050 - x} \approx \frac{x^2}{0.050}$$

                                        ↖ making the usual approximation

$$x^2 \approx 3.0 \times 10^{-4}$$
$$x \approx 1.7 \times 10^{-2}$$

Check the assumption:

$$\frac{x}{[Fe(OH_2)_6^{3+}]_0}(100) = \frac{1.7 \times 10^{-2}}{5.0 \times 10^{-2}} \times 100 = 34\%$$

Thus the approximation $[HA]_0 - x \approx [HA]_0$ is *not* valid. To calculate the correct answer, use the quadratic formula:

$$\frac{x^2}{0.050 - x} = 6.0 \times 10^{-3}$$
$$x^2 = (3.0 \times 10^{-4}) - (6.0 \times 10^{-3})x$$
$$x^2 + (6.0 \times 10^{-3})x - (3.0 \times 10^{-4}) = 0$$

which has the form $ax^2 + bx + c = 0$ where $a = 1$, $b = 6.0 \times 10^{-3}$, and $c = -3.0 \times 10^{-4}$. Then

$$x = \frac{-b \pm \sqrt{b^2 - 4ac}}{2a} = \frac{-6.0 \times 10^{-3} \pm \sqrt{(6.0 \times 10^{-3})^2 - (4)(1)(-3.0 \times 10^{-4})}}{(2)(1)}$$

Disregarding the negative root,

$$x = 1.5 \times 10^{-2} = [H^+]$$
$$pH = 1.82$$

TEST 5–1

Calculate the pH of $2.00 \times 10^{-3} \ M$ HNO_2 ($K_a = 4.0 \times 10^{-4}$). Be sure to follow the usual steps.

5.3 ACID SOLUTIONS IN WHICH WATER CONTRIBUTES TO [H⁺]

In all previous calculations involving acids and bases, we have been able to ignore the contribution of water to the total [H⁺] in solution. This assumption is usually valid, but complications occur when the acid is very weak or very dilute, or both.

a. *Very Dilute Solutions of Strong Acids*

Sample Problem 5–3

Calculate the [H⁺] in a $1.0 \times 10^{-7} \ M$ HCl solution.

Solution

The solution contains the major species:

$$H^+, \ Cl^-, \ H_2O$$

Normally, the H⁺ from the strong acid dominates. However, in this case, the strong acid is so dilute that water will make a comparable contribution.

One possible way to approach this problem would be to add the [H⁺] from the HCl to the [H⁺] normally found in pure water.

$$[H^+]_{total} \overset{?}{=} 1.0 \times 10^{-7} + 1.0 \times 10^{-7} = 2.0 \times 10^{-7} \ M$$

Is this a valid approach?

The answer is no, because the H⁺ from the strong acid will cause the water equilibrium

$$H_2O \rightleftarrows H^+ + OH^-$$

to shift to the left. This causes the contribution from the dissociation of H_2O to be less than $1.0 \times 10^{-7} \ M$. We must use a more elaborate method.

The best way to handle this problem is to recognize that the net charge on this solution must be zero. That is, the positive charge carried by the cations must be exactly equal to the negative charge carried by the anions. This leads to the **charge balance** expression:

$$\text{Concentration of} \atop \text{positive charge} = {\text{Concentration of} \atop \text{negative charge}}$$

In the 10^{-7} M HCl solution, the only cation is H^+ and the only anions are Cl^- and OH^-. Thus in this solution

$$[H^+] = [Cl^-] + [OH^-] \qquad \text{charge balance equation}$$

The Cl^- in this solution comes from the dissolved HCl. Thus

$$[Cl^-] = 1.0 \times 10^{-7} \, M$$
$$[H^+] = [Cl^-] + [OH^-] = 1.0 \times 10^{-7} \, M + [OH^-].$$

This equation can be put in terms of one unknown ($[H^+]$) by remembering that

$$[H^+] [OH^-] = K_w = 1.0 \times 10^{-14}$$

or

$$[OH^-] = \frac{1.0 \times 10^{-14}}{[H^+]}$$

Thus

$$[H^+] = [Cl^-] + [OH^-] = [Cl^-] + \frac{1.0 \times 10^{-14}}{[H^+]}$$
$$= 1.0 \times 10^{-7} + \frac{1.0 \times 10^{-14}}{[H^+]}$$
$$\nwarrow \text{from the HCl}$$

or

$$[H^+] - \frac{1.0 \times 10^{-14}}{[H^+]} = 1.0 \times 10^{-7}$$

Multiplying both sides of this equation by $[H^+]$ gives

$$[H^+]^2 - (1.0 \times 10^{-14}) = (1.0 \times 10^{-7})[H^+]$$

or

$$[H^+]^2 - (1.0 \times 10^{-7})[H^+] - (1.0 \times 10^{-14}) = 0$$

This is a quadratic equation in standard form where $a = 1$, $b = -1.0 \times 10^{-7}$, and $c = 1.0 \times 10^{-14}$. Substitution into the quadratic formula gives

$$[H^+] = \frac{-b \pm \sqrt{b^2 - 4ac}}{2a}$$
$$= \frac{-(-1.0 \times 10^{-7}) \pm \sqrt{(-1.0 \times 10^{-7})^2 - (4)(1)(-1.0 \times 10^{-14})}}{2(1)}$$
$$= 1.6 \times 10^{-7} \, M$$

Thus the $[H^+]$ in a 1.0×10^{-7} M HCl solution is 1.6×10^{-7} M. Since 1.0×10^{-7} M H^+ comes from the dissolved HCl, 0.6×10^{-7} M comes from water. This shows that the position of the water equilibrium,

$$H_2O \rightleftarrows H^+ + OH^-$$

is shifted to the left by the common ion, H^+.

For the 1.0×10^{-7} M HCl solution,

$$pH = -\log[H^+] = -\log(1.6 \times 10^{-7}) = 6.80$$

Sample Problem 5–4

Calculate the pH of 1.0×10^{-10} M HNO_3.

Solution

Here is a case where considering only the H^+ from the strong acid (HNO_3) leads to a clearly ridiculous result. The ionization of 1.0×10^{-10} M HNO_3 produces 1.0×10^{-10} M H^+. Then

$$pH = -\log(1.0 \times 10^{-10}) = 10.0$$

This cannot be correct. Adding an acid to water cannot produce a basic solution. Clearly, water must be considered as a source of H^+.

To handle this problem, again consider the charge balance equation.

$$[H^+] = [NO_3^-] + [OH^-]$$

$$\nearrow \qquad \nwarrow \qquad \nwarrow$$

from HNO_3 from HNO_3 from H_2O
and H_2O

$$[NO_3^-] = 1.0 \times 10^{-10} \ M$$

Using the K_w expression:

$$[OH^-] = \frac{K_w}{[H^+]} = \frac{1.0 \times 10^{-14}}{[H^+]}$$

Substituting in the above equation gives

$$[H^+] = (1.0 \times 10^{-10}) + \frac{1.0 \times 10^{-14}}{[H^+]}$$

Multiplying both sides by $[H^+]$ gives

$$[H^+]^2 = (1.0 \times 10^{-10})[H^+] + (1.0 \times 10^{-14})$$

or

$$[H^+]^2 - (1.0 \times 10^{-10})[H^+] - (1.0 \times 10^{-14}) = 0$$

Use of the quadratic formula gives

$$[H^+] = 1.0 \times 10^{-7} \, M$$
$$pH = 7.00$$

Note that the pH is the same as that for pure water within the number of significant figures allowed by the data. This is not really surprising. The amount of HNO_3 added is very small compared with the $[H^+]$ from water:

$$10^{-10} << 10^{-7}$$

In this solution water is the dominant source of H^+.

TEST 5–2

A. Calcualte the $[H^+]$ in a $2.0 \times 10^{-8} \, M$ solution of HNO_3.

B. The considerations involved in treating dilute solutions of strong bases are similar to those for strong acids. Try this problem:
    Calculate the $[OH^-]$ in a $1.0 \times 10^{-7} \, M$ solution of NaOH.
    1. What ions are present?
    2. What is the charge balance equation?
    3. What is the $[Na^+]$?
    4. What is $[H^+]$ in terms of K_w and $[OH^-]$?
    5. Solve for $[OH^-]$.

C. The method for calculating the $[H^+]$ using the charge balance equation also gives the correct answer for more concentrated strong acid solutions (the usual case). Show this by using the method to calculate the pH for a 0.10 M HCl solution.

b. *Very Weak Acids or Dilute Solutions of Weak Acids*

This situation is more complicated than that of a strong acid, since two equilibria must be considered:

$$H_2O \rightleftarrows H^+ + OH^- \qquad K_w$$
$$HA \rightleftarrows H^+ + A^- \qquad K_a$$

Note that there are four unknowns in this system: $[H^+]$, $[OH^-]$, $[HA]$, and $[A^-]$. To solve for four unknowns requires four equations. The equilibrium equations are two of these. Another useful relationship is the charge balance equation:

$$[H^+] = [A^-] + [OH^-]$$

Knowing that all of the HA originally dissolved must be present at equilibrium either as A^- or HA leads to the equation

$$[HA]_0 = [HA] + [A^-]$$

$\nwarrow$
original amount of
HA dissolved

This is called the **material balance** equation.

These four equations can be used to derive an equation involving only $[H^+]$, as follows:

$$K_a = \frac{[H^+][A^-]}{[HA]}$$

To express $[A^-]$ and $[HA]$ in terms of $[H^+]$, use the charge balance equation

$$[H^+] = [A^-] + [OH^-]$$

where

$$[OH^-] = \frac{K_w}{[H^+]} \qquad \text{from the } K_w \text{ expression}$$

The charge balance equation becomes

$$[H^+] = [A^-] + \frac{K_w}{[H^+]}$$

or

$$[A^-] = [H^+] - \frac{K_w}{[H^+]}$$

This gives $[A^-]$ in terms of $[H^+]$.

The material balance equation is

$$[HA]_0 = [HA] + [A^-] \qquad \text{or} \qquad [HA] = [HA]_0 - [A^-]$$

Since

$$[A^-] = [H^+] - \frac{K_w}{[H^+]}$$
$$[HA] = [HA]_0 - \left([H^+] - \frac{K_w}{[H^+]}\right)$$

Now substitute into the K_a expression:

$$K_a = \frac{[H^+][A^-]}{[HA]} = \frac{[H^+]\left([H^+] - \dfrac{K_w}{[H^+]}\right)}{[HA]_0 - \left([H^+] - \dfrac{K_w}{[H^+]}\right)} = \frac{[H^+]^2 - K_w}{[HA]_0 - \dfrac{[H^+]^2 - K_w}{[H^+]}}$$

This expression permits the calculation of the $[H^+]$ in a solution containing a weak acid. It gives the correct $[H^+]$ for any solution made by dissolving a weak acid in pure water.

The equation can be solved by simple trial and error or by the more systematic method of successive approximations. The usual way of doing successive approximations is to substitute a guessed value of the variable of interest ($[H^+]$ in this case) into the equation everywhere it appears except one place. The equation is then solved to obtain a value of the variable, which becomes the "guessed value" in the next round. The process is continued until the calculated value equals the guessed value.

Even though the full equation can be solved in this manner, the process is tedious and time-consuming. We would certainly like to use the simpler method (ignoring the contribution of water to the $[H^+]$) wherever possible. Thus, a key question is: Under what conditions can problems involving a weak acid be done the simple way? This question will be answered in the following paragraphs.

Notice that the term $[H^+]^2 - K_w$ appears twice in the full equation:

$$K_a = \frac{[H^+]^2 - K_w}{[HA]_0 - \dfrac{[H^+]^2 - K_w}{[H^+]}}$$

Under conditions where

$$[H^+]^2 >> K_w$$

and thus

$$[H^+]^2 - K_w \approx [H^+]^2$$

the full equation reduces as follows:

$$K_a = \frac{[H^+]^2 - K_w}{[HA]_0 - \dfrac{[H^+]^2 - K_w}{[H^+]}} \approx \frac{[H^+]^2}{[HA]_0 - \dfrac{[H^+]^2}{[H^+]}} = \frac{[H^+]^2}{[HA]_0 - [H^+]}$$

$$= \frac{x^2}{[HA]_0 - x}$$

where $x = [H^+]$ at equilibrium.

This is an important result: If $[H^+]^2 >> K_w$, the full equation reduces to the simple expression for a weak acid derived in Chapter 2, ignoring water as a source of H^+. Let's arbitrarily decide that "much greater than" means at least a factor of 100 times greater. Since $K_w = 1.0 \times 10^{-14}$, the $[H^+]^2$ must be at least 100×10^{-14} or 10^{-12}. This value of $[H^+]^2$ requires that $[H^+] = 10^{-6}$. Thus if $[H^+]$ is greater than or equal to 10^{-6} M, the complicated equation reduces to the simple equation: i.e., you get *same answer* by using either equation.

How do we decide when it is necessary to use the complicated equation? The best way to proceed is as follows:

Calculate the $[H^+]$ in the normal way, ignoring H_2O. If $[H^+]$ from this calculation is greater than or equal to 10^{-6} M, the answer is correct; i.e., the complicated equation will give the same answer. If $[H^+]$ is less than 10^{-6} M, you must use the full equation, i.e., water must be considered as a source of H^+.

Sample Problem 5–5

A. Calculate the $[H^+]$ in 1.0 M HCN ($K_a = 6.2 \times 10^{-10}$).

Solution

First do the weak acid problem the "normal" way. This leads to the expression

$$\frac{x^2}{1.0-x} = 6.2 \times 10^{-10} \approx \frac{x^2}{1.0}$$

and

$$x = 2.5 \times 10^{-5} \ M = [H^+]$$

Note that $[H^+]$ is greater than 10^{-6} M, so we are finished.

TEST 5–3

Show that $[H^+] = 2.5 \times 10^{-5}$ M also satisfies the full equation (where H_2O is taken into account) for a 1.0 M HCN solution.

B. Calculate the $[H^+]$ in 1.0×10^{-4} M HCN ($K_a = 6.2 \times 10^{-10}$).

Solution

First do the weak acid problem the "normal" way. This leads to the expression

$$K_a = 6.2 \times 10^{-10} = \frac{x^2}{1.0 \times 10^{-4} - x} \approx \frac{x^2}{1.0 \times 10^{-4}}$$

$$x \approx 2.5 \times 10^{-7} \ M$$

Here $[H^+]$ from HCN is less than 10^{-6} M, so the full equation must be used:

$$6.2 \times 10^{-10} = K_a = \frac{[H^+]^2 - 10^{-14}}{1.0 \times 10^{-4} - \dfrac{[H^+]^2 - 10^{-14}}{[H^+]}}$$

Solve for $[H^+]$ by use of successive approximations. First determine a reasonable guess for $[H^+]$. Note from the above simple calculation that the $[H^+]$, ignoring the contribution from water, is 2.5×10^{-7} M. Will the actual $[H^+]$ be larger or smaller than this?

It will be a little larger because of the contribution from H_2O. Guess $[H^+] = 3.0 \times 10^{-7}$ M. Substitute this value for $[H^+]$ into the denominator of the equation to give

$$K_a = 6.2 \times 10^{-10} = \frac{[H^+]^2 - 1.0 \times 10^{-14}}{1.0 \times 10^{-4} - \dfrac{(3.0 \times 10^{-7})^2 - 1.0 \times 10^{-14}}{3.0 \times 10^{-7}}}$$

or

$$6.2 \times 10^{-10} = \frac{[H^+]^2 - 1.0 \times 10^{-14}}{1.0 \times 10^{-4} - 2.67 \times 10^{-7}}$$

Now rearrange this equation so that a value for $[H^+]$ can be calculated.

$$[H^+]^2 = 6.2 \times 10^{-14} - 1.66 \times 10^{-16} + 1.0 \times 10^{-14} = 7.2 \times 10^{-14}$$

$$[H^+] = \sqrt{7.2 \times 10^{-14}} = 2.68 \times 10^{-7}$$

The original guessed value of $[H^+]$ was 3.0×10^{-7}. Since the calculated value and the guessed value do not agree, use 2.68×10^{-7} as the new guessed value:

$$K_a = 6.2 \times 10^{-10} = \frac{[H^+]^2 - 1.0 \times 10^{-14}}{1.0 \times 10^{-4} - \dfrac{[H^+]^2 - 1.0 \times 10^{-14}}{[H^+]}}$$

$$= \frac{[H^+]^2 - 1.0 \times 10^{-14}}{1.0 \times 10^{-4} - \dfrac{(2.68 \times 10^{-7})^2 - 1.0 \times 10^{-14}}{2.68 \times 10^{-7}}}$$

Solving for $[H^+]$ gives

$$[H^+] = 2.68 \times 10^{-7} = 2.7 \times 10^{-7} \, M$$

Since the guessed value and the calculated value agree, this is the correct answer, which takes into account both the contribution of H^+ from water and from HCN.

$$pH = -\log(2.7 \times 10^{-7}) = 6.57$$

TEST 5–4

Calculate the $[H^+]$ in a 2.0×10^{-4} M solution of phenol (C_6H_5OH, $K_a = 1.3 \times 10^{-10}$).

A. Do the problem the "normal" way.

B. How does the concentration of H^+ calculated in A compare to 10^{-6} M?

C. Must the full equation be used?

D. What might be a reasonable guess for the $[H^+]$?

E. Calculate the $[H^+]$.

5.4   POLYPROTIC ACIDS

a. *Introduction*

Some acids have more than one acidic hydrogen. For example, the common strong acid, sulfuric acid, produces two protons per molecule:

$$H_2SO_4(aq) \xrightarrow{\hspace{1cm}} H^+ + HSO_4^- \qquad K_{a_1} \text{ very large}$$
$$HSO_4^-(aq) \rightleftharpoons H^+ + SO_4^{2-} \qquad K_{a_2} = 1.2 \times 10^{-2}$$

Sulfuric acid is said to be a *diprotic acid*; the general term for acids which dissociate two or more H^+ ions per molecule is *polyprotic*. Two characteristics of polyprotic acids which normally can be assumed are:
1. The protons dissociate stepwise, that is, two or more H^+ ions do not dissociate simultaneously.
2. The first dissociation occurs to the greatest extent, and subsequent dissociation steps have much smaller equilibrium constants.

To illustrate these concepts, consider phosphoric acid:

$$H_3PO_4(aq) \rightleftharpoons H^+(aq) + H_2PO_4^-(aq) \qquad K_{a_1} = 7.5 \times 10^{-3}$$
$$H_2PO_4^-(aq) \rightleftharpoons H^+(aq) + HPO_4^{2-}(aq) \qquad K_{a_2} = 6.2 \times 10^{-8}$$
$$HPO_4^{2-}(aq) \rightleftharpoons H^+(aq) + PO_4^{3-}(aq) \qquad K_{a_3} = 4.8 \times 10^{-13}$$

Note that H^+ dissociation occurs in successive steps with decreasing equilibrium constants; the conjugate base of the first dissociation becomes and the acid for the second dissociation, and so on.

Phosphoric acid illustrates a third characteristic which is usually (but not always) true for polyprotic acids: the successive K_a's often differ by a factor of 10^3 or more. For H_3PO_4

$$\frac{K_{a_1}}{K_{a_2}} = \frac{7.5 \times 10^{-3}}{6.2 \times 10^{-8}} = 1.2 \times 10^5$$

$$\frac{K_{a_1}}{K_{a_2}} = \frac{6.2 \times 10^{-8}}{4.8 \times 10^{-13}} = 1.3 \times 10^5$$

This characteristic causes pH calculations involving polyprotic acids to be much easier than might be initially expected. Under most circumstances, each successive acid (e.g., H_3PO_4, $H_2PO_4^-$, and HPO_4^{2-}) can be treated independently of the others. Thus, the concepts learned for monoprotic acids can be applied to polyprotic acids with little modification.

b. Calculations for Typical Polyprotic Acids

This section presents problems involving polyprotic acids with the three characteristics discussed above.

Sample Problem 5–6

Calculate the pH of 1.00 M solution of H_3PO_4, for which $K_{a_1} = 7.5 \times 10^{-3}$, $K_{a_2} = 6.2 \times 10^{-8}$, and $K_{a_3} = 4.8 \times 10^{-13}$.

Solution

As always, first write the major species in solution:

$$H_3PO_4, H_2O$$

(None of the dissociation products of H_3PO_4 are written because all of the K_a's are small and these will be minor species.) Do this problem assuming that H_3PO_4 is the dominant acid ($K_{a_1} \gg K_{a_2} \gg K_{a_3}$). Under these conditions, this becomes a standard weak acid problem.

The dominant equilibrium is

$$H_3PO_4 \rightleftarrows H^+ + H_2PO_4^- \qquad K_a = 7.5 \times 10^{-3}$$

$$K_a = \frac{[H^+][H_2PO_4^-]}{[H_3PO_4]} = 7.5 \times 10^{-3}$$

Initial Concentrations (before any dissociation)		Equilibrium Concentrations
$[H_3PO_4]_0 = 1.00\ M$		$[H_3PO_4] = 1.00 - x$
$[H_2PO_4^-]_0 = 0$	Let x moles/ℓ ──H_3PO_4──→ dissociate	$[H_2PO_4^-] = x$
$[H^+]_0 \approx 0$ (ignoring H^+ from H_2O)		$[H^+] = x$

Solving for x by substituting into K_a and solving the easy way ($[H_3PO_4]_0 - x \approx [H_3PO_4]$) gives

$$x \approx 8.7 \times 10^{-2}$$

In this case

$$\frac{x}{[H_3PO_4]_0} \times 100 = 8.7\%$$

so according to the 5% rule, the quadratic equation should be used. When this is done (do it for practice),

$$x = 8.3 \times 10^{-2}\, M = [H^+] = [H_2PO_4^-]$$

It has been assumed to this point that only the first dissociation of H_3PO_4 makes an important contribution to $[H^+]$. To check the validity of this assumption, substitute the calculated $[H^+]$ into the equilibrium expressions for the latter dissociations. For example, consider the second dissociation

$$H_2PO_4^- \rightleftharpoons H^+ + HPO_4^{2-},$$

where the equilibrium expression is

$$K_{a_2} = 6.2 \times 10^{-8} = \frac{[H^+][HPO_4^{2-}]}{[H_2PO_4^-]} = \frac{(8.3 \times 10^{-2})\,(HPO_4^{2-})}{(8.3 \times 10^{-2})}$$

$\swarrow 8.3 \times 10^{-2}\, M$ (from dissociation of H_3PO_4)

$\nwarrow 8.3 \times 10^{-2}\, M$ (from dissociation of H_3PO_4)

$$[HPO_4^{2-}] = 6.2 \times 10^{-8} = K_{a_2}$$

Thus dissociation of $H_2PO_4^-$ to produce $H^+ + HPO_4^{2-}$ proceeds only to a very slight extent (only $6.2 \times 10^{-8}\, M$ HPO_4^{2-} is produced).

A similar calculation can be performed involving the third dissociation:

$$4.8 \times 10^{-13} = K_{a_3} = \frac{[H^+][PO_4^{3-}]}{[HPO_4^{2-}]} = \frac{(8.3 \times 10^{-2})\,[PO_4^{3-}]}{6.2 \times 10^{-8}}$$

$\swarrow 8.3 \times 10^{-2}\, M$ (from first step)

$\nwarrow 6.2 \times 10^{-8}\, M$ (from the second step)

$$[PO_4^{3-}] = \frac{(4.8 \times 10^{-13})\,(6.2 \times 10^{-8})}{8.3 \times 10^{-2}} = 3.6 \times 10^{-19}\, M$$

Thus the third dissociation, $HPO_4^{2-} \rightleftharpoons H^+ + PO_4^{3-}$, occurs only to a minute extent.

All of this shows that, to calculate the pH of a $1.0\, M$ H_3PO_4 solution, only the first dissociation need be considered:

$$[H^+] = 8.3 \times 10^{-2}\, M$$
$$pH = 1.08$$

If the concentrations of HPO_4^{2-} or PO_4^{3-} are desired, they can be obtained from the K_{a_2} or K_{a_3} expressions as illustrated above.

TEST 5–5

A. Calculate the pH of a $0.1\, M$ solution of carbonic acid (H_2CO_3), where

$$H_2CO_3 \rightleftharpoons H^+ + HCO_3^- \qquad K_{a_1} = 4.3 \times 10^{-7}$$
$$HCO_3^- \rightleftharpoons H^+ + CO_3^{2-} \qquad K_{a_2} = 5.6 \times 10^{-11}$$

   B.   Calculate $[CO_3^{2-}]$ in this solution.

c.   *Calculations Involving Sulfuric Acid*

   Sulfuric acid is a special case because the first acid (H_2SO_4) is a strong acid, but the second acid (HSO_4^-) is a weak acid. This special nature must be taken into account when equilibrium calculations are carried out.

Sample Problem 5–7

Calculate the $[H^+]$ in a 1.00 M H_2SO_4 solution, where

$$H_2SO_4 \rightleftharpoons H^+ + HSO_4^- \qquad K_{a_1} \text{ very large}$$
$$HSO_4^- \rightleftharpoons H^+ + SO_4^{2-} \qquad K_{a_2} = 1.2 \times 10^{-2}$$

Solution

   As mentioned above, the first acid is a strong acid and the second is weak. With this in mind, what are the major species in a 1.00 M H_2SO_4 solution? Since H_2SO_4 dissociates essentially completely to HSO_4^- and H^+, these species are

$$H^+, \ HSO_4^-, \ H_2O$$

The question which must now be answered is: To what extent does HSO_4^- dissociate? To answer this question, do an equilibrium calculation where HSO_4^- is the weak acid:

$$HSO_4^- \rightleftharpoons H^+ + SO_4^{2-}$$

$$1.2 \times 10^{-2} = \frac{[H^+][SO_4^{2-}]}{[HSO_4^-]}$$

Initial Concentrations   *Equilibrium Concentrations*
(before dissociation of HSO_4^-)
$[HSO_4^-]_0 = 1.00 \ M$ $\Big\}$ from complete   Let x moles/ℓ $[HSO_4^-] = 1.00 - x$
$[H^+]_0 = 1.00 \ M$ $\Big\}$ dissociation of $\xrightarrow{\text{HSO}_4^-}$ $[H^+] = 1.00 + x$
$[SO_4^{2-}]_0 = 0$ H_2SO_4 dissociate $[SO_4^{2-}] = x$

$$1.2 \times 10^{-2} = K_{a_2} = \frac{[H^+][SO_4^{2-}]}{[HSO_4^-]} = \frac{(1.00+x)\,(x)}{1.00-x} \approx \frac{(1.00)\,(x)}{1.00}$$

$$x \approx 1.2 \times 10^{-2} \ M$$

Since 1.2×10^{-2} is only 1.2% of 1.0, the simplifying approximation is valid.

$$[H^+] = 1.00 + x = 1.00 + 0.012 = 1.01 \ M$$
$$[HSO_4^-] = 1.00 - x = 1.00 - 0.012 = 0.99 \ M$$

Note that in this case dissociation of HSO_4^- contributes only 1% of the total $[H^+]$.

Even though the dissociation of HSO_4^- makes only a small contribution to the total $[H^+]$, it is the only source of SO_4^{2-} in the solution. Thus to calculate the $[SO_4^{2-}]$, the equilibrium involving the dissociation of HSO_4^- must be used:

$$HSO_4^- \rightleftarrows H^+ + SO_4^{2-}$$

From the above calculations

$$[H^+] = 1.01 \ M$$
$$[HSO_4^-] = 0.99 \ M$$

$$1.2 \times 10^{-2} = K_{a_2} = \frac{[H^+][SO_4^{2-}]}{[HSO_4^-]} = \frac{(1.01)[SO_4^{2-}]}{(0.99)}$$

$$[SO_4^{2-}] = \frac{0.99}{1.01}(1.2 \times 10^{-2}) = 1.17 \times 10^{-2} \ M = 1.2 \times 10^{-2} \ M$$

(rounding to the correct number of significant figures)

Sulfuric acid is the only common polyprotic acid for which the first acid is strong and the others are weak. The more common case is that in which each successive acid is a weak acid (e.g., H_3PO_4).

TEST 5–6

Calculate the pH and the $[SO_4^{2-}]$ in a 5.0 M H_2SO_4 solution. (For H_2SO_4, K_{a_1} is very large and $K_{a_2} = 1.2 \times 10^{-2}$.)

d. Calculations Involving Amphoteric Anions

So far, polyprotic acids have been dealt with using the procedures developed from the treatment of strong and weak monoprotic acids. However, there is one case commonly encountered in connection with polyprotic acids which does require some fresh thinking. This case occurs in solutions which contain, *as the only major species*, an "amphoteric anion." To understand this situation, consider H_3PO_4 again:

$$H_3PO_4 \rightleftarrows H^+ + H_2PO_4^-$$
$$H_2PO_4^- \rightleftarrows H^+ + HPO_4^{2-}$$
$$HPO_4^{2-} \rightleftarrows H^+ + PO_4^{3-}$$

Notice that

$$H_3PO_4 \text{ is an acid only}$$
$$PO_4^{3-} \text{ is a base only}$$

but

$$H_2PO_4^- \text{ is both an acid and a base (amphoteric)}$$
$$HPO_4^{2-} \text{ is both an acid and a base (amphoteric)}$$

These latter two ions are examples of the amphoteric anions referred to above.

When a solution, such as a NaH_2PO_4 solution, contains $H_2PO_4^-$ as *the only major species*, both the acid and the base properties of $H_2PO_4^-$ must be taken into account for calculating the pH. This situation arises because $H_2PO_4^-$ can lose a proton:

$$H_2PO_4^- \rightleftharpoons H^+ + HPO_4^{2-}$$

or gain a proton:

$$H_2PO_4^- + H^+ \rightleftharpoons H_3PO_4$$

Of major species in solution, $H_2PO_4^-$ is both the best acid and the best base.

To treat this situation requires consideration of these equilibria simultaneously, which involves fairly complicated algebra that will not be considered here. Only the result will be given.

For every case to be encountered here, the pH of a NaH_2PO_4 solution can be calculated from the expression

$$pH = \frac{pK_{a_1} + pK_{a_2}}{2}$$

where pK_{a_1} and pK_{a_2} are the negative logs of the dissociation constants for H_3PO_4 (K_{a_1}) and $H_2PO_4^-$ (K_{a_2}).

Sample Problem 5–8

Calculate the pH of a 1.0 M solution of Na_2HPO_4. (For H_3PO_4, $K_{a_1} = 7.5 \times 10^{-3}$, $K_{a_2} = 6.2 \times 10^{-8}$, $K_{a_3} = 4.8 \times 10^{-13}$.)

Solution

The major species in solution are:

$$Na^+, \ HPO_4^{2-}, \ H_2O$$

This is an example of a solution containing the amphoteric anion HPO_4^{2-}. HPO_4^{2-} is at the same time the best acid and the best base in the solution. Both properties must be considered to calculate the pH correctly. Use the formula involving the average of the pK's. In this case, since HPO_4^{2-} is the second amphoteric anion of H_3PO_4 ($H_2PO_4^-$ is the first), the pK_{a_2} and pK_{a_3} must be used:

$$pH = \frac{pK_{a_2} + pK_{a_3}}{2} = \frac{7.21 + 12.32}{2} = 9.76$$

To summarize this situation:

Major Species	pH
$H_2PO_4^-$	$\dfrac{pK_{a_1} + pK_{a_2}}{2}$
HPO_4^{2-}	$\dfrac{pK_{a_2} + pK_{a_3}}{2}$

Sample Problem 5–9

Calculate the pH of a 0.10 M solution of $NaHCO_3$. (For H_2CO_3, $K_{a_1} = 4.3 \times 10^{-7}$ and $K_{a_2} = 5.6 \times 10^{-11}$.)

Solution

The major species in solution are Na^+, HCO_3^-, H_2O.
HCO_3^- is the amphoteric anion associated with H_2CO_3. In a solution where HCO_3^- is the major species

$$pH = \frac{pK_{a_1} + pK_{a_2}}{2} = \frac{-\log(4.3 \times 10^{-7}) - \log(5.6 \times 10^{-11})}{2}$$

$$= \frac{6.37 + 10.25}{2} = \frac{16.62}{2} = 8.31$$

Sample Problem 5–10

Calculate the pH of a solution containing 0.100 M $NaHCO_3$ and 0.100 M Na_2CO_3. (For H_2CO_3, $K_{a_1} = 4.3 \times 10^{-7}$, $K_{a_2} = 5.6 \times 10^{-11}$.)

Solution

The major species in solution are: Na^+, HCO_3^-, CO_3^{2-}, H_2O.
Under these conditions, it might be tempting to assume, since HCO_3^- is present, that
$$pH = \frac{pK_1 + pK_2}{2}$$ can be used. This formula *does not* give the correct answer in this case because the solution contains large amounts of both HCO_3^- and CO_3^{2-}. Therefore

$$CO_3^{2-} \text{ is the strongest base}$$
$$HCO_3^- \text{ is the strongest acid}$$

Thus only the acidic properties of HCO_3^- need be considered in this case (since the much stronger base CO_3^{2-} is present). The equilibrium which will dominate in this solution is the one involving both HCO_3^- and CO_3^{2-}:

$$HCO_3^- \rightleftharpoons H^+ + CO_3^{2-}$$

$$K_{a_2} = \frac{[H^+][CO_3^{2-}]}{[HCO_3^-]} = 5.6 \times 10^{-11}$$

Initial Concentrations   *Equilibrium Concentrations*

$[HCO_3^-]_0 = 0.100\ M$ $[HCO_3^-] = 0.100 - x$

$[CO_3^{2-}]_0 = 0.100\ M$ $[CO_3^{2-}] = 0.100 + x$

$[H^+]_0 \approx 0$ (Ignoring H^+ $[H^+] = x$

from H_2O)

Let x moles/ℓ HCO_3^- dissociate

$$5.6 \times 10^{-11} = K_{a_2} = \frac{[H^+][CO_3^{2-}]}{[HCO_3^-]} = \frac{(x)(0.100 + x)}{0.100 - x} \approx \frac{(x)(0.100)}{0.100}$$

$x = 5.6 \times 10^{-11}\ M$

$pH = -\log(5.6 \times 10^{-11}) = 10.25$

Summary

When a solution contains an amphoteric anion as the *only major species*,

$$pH = \frac{pK_n + pK_m}{2}$$

where $n = 1$, $m = 2$ for the first amphoteric anion

$n = 2$, $m = 3$ for the second amphoteric anion (when the parent acid is triprotic)

When a solution contains large quantities of both an amphoteric anion and its conjugate acid or base, the pH is calculated using the appropriate dissociation equilibrium.

TEST 5–7

Calculate the pH of each of the following solutions: (for H_3AsO_4, $K_{a_1} = 5.0 \times 10^{-3}$, $K_{a_2} = 8.3 \times 10^{-8}$, $K_{a_3} = 6.0 \times 10^{-10}$)

A. 0.100 M NaH_2AsO_4

B. 0.100 M Na_2HAsO_4

C. 0.100 M in both NaH_2AsO_4 and Na_2HAsO_4

e. *Titration of Polyprotic Acids*

Like the other pH calculations involving polyprotic acids, titrations can mostly be treated using the procedures for monoprotic acids.

Sample Problem 5–11

Consider the titration of 100.00 mℓ of 1.0 M phthalic acid ($H_2C_8H_4O_4$, $K_{a_1} = 1.3 \times 10^{-3}$, $K_{a_2} = 3.9 \times 10^{-6}$) with 1.0 M NaOH.

A. Calculate the pH of the solution before any NaOH is added. Do this as a test. (**Test 5–8**) (Hint: as always, first write down the major species and pick out the strongest acid.)

B. Calculate the pH after 25.0 mℓ (total) of 1.0 M NaOH has been added.

The mixed solution before any reaction occurs contains

$$Na^+, OH^-, H_2C_8H_4O_4, \text{ and } H_2O.$$

What reaction will occur? There is only one logical choice.

$$OH^- + H_2C_8H_4O_4 \rightarrow H_2O + HC_8H_4O_4^-$$

Do the stoichiometry problem:

	OH^-	+	$H_2C_8H_4O_4 \rightarrow$	H_2O +	$HC_8H_4O_4^-$
Before the reaction	25.0 mmole		100.0 mmole		0
After the reaction	0		75.0 mmole		25.0 mmole

The stoichiometry problem is done. Now do the equilibrium problem.
In solution (after the above reaction has gone to completion) the species are:

$$H_2C_8H_4O_4, \quad HC_8H_4O_4^-, \ Na^+, \ H_2O$$

strongest   strongest
acid   base

The equilibrium which will dominate in this solution is

$$H_2C_8H_4O_4 \rightleftarrows H^+ + HC_8H_4O_4^-$$

Complete the problem to test your knowledge. (**Test 5–9**)

C. Calculate the pH after 50.0 mℓ (total) of 1.0 M NaOH has been added. (**Test 5–10**)

D. Calculate the pH after 100.0 mℓ of 1.0 M NaOH has been added.

This corresponds to the first equivalence point: 100.0 mmoles of OH^- have been added, which react with the original 100.0 mmoles of $H_2C_8H_4O_4$ to produce 100.0 mmoles of $HC_8H_4O_4^-$. Thus, after the titration reaction has run to completion, the solution contains

$$Na^+, HC_8H_4O_4^-, H_2O$$

How is this case handled?

It is tempting to note that $HC_8H_4O_4^-$ is a weak acid and use K_{a_2} to solve for the $[H^+]$. This will give an incorrect answer. What has been forgotten?

$HC_8H_4O_4^-$ is a base as well as an acid. (It is both the best acid and the best base in this solution.) Thus this is the special case described above (amphoteric anion):

$$pH = \frac{pK_{a_1} + pK_{a_2}}{2} = \frac{-\log(1.3 \times 10^{-3}) - \log(3.9 \times 10^{-6})}{2}$$

$$= \frac{2.89 + 5.41}{2} = \frac{8.30}{2} = 4.15$$

E. Calculate the pH after 125.0 mℓ of 1.0 M NaOH has been added.

This is 25.0 mℓ past the first equivalence point. Recall that

OH^-	+	$H_2C_8H_4O_4$	$\rightarrow$	H_2O	+	$HC_8H_4O_4^-$
100.0 mmoles		100.0 mmoles				100.0 mmoles

requires 100.0 ml
of 1.0 M NaOH

When the $H_2C_8H_4O_4$ has been consumed, the OH^- begins to react with the $HC_8H_4O_4^-$:

	OH^-	+	$HC_8H_4O_4^-$	$\rightarrow$	$C_8H_4O_4^{2-}$	+	H_2O
Before reaction	*25.0 mℓ × 1.0 M = 25.0 mmoles		100.0 mmoles		0		
After reaction	0		75.0 mmoles		25.0 mmoles		

*First 100.0 mℓ of NaOH was consumed by reacting with $H_2C_8H_4O_4$.

The stoichiometry problem is complete. Now do the equilibrium problem. The solution now contains

$$HC_8H_4O_4^-, C_8H_4O_4^{2-}, Na^+, H_2O$$

What equilibrium will control the pH?

The strongest acid is $HC_8H_4O_4^-$, for which $C_8H_4O_4^{2-}$ is the conjugate base. Thus the equilibrium of interest is

$$HC_8H_4O_4^- \rightleftarrows H^+ + C_8H_4O_4^{2-}$$

Now do the weak acid problem.

Initial Concentrations
(before dissociation of
$HC_8H_4O_4^-$)

Equilibrium Concentrations

$$[HC_8H_4O_4^-]_0 = \frac{75.0}{100 + 125}$$

$$[C_8H_4O_4^{2-}]_0 = \frac{25.0}{100 + 125}$$

$$[H^+]_0 = 0$$

Let x moles/ℓ
$\xrightarrow{HC_8H_4O_4^-}$
dissociate

$$[HC_8H_4O_4^-] = \frac{75}{225} - x$$

$$[C_8H_4O_4^{2-}] = \frac{25}{225} + x$$

$$[H^+] = x$$

Substitute into K_{a_2} and solve for x

$$x = 1.2 \times 10^{-5}\ M = [H^+];\ \text{pH} = 4.93$$

F.   Calculate the pH after 150.0 mℓ of 1.0 M NaOH has been added. (**Test 5–11**)

G.   Calculate the pH after 200.0 mℓ of 1.0 M has been added.

   This is the second stoichiometric point; 100.0 mmoles of $C_8H_4O_4^{2-}$ have been formed from the original 100.0 mmoles of $H_2C_8H_4O_4$. In solution are

$$Na^+,\ C_8H_4O_4^{2-},\ H_2O$$

What equilibrium will dominate? Do the problem. (**Test 5–12**)

$\left(\text{Hint:}\quad K_b \text{ for } C_8H_4O_4^{2-} = \dfrac{K_w}{K_{a_2}}\right)$

   All of the concepts concerning titrations of polyprotic acids which have been discussed can be summarized on the following diagram for the titration of H_3A with NaOH.

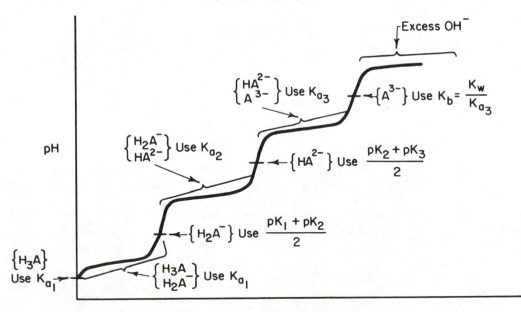

Vol. NaOH

5.5 EQUILIBRIUM CALCULATIONS FOR SOLUTIONS WHERE PRECIPITATION OCCURS

In Chapter 4, precipitation reactions occurring when appropriate solutions are mixed were considered. At that time, treatment of these solutions was limited to predicting whether or not precipitation would occur. In this section, equilibrium concentrations will be calculated.

Sample Problem 5–12

Calculate the equilibrium concentrations of Pb^{2+} and I^- in a solution prepared by mixing 100.0 mℓ of **0.0500 M Pb(NO₃)₂** and **200.0** mℓ of 0.100 M NaI. (K_{sp} for PbI₂ is 1.4×10^{-8}.)

Solution

First determine whether $PbI_2(s)$ will form. To do this, calculate the original concentrations (before any reaction occurs) of Pb^{2+} and I^- in the mixed solution.

$$[Pb^{2+}]_{original} = \frac{\text{mmoles } Pb^{2+}}{\text{m}\ell \text{ of solution}} = \frac{(100.0 \text{ m}\ell)(0.0500 \text{ } M)}{300.0 \text{ m}\ell} = 1.67 \times 10^{-2} \text{ } M$$

$$[I^-]_{original} = \frac{\text{mmoles } I^-}{\text{m}\ell \text{ of solution}} = \frac{(200.0 \text{ m}\ell)(0.100 \text{ } M)}{300.0 \text{ m}\ell} = 6.67 \times 10^{-2} \text{ } M$$

For $PbI_2(s)$ ($PbI_2(s) \rightleftarrows Pb^{2+} + 2I^-$), the ion product expression is

$$Q = [Pb^{2+}]_0[I^-]_0^2 = (1.67 \times 10^{-2})(6.67 \times 10^{-2})^2$$
$$= 7.43 \times 10^{-5}$$

Thus $Q > K_{sp}$ and $PbI_2(s)$ will form.

Note that for $PbI_2(s)$ the equilibrium constant (K_{sp}) for the reaction

$$PbI_2(s) \rightleftarrows Pb^{2+} + 2I^-$$

is 1.4×10^{-8}. This means that the position of this equilibrium lies far to the left and that a solution cannot contain large concentrations of Pb^{2+} and I^-. Another way of saying this is that Pb^{2+} and I^- will react essentially to completion.

As with any situation where a reaction goes essentially to completion, the math is easiest if the reaction is considered to be complete and then the equilibrium calculations are made. So let the system go completely in the direction it tends toward, and then adjust it back to equilibrium.

The next step, then, is to let Pb^{2+} and I^- react to completion:

	Pb^{2+}	+	2I$^-$	$\rightarrow$	PbI$_2$(s)
Before the reaction	(100.0 mℓ)(0.0500 M) = 5.00 mmoles		(200.0 mℓ)(0.100 M) = 20.0 mmoles		The amount of PbI$_2$(s) does not influence the equilibrium
After the reaction	0		20.0 − 2(5.00) = 10.0 mmoles		

At equilibrium the [Pb^{2+}] is not really zero (the reaction does not quite go to completion). Correct for this by considering that some of the PbI$_2$(s) formed in the reaction will dissolve:

$$PbI_2(s) \rightleftarrows Pb^{2+} + 2I^-$$
$$K_{sp} = [Pb^{2+}][I^-]^2 = 1.4 \times 10^{-8}$$

Initial Concentrations
(after the reaction between
Pb^{2+} and I$^-$ has gone to
completion)
$$[Pb^{2+}]_0 = 0$$
$$[I^-]_0 = \frac{10.0 \text{ mmoles}}{300.0 \text{ m}\ell} = 0.0333 \ M$$

$$\xrightarrow[\substack{\text{—PbI}_2\text{(s)}\longrightarrow \\ \text{dissolve to} \\ \text{come to equilibrium}}]{\text{Let } x \text{ moles}/\ell}$$

*Equilibrium
Concentrations*
$$[Pb^{2+}] = x$$
$$[I^-] = 0.0333 + 2x$$

$$1.4 \times 10^{-8} = K_{sp} = [Pb^{2+}][I^-]^2 = (x) (0.0333 + 2x)^2 \approx (x) (0.0333)^2$$

x is expected to be very small (PbI$_2$(s) is very insoluble). Thus

$$x \approx \frac{1.4 \times 10^{-8}}{(3.33 \times 10^{-2})^2} = 1.26 \times 10^{-5} \text{ moles}/\ell$$

Note that 0.033 $\gg$ 2x = 2(1.26 $\times$ 10^{-5}). Thus at equilibrium

$$[Pb^{2+}] = x = 1.26 \times 10^{-5} \ M$$
$$[I^-] = 3.33 \times 10^{-2} \ M + 2x \approx 3.33 \times 10^{-2} \ M$$

In summary, the steps involved in this type of problem are:
1) Determine whether or not precipjitation occurs (use Q to do this). If precipitation occurs:
2) Run the precipitation reaction to completion. (Do the stoichiometry problem.)
3) Compute the initial concentrations (after the precipitation reaction goes to completion).
4) Adjust the system to equilibrium.
   a) Define x.
   b) Represent the equilibrium concentrations in terms of x.
   c) Solve for x by plugging the equilibrium concentrations into the K_{sp} expression (neglect x where possible).

Sample Problem 5–13

To help you appreciate the simplifications that are possible using the previous method, consider this problem using a different strategy: allow the system to come to equilibrium directly as it reacts to form $PbI_2(s)$.

Initial Concentrations
(before any reaction occurs between Pb^{2+} and I^-)

$[Pb^{2+}]_0 = 1.67 \times 10^{-2}\ M$

$[I^-]_0 = 6.67 \times 10^{-2}\ M$

Let y moles/ℓ Pb^{2+}
——react with $2y$ moles/ℓ——→
of I^- to come to equilibrium

Equilibrium Concentrations

$[Pb^{2+}] = 1.67 \times 10^{-2} - y$

$[I^-] = 6.67 \times 10^{-2} - 2y$

$$1.4 \times 10^{-8} = K_{sp} = [Pb^{2+}][I^-]^2 = (1.67 \times 10^{-2} - y)(6.67 \times 10^{-2} - 2y)^2$$

Can y be neglected? Clearly it cannot because the Pb^{2+} and the I^- will react until the Pb^{2+} is almost consumed ($PbI_2(s)$ being very insoluble); to solve the problem involves some very complicated algebra. Eventually one will obtain the same answer as by the previous method, but only after much harder math.

The point is that in dealing with substances that react almost to completion, it is best to run the reaction to completion first and then adjust to equilibrium. This is not the way nature does it, but the math is much easier and the answer will be correct.

TEST 5–13

A solution is prepared by mixing 50.0 mℓ of $1.0 \times 10^{-3}\ M$ $Pb(NO_3)_2$ with 50.0 mℓ of $1.0 \times 10^{-2}\ M$ HCl. Calculate the concentrations of Pb^{2+} and Cl^- at equilibrium. (The K_{sp} for $PbCl_2(s)$ is 1.0×10^{-4}.)

A. Does $PbCl_2(s)$ precipitate?

B. Calculate the concentrations of Pb^{2+} and Cl^-.

TEST 5–14

A solution is prepared by mixing 150.0 mℓ of $1.00 \times 10^{-2}\ M$ $Mg(NO_3)_2$ and 250.0 mℓ of $1.00 \times 10^{-1}\ M$ NaF. Calculate the concentrations of Mg^{2+} and F^- at equilibrium. (The K_{sp} for $MgF_2(s)$ is 6.4×10^{-9}.)

A. Does $MgF_2(s)$ form?

B. Run the reaction to completion. (Do the stoichiometry problem.)

C. Calculate the initial concentrations of Mg^{2+} and F^- (after the precipitation reaction is run to completion but before some $MgF_2(s)$ redissolves to come to equilibrium).

D. Define x.

E. Represent the equilibrium concentrations in terms of x.

F. Solve for x by plugging the equilibrium concentrations into the K_{sp} expression.

G. Calculate the equilibrium concentrations of Mg^{2+} and F^-.

5.6   EQUILIBRIA INVOLVING COMPLEX IONS

A complex ion is a charged species consisting of a metal ion surrounded by ligands. A ligand is typically an anion or neutral molecule which has an unshared electron pair (lone pair) that can be shared with an empty metal ion orbital to form a metal-ligand bond. Some common ligands are H_2O, NH_3, Cl^-, and CN^-.

The number of ligands attached to a metal ion is called the coordination number. The most common coordination numbers are six (as in $Co(OH_2)_6^{2+}$ and $Ni(NH_3)_6^{2+}$), four (as in $CoCl_4^{2-}$ and $Cu(NH_3)_4^{2+}$), and two (as in $Ag(NH_3)_2^+$), although others are known.

Metal ions add ligands one at a time in steps characterized by equilibrium constants called *formation constants*. For example, when solutions containing Ag^+ and NH_3 are mixed, the following reactions take place:

$$Ag^+ + NH_3 \rightleftarrows Ag(NH_3)^+ \qquad K_1 = 2.1 \times 10^3$$
$$Ag(NH_3)^+ + NH_3 \rightleftarrows Ag(NH_3)_2^+ \qquad K_2 = 8.2 \times 10^3$$

In a solution containing Ag^+ and NH_3, all of the species NH_3, Ag^+, $Ag(NH_3)^+$, and $Ag(NH_3)_2^+$ exist at equilibrium. Calculating the concentrations of all these components can be a complicated problem. However, in the most common case, where the total ligand concentration is much larger than the total metal ion concentration, certain approximations are possible which greatly simplify the algebra. This is the only case which will be considered here.

Sample Problem 5–14

Calculate the equilibrium concentrations of NH_3, Ag^+, $Ag(NH_3)^+$, and $Ag(NH_3)_2^+$ in a solution prepared by mixing 100.0 mℓ of 2.0 M NH_3 with 100.0 mℓ of 1.0×10^{-3} M $AgNO_3$.

Solution

Since equal volumes of the solutions have been mixed, the concentrations are halved. Thus, in the mixed solution before any reaction takes place:

$$[Ag^+]_{original} = \frac{1.0 \times 10^{-3} \, M}{2} = 5.0 \times 10^{-4} \, M$$

$$[NH_3]_{original} = \frac{2.0 \, M}{2} = 1.0 \, M$$

As usual, when two solutions are mixed, the first thing to do is to decide whether any reaction occurs which goes essentially to completion. If such a reaction exists, consider it completed first, and then make adjustments to allow the system to come to equilibrium; i.e., do the stoichiometry problem first and then worry about the equilibrium calculations. This strategy allows simplification of the algebra.

In this case, Ag^+ first reacts with NH_3 to form $Ag(NH_3)^+$. Since K_1 and the $[NH_3]_{original}$ are both large, this reaction would be expected to go essentially to completion.

The next step is the reaction of $Ag(NH_3)^+$ with NH_3 to form $Ag(NH_3)_2^+$. Again, since there is still a large amount of NH_3 available and since K_2 is large, this reaction will also essentially go to completion.

To summarize the situation:

1. $[NH_3]_{original} \gg [Ag^+]_{original}$
2. K_1 and K_2 are both large.

One concludes that at equilibrium most of the Ag^+ originally in the solution will be present as $Ag(NH_3)_2^+$. This is equivalent to writing the net reaction in the given solution as

$$Ag^+ + 2NH_3 \rightarrow Ag(NH_3)_2^+$$

Under the conditions of this problem, 5×10^{-4} mole/ℓ Ag^+ reacts with $2(5 \times 10^{-4}$ mole/$\ell)$ NH_3 to produce 5×10^{-4} mole/ℓ $Ag(NH_3)_2^+$. Thus the equilibrium concentration of $Ag(NH_3)_2$ can be estimated to be 5.0×10^{-4} M.

What about the concentration of NH_3 at equilibrium? The solution originally contains 1.0 M NH_3, of which $2(5.0 \times 10^{-4}$ $M)$ is consumed to form 5.0×10^{-4} M $Ag(NH_3)_2^+$. At equilibrium

$$[NH_3] \approx 1.0\ M - 2(5.0 \times 10^{-4}\ M) \approx 1.0\ M$$

(Note that this discussion ignores the fact that NH_3 is a Brønsted base and reacts with H_2O. The amount of NH_3 consumed in this reaction is negligible.)

Next calculate the equilibrium concentration of $Ag(NH_3)^+$. To do this, recall the step-wise equilibria

$$Ag^+ + NH_3 \rightleftarrows Ag(NH_3)^+ \qquad K_1 = 2.1 \times 10^3$$
$$Ag(NH_3)^+ + NH_3 \rightleftarrows Ag(NH_3)_2^+ \qquad K_2 = 8.2 \times 10^3$$

Note that $Ag(NH_3)^+$ is involved in both equilibria. Which one should be used to calculate the $[Ag(NH_3)^+]$? The answer is that K_2 should be used, since the approximate equilibrium concentrations of NH_3 and $Ag(NH_3)_2^+$ are known.

$$8.2 \times 10^3 = K_2 = \frac{[Ag(NH_3)_2^+]}{[Ag(NH_3)^+][NH_3]} = \frac{(5.0 \times 10^{-4})}{[Ag(NH_3)^+](1.0)}$$

$$[Ag(NH_3)^+] = \frac{(5.0 \times 10^{-4})}{(8.2 \times 10^3)(1.0)} = 6.1 \times 10^{-8}\ M$$

Now calculate the equilibrium concentration of Ag^+, using K_1:

$$2.1 \times 10^3 = K_1 = \frac{[Ag(NH_3)^+]}{[Ag^+][NH_3]} = \frac{(6.1 \times 10^{-8})}{[Ag^+](1.0)}$$

$$[Ag^+] = \frac{(6.1 \times 10^{-8})}{(2.1 \times 10^3)\,(1.0)} = 2.9 \times 10^{-11}\ M$$

So far the assumption has been made that $Ag(NH_3)_2^+$ is the dominant silver-containing species in solution. The validity of this assumption can now be demonstrated. The calculated concentrations are

$$[Ag(NH_3)_2^+] = 5.0 \times 10^{-4}\ M$$
$$[Ag(NH_3)^+] = 6.1 \times 10^{-8}\ M$$
$$[Ag^+] = 2.9 \times 10^{-11}\ M$$

These values clearly support the conclusion that

$$[Ag(NH_3)_2^+] \gg [Ag(NH_3)^+] \gg [Ag^+]$$

Thus the assumption that $[Ag(NH_3)_2^+]$ is dominant is valid and the calculated concentrations are correct.

To review the strategy for dealing with a complex ion problem where $[L]_{original} \gg [M^{n+}]_{original}$ (L = ligand; M^{n+} = metal ion):

1. Since the formation equilibrium constants are typically large, assume that the complex ion containing the most ligands will be dominant.

2. Calculate the equilibrium concentration of the ligand. This will be

   $[L]_{original}$ − ligand consumed to form dominant species

3. Calculate the concentrations of the intermediate species by using the stepwise formation constants.

TEST 5–15

Calculate the concentrations of Ag^+, $Ag(S_2O_3)^-$ and $Ag(S_2O_3)_2^{3-}$ in a solution prepared by mixing 150.0 mℓ of $1.00 \times 10^{-3}\ M$ $AgNO_3$ with 200.0 mℓ of 5.00 M $Na_2S_2O_3$. The stepwise formation equilibria are:

$$Ag^+ + S_2O_3^{2-} \rightleftarrows Ag(S_2O_3)^- \qquad K_1 = 7.4 \times 10^8$$
$$Ag(S_2O_3)^- + S_2O_3^{2-} \rightleftarrows Ag(S_2O_3)_2^{3-} \qquad K_2 = 3.9 \times 10^4$$

A. Calculate the original concentrations of Ag^+ and $S_2O_3^{2-}$.

B. What will be the dominant silver-containing species? Calculate its approximate concentration at equilibrium.

C. What is the concentration of $S_2O_3^{2-}$ at equilibrium?

D. Calculate the equilibrium concentrations of $Ag(S_2O_3)^-$ and Ag^+.

E. Are all of the assumptions about relative concentrations valid?

TEST 5–16

Calculate the equilibrium concentrations of NH_3, Cu^{2+}, $Cu(NH_3)^{2+}$, $Cu(NH_3)_2^{2+}$, $Cu(NH_3)_3^{2+}$, and $Cu(NH_3)_4^{2+}$ in a solution prepared by mixing 500.0 mℓ of 3.00 M NH_3 with 500.0 mℓ of 2.00×10^{-3} M $Cu(NO_3)_2$. The stepwise equilibria are

$$Cu^{2+} + NH_3 \rightleftarrows Cu(NH_3)^{2+} \qquad K_1 = 1.86 \times 10^4$$
$$Cu(NH_3)^{2+} + NH_3 \rightleftarrows Cu(NH_3)_2^{2+} \qquad K_2 = 3.88 \times 10^3$$
$$Cu(NH_3)_2^{2+} + NH_3 \rightleftarrows Cu(NH_3)_3^{2+} \qquad K_3 = 1.00 \times 10^3$$
$$Cu(NH_3)_3^{2+} + NH_3 \rightleftarrows Cu(NH_3)_4^{2+} \qquad K_4 = 1.55 \times 10^2$$

5.7 DISSOLVING SOLIDS THAT ARE VERY INSOLUBLE IN WATER

a. *Introduction*

On many occasions, a chemist must dissolve ionic compounds which are very insoluble in water. To understand how this might be done, consider the solubility equilibrium for a general salt, $MX(s)$, which is quite insoluble in water (very small K_{sp} value):

$$MX(s) \rightleftarrows M^+ + X^-$$

For significant quantities of $MX(s)$ to dissolve, this equilibrium must somehow be shifted to the right. This can be accomplished by lowering the concentration of either M^+ or X^- by introducing a substance which will react with one of these ions.

If X^- is a good base (that is, if HX is a weak acid), the usual strategy is to add a strong acid. This will produce the reaction

$$H^+ + X^- \rightleftarrows HX$$

where the equilibrium position lies far to the right. As the H^+ reacts with X^-, lowering its concentration, the solubility equilibrium

$$MX(s) \rightleftarrows M^+ + X^-$$

will be shifted to the right, thus increasing the solubility of $MX(s)$. For example, the solubility of $Ag_3PO_4(s)$ is much greater in strong acid than in pure water. On the other hand, $AgCl(s)$ has the same solubility in strong acid as in pure water. PO_4^{3-} is a strong base and reacts with H^+ to form HPO_4^{2-}, whereas Cl^- is a very weak base (HCl is a very strong acid in water) and virtually no HCl is formed.

How can one increase the solubility of a solid such as AgCl(s) which is very insoluble in both water and acid? The usual strategy in cases where X^- is not a strong base is to add a ligand to the solution which forms a stable complex ion with the metal ion from the solid. For example, Ag^+ forms the stable complex ion $Ag(NH_3)_2^+$ in solutions containing NH_3. As a result, AgCl(s) is quite soluble in concentrated NH_3 solutions. The relevant reactions are

$$AgCl(s) \rightleftarrows Ag^+ + Cl^-$$
$$Ag^+ + NH_3 \rightleftarrows Ag(NH_3)^+$$
$$Ag(NH_3)^+ + NH_3 \rightleftarrows Ag(NH_3)_2^+$$

The Ag^+ produced by dissolving AgCl(s) is combined with the NH_3 to form $Ag(NH_3)_2^+$, which causes more AgCl(s) to dissolve, until

$$[Ag^+][Cl^-] = K_{sp} = 1.6 \times 10^{-10}$$
$\nwarrow$ free Ag^+ only; $Ag(NH_3)^+$ and $Ag(NH_3)_2^+$ are not included.

b. *Strategies for Dissolving Water-Insoluble Ionic Solids*

Consider the salt MX(s).
1. If X^- is a strong base (HX is a weak acid), add H^+ to form HX, thus lowering the X^- concentration. Examples of common anions which are good bases are OH^-, S^{2-}, CO_3^{2-}, PO_4^{3-}, $C_2O_4^{2-}$, and CrO_4^{2-}. Salts containing these anions are much more soluble in acid than in pure water.
2. If X^- is not a strong base (HX is a strong acid), add a ligand which will form stable complex ions with M^+.

c. *Equilibrium Calculations*

These cases will now be treated quantitatively.

Dissolving Salts in Strong Acid Solution

Sample Problem 5–15

Calculate the solubility of Ag_3PO_4(s) ($K_{sp} = 1.8 \times 10^{-18}$) in a 10.0 M HNO_3 solution. (For H_3PO_4, $K_{a_1} = 7.5 \times 10^{-3}$, $K_{a_2} = 6.2 \times 10^{-8}$, and $K_{a_3} = 4.8 \times 10^{-13}$.)

Solution

This is a complicated problem, and must be thought about carefully.
First, review the calculation of the solubility of Ag_3PO_4(s) in pure water. The equilibrium is

$$Ag_3PO_4(s) \rightleftarrows 3Ag^+ + PO_4^{3-}$$
$$K_{sp} = [Ag^+]^3[PO_4^{3-}] = 1.8 \times 10^{-18}$$

Let x = solubility in water. Then

$$[Ag^+] = 3x$$
$$[PO_4^{3-}] = x$$

$$1.8 \times 10^{-18} = K_{sp} = (3x)^3(x) = 27x^4$$
$$x^4 = \frac{1.8 \times 10^{-18}}{27} = 6.7 \times 10^{-20}$$
$$x = 1.6 \times 10^{-5} \text{ moles/}\ell = \text{solubility in pure water}$$

Those of you who are thinking carefully about this problem may wonder how the strong basicity of PO_4^{3-} (the K_a for HPO_4^{2-} is only 4.8×10^{-13}) may affect the solubility of $Ag_3PO_4(s)$ in water. (In the problem above, the properties of PO_4^{3-} as a base have been ignored.) Actually, the solubility of $Ag_3PO_4(s)$ in water is greater than the value calculated above, because some of the PO_4^{3-} from the dissolved Ag_3PO_4 reacts with water. The equilibria involved are

$$Ag_3PO_4(s) \rightleftarrows 3Ag^+ + PO_4^{3-}$$
$$PO_4^{3-} + H_2O \rightleftarrows HPO_4^{2-} + OH^-$$

The actual solubility of $Ag_3PO_4(s)$ in water is greater than 1.6×10^{-5} moles/ℓ because the second reaction lowers the $[PO_4^{3-}]$ and thus shifts the first equilibrium to the right.

If you are interested in the details of this problem, it is considered in the following optional test.

TEST 5–17 (optional)

Calculate accurately the solubility of $Ag_3PO_4(s)$ ($K_{sp} = 1.8 \times 10^{-18}$) in pure water. For H_3PO_4, $K_{a_1} = 7.5 \times 10^{-3}$, $K_{a_2} = 6.2 \times 10^{-8}$, and $K_{a_3} = 4.8 \times 10^{-13}$.)

Now calculate the solubility of $Ag_3PO_4(s)$ in 10.0 M HNO_3. The reactions that must be considered are

$$Ag_3PO_4(s) \rightleftarrows 3Ag^+ + PO_4^{3-} \qquad K_{sp} = 1.8 \times 10^{-18}$$

$$H^+ + PO_4^{3-} \rightleftarrows HPO_4^{2-} \qquad K = \frac{1}{K_{a_3}} = 2.1 \times 10^{12}$$

$$HPO_4^{2-} + H^+ \rightleftarrows H_2PO_4^- \qquad K = \frac{1}{K_{a_2}} = 1.6 \times 10^7$$

$$H_2PO_4^- + H^+ \rightleftarrows H_3PO_4 \qquad K = \frac{1}{K_{a_1}} = 1.3 \times 10^2$$

The $Ag_3PO_4(s)$ dissolves to produce PO_4^{3-}, which reacts with the H^+ from the 10.0 M HNO_3.

Note that the equilibrium of each of the protonation steps lies far to the right. Thus, in the presence of a high concentration of H^+, it is reasonable to assume that almost all of the PO_4^{3-} from the Ag_3PO_4 ends up as H_3PO_4. To simplify this problem, assume that H_3PO_4 is the dominant phosphate-containing species in the solution. This is the same as assuming that the net reaction is

$$Ag_3PO_4(s) + 3H^+ \rightarrow H_3PO_4 + 3Ag^+$$

which is the sum of the four reactions listed above. The K for this equilibrium is the product of the K values for the four reactions:

$$K = \frac{[H_3PO_4][Ag^+]^3}{[H^+]^3} = \frac{K_{sp}}{K_{a1} \cdot K_{a2} \cdot K_{a3}} = 8.1 \times 10^3$$

Let x = solubility of Ag_3PO_4. Then xAg_3PO_4 reacts with $3xH^+$ to produce xH_3PO_4 plus $3xAg^+$. At equilibrium (assuming 1 ℓ of solution):

$$[H_3PO_4] = x$$
$$[Ag^+] = 3x$$
$$[H^+] = 10.0 - \text{amount consumed} = 10.0 - 3x$$

$$K = 8.1 \times 10^3 = \frac{(x)(3x)^3}{(10.0 - 3x)^3}$$

At this point a crucial question arises: Is $10 >> 3x$? The answer is "probably not." Note that the K for this reaction is quite large. A large amount of H^+, therefore, will be consumed as the reaction comes to equilibrium. The equation can be solved by trial and error, or by adopting a different strategy. Since the reaction

$$Ag_3PO_4(s) + 3H^+ \rightarrow H_3PO_4 + 3Ag^+$$

goes nearly to completion, a more reasonable strategy is to assume the reaction goes to completion and then adjust it to equilibrium.

	$Ag_3PO_4(s)$ +	$3H^+$	$\rightarrow$	H_3PO_4	+	$3Ag^+$
Before reaction	excess	10.0 moles		0		0
After reaction	excess	0		3.33 moles		10.0 moles

Now let the system come back to equilibrium by considering the reverse reaction:

Initial Concentrations (above reaction has gone to completion)		*Equilibrium Concentrations*
$[Ag^+]_0 = 10.0\ M$	Let y moles/ℓ	$[Ag^+] = 10.0 - 3y$
$[H_3PO_4]_0 = 3.33\ M$	$\xrightarrow{\ \ H_3PO_4\ \ }$ react with Ag^+	$[H_3PO_4] = 3.33 - y$
$[H^+]_0 = 0$		$[H^+] = 3y$

Now substitute into the equilibrium expression:

$$K = 8.1 \times 10^3 = \frac{[Ag^+]^3[H_3PO_4]}{[H^+]^3} = \frac{(10-3y)^3(3.33-y)}{(3y)^3}$$

Assume $10 \gg 3y$ or $3.33 \gg y$ so that

$$8.1 \times 10^3 \approx \frac{(10)^3(3.33)}{(3y)^3} = \frac{3.33 \times 10^3}{27y^3}$$

$$y^3 = \frac{3.33 \times 10^3}{(27)(8.1 \times 10^3)}$$

$$y = 0.25 \text{ moles/}\ell$$

Note that $3y = 0.75$ moles/ℓ. Comparing $3y$ to 10.0:

$$\frac{0.75}{10.0} \times 100 = 7.5\%$$

To continue to abide by the "5% rule," this should be solved more exactly. Solving by trial and error produces a value of $y = 0.23$ moles/ℓ.

Now check the assumption that H_3PO_4 is the dominant species. Using K_{a_1}:

$$K_{a_1} = 7.5 \times 10^{-3} = \frac{[H^+][H_2PO_4^-]}{[H_3PO_4]}$$

$$[H^+] = 3y = 0.69 \ M$$

$$\frac{[H_3PO_4]}{[H_2PO_4^-]} = \frac{[H^+]}{K_{a_1}} = \frac{0.69}{7.5 \times 10^{-3}} = \frac{92}{1}$$

Thus $[H_3PO_4] \gg [H_2PO_4^-]$.

Using K_{a_2}:

$$K_{a_2} = \frac{[H^+][HPO_4^{2-}]}{[H_2PO_4^-]} = 6.2 \times 10^{-8}$$

$$\frac{[H_2PO_4^-]}{[HPO_4^{2-}]} = \frac{[H^+]}{K_{a_2}} = \frac{0.69}{6.2 \times 10^{-8}} = 1.1 \times 10^7$$

Thus $[H_2PO_4^-] \gg [HPO_4^{2-}]$.

Using K_{a_3}:

$$K_{a_3} = \frac{[H^+][PO_4^{3-}]}{[HPO_4^{2-}]} = 4.8 \times 10^{-13}$$

$$\frac{[HPO_4^{2-}]}{[PO_4^{3-}]} = \frac{[H^+]}{K_{a_3}} = \frac{0.69}{4.8 \times 10^{-13}} = 1.4 \times 10^{12}$$

Thus $[HPO_4^{2-}] \gg [PO_4^{3-}]$.

To summarize: $[H_3PO_4] \gg [H_2PO_4^-] \gg [HPO_4^{2-}] \gg [PO_4^{3-}]$.

The original assumption that H_3PO_4 is dominant is valid; that is, the net reaction is

$$Ag_3PO_4(s) + 3H^+ \rightarrow H_3PO_4 + 3Ag^+$$

The total solubility is equal to the concentration of H_3PO_4 at equilibrium. From the above calculations,

$$[H_3PO_4] = 3.33\ M - y = 3.33 - 0.23 = 3.10 \text{ moles}/\ell$$

Therefore the solubility of $Ag_3PO_4(s)$ in 10.0 M HNO_3 is 3.10 moles/ℓ. Compare this with a solubility of $\sim 10^{-5}$ moles/ℓ in pure water. The acid dramatically increases the solubility of $Ag_3PO_4(s)$.

Strategies for Attacking this Type of Problem

1. Write the reactions that occur.

2. Determine whether one species is dominant.

3. If so, write the net reaction that occurs.

4. Solve the equilibrium problem using the net reaction. (When equations are added, K for the net reaction is the product of the individual K values.)

TEST 5–18

Calculate the solubility of $CuS(s)$ $(K_{sp} = 8.5 \times 10^{-45})$ in 10.0 M strong acid. (For H_2S, $K_{a_1} = 1.02 \times 10^{-7}$; $K_{a_2} = 1.29 \times 10^{-13}$.)

A. Write the steps (reactions) that occur as $CuS(s)$ dissolves in this solution.

B. Determine which species containing S is most likely to be dominant.

C. Write the net reaction that most likely occurs.

D. Write the equilibrium expression for the net reaction and compute the K value.

E. Do the equilibrium calculations. (Hint: Let x = solubility of $CuS(s)$.)

Dissolving Salts in Solutions Containing a Ligand

Sample Problem 5–16

Calculate the solubility of $AgCl(s)$ $(K_{sp} = 1.6 \times 10^{-10})$ in 10.0 M NH_3. Ag^+ reacts with NH_3 to form $Ag(NH_3)^+$, $K_1 = 2.1 \times 10^3$, and $Ag(NH_3)_2^+$, $K_2 = 8.2 \times 10^3$.

Solution

As the AgCl(s) dissolves, the Ag^+ reacts with NH_3 to produce $Ag(NH_3)^+$ and $Ag(NH_3)_2^+$. The relevant reactions are

$$AgCl(s) \rightleftarrows Ag^+ + Cl^- \qquad\qquad K_{sp} = 1.6 \times 10^{-10}$$
$$Ag^+ + NH_3 \rightleftarrows Ag(NH_3)^+ \qquad\qquad K_1 = 2.1 \times 10^3$$
$$Ag(NH_3)^+ + NH_3 \rightleftarrows Ag(NH_3)_2^+ \qquad K_2 = 8.2 \times 10^3$$

Note that the equilibrium in each of the complexation reactions lies far to the right. Thus, in the presence of excess NH_3, $Ag(NH_3)_2^+$ would be expected to be the dominant silver-containing species. This means that the net reaction will be

$$AgCl(s) + 2NH_3 \rightleftarrows Ag(NH_3)_2^+ + Cl^-$$

which is the sum of the three reactions given above.

$$K = \frac{[Ag(NH_3)_2^+][Cl^-]}{[NH_3]^2} = K_{sp}K_1K_2$$
$$= (1.6 \times 10^{-10})\,(2.1 \times 10^3)\,(8.2 \times 10^3)$$
$$= 2.8 \times 10^{-3}$$

Let x = solubility of AgCl. Then xAgCl(s) reacts with $2x$NH$_3$ to produce xAg(NH$_3$)$_2^+$ plus xCl$^-$. Thus at equilibrium

$$[Cl^-] = x$$
$$[Ag(NH_3)_2^+] = x$$
$$[NH_3] = \text{initial amount} - \text{amount consumed} = 10.0 - 2x$$

$$K = 2.8 \times 10^{-3} = \frac{[Ag(NH_3)_2^+]\,[Cl^-]}{[NH_3]^2} = \frac{(x)\,(x)}{(10.0 - 2x)^2}$$

Since K is small, assume that $10.0 \gg 2x$, and thus that $10.0 - 2x \approx 10.0$

$$2.8 \times 10^{-3} = \frac{(x)\,(x)}{(10.0 - 2x)^2} \approx \frac{x^2}{(10.0)^2}$$
$$x^2 \approx (10.0)^2(2.8 \times 10^{-3}) = 2.8 \times 10^{-1}$$
$$x \approx 0.53 \text{ moles}/\ell$$

Check the assumption: $2x = 2(0.53) = 1.06$

$$\frac{2x}{10} \times 100 = \frac{1.06}{10} \times 100 = 10.6\%$$

Thus the assumption that $10.0 - 2x \approx 10.0$ is *not* valid. The equation must be solved exactly (take the square root of both sides). This gives $x = 0.48$ moles/ℓ.

$$[NH_3] = 10.0 - 2x = 10.0 - 0.96 = 9.0 \ M$$

Now check the assumption that $Ag(NH_3)_2^+$ is the dominant species. Using K_2:

$$K_2 = \frac{[Ag(NH_3)_2^+]}{[Ag(NH_3)^+][NH_3]}$$

$$\frac{[Ag(NH_3)_2^+]}{[Ag(NH_3)^+]} = [NH_3] \cdot K_2 = (9.0)(8.2 \times 10^3) = 7.4 \times 10^4$$

Thus $[Ag(NH_3)_2^+] \gg [Ag(NH_3)^+]$.
Using K_1:

$$K_1 = \frac{[Ag(NH_3)^+]}{[Ag^+][NH_3]}$$

$$\frac{[Ag(NH_3)^+]}{[Ag^+]} = K_1[NH_3] = (2.1 \times 10^3)(9.0) = 1.9 \times 10^4$$

Thus $[Ag(NH_3)^+] \gg [Ag^+]$.
    Summary: $[Ag(NH_3)_2^+] \gg [Ag(NH_3)^+] \gg [Ag^+]$.
        $Ag(NH_3)_2^+$ is the dominant species.
        Solubility of AgCl(s) in 10.0 M NH_3 is 0.48 mole/ℓ.

TEST 5–19

Calculate the solubility of AgI(s) ($K_{sp} = 1.5 \times 10^{-16}$) in a 5.0 M $Na_2S_2O_3$ solution. Ag^+ reacts with $S_2O_3^{2-}$ to form $Ag(S_2O_3)^-$, $K_1 = 7.4 \times 10^8$, and $Ag(S_2O_3)_2^{3-}$, $K_2 = 3.9 \times 10^4$.

A. Write the series of reactions that occurs when AgI(s) dissolves in this solution.

B. Decide which silver-containing species will be dominant.

C. Write the net reaction that occurs in this solution.

D. Write the equilibrium expression for the net reaction and calculate the value of K.

E. Solve the equilibrium problem.

Exercises

1. Calculate the pH of a 0.0100 M solution of chloroacetic acid ($HC_2H_2O_2Cl$, $K_a = 1.4 \times 10^{-3}$).

2. Calculate the pH of a 5.0×10^{-8} M HNO_3 solution.

3. Calculate the pH of a 1.0×10^{-2} M solution of $Fe(NO_3)_3$. (Fe^{3+} is hydrated and the K_a for $Fe(OH_2)_6^{3+}$ is 6.0×10^{-3}.)

4. Calculate the pH of a 5.0×10^{-5} M solution of HCN ($K_a = 6.2 \times 10^{-10}$).

5. Calculate the pH of a 1.00 M solution of oxalic acid ($H_2C_2O_4$, $K_{a_1} = 6.5 \times 10^{-2}$, $K_{a_2} = 6.1 \times 10^{-5}$).

6. Calculate the pH for each of the following:
   a) 0.100 M H_3AsO_4 ($K_{a_1} = 5.0 \times 10^{-3}$, $K_{a_2} = 8.3 \times 10^{-8}$, $K_{a_3} = 6.0 \times 10^{-10}$).
   b) 0.100 M NaH_2AsO_4.
   c)   A solution prepared by mixing 500.0 mℓ of 0.100 M NaOH and 500.0 mℓ of 0.200 M H_3AsO_4.
   d) 0.100 M Na_3AsO_4.

7. Calculate the pH of a 0.90 M H_2SO_4 solution ($K_{a_2} = 1.2 \times 10^{-2}$).

8. Consider 75.0 mℓ of a 0.30 M H_3PO_4 solution (for H_3PO_4, $K_{a_1} = 7.5 \times 10^{-3}$, $K_{a_2} = 6.2 \times 10^{-8}$, $K_{a_3} = 4.8 \times 10^{-13}$).
   a)   Calculate the pH of this solution.
   b)   Calculate the pH after 10.0 mℓ of 1.0 M NaOH is added.

9. Calculate the pH of a solution containing 1.00×10^{-3} M HCl and 1.0 M acetic acid ($K_a = 1.8 \times 10^{-5}$).

10. A solution is prepared by mixing 100.0 mℓ of 0.100 M KIO_3 and 100.0 mℓ of 1.00×10^{-2} M $Ce(NO_3)_3$. Calculate the concentrations of Ce^{3+} and IO_3^- at equilibrium. (The K_{sp} for $Ce(IO_3)_3(s)$ is 3.5×10^{-10}.)

11. A solution is prepared by mixing 100.0 mℓ of 1.00×10^{-4} M $Be(NO_3)_2$ and 100.0 mℓ of 8.00 M NaF.

$$Be^{2+} + F^- \rightleftarrows BeF^+ \qquad K_1 = 7.9 \times 10^4$$
$$BeF^+ + F^- \rightleftarrows BeF_2 \qquad K_2 = 5.8 \times 10^3$$
$$BeF_2 + F^- \rightleftarrows BeF_3^- \qquad K_3 = 6.1 \times 10^2$$
$$BeF_3^- + F^- \rightleftarrows BeF_4^{2-} \qquad K_4 = 2.7 \times 10^1$$

Calculate the equilibrium concentrations of F^-, Be^{2+}, BeF^+, BeF_2, BeF_3^-, and BeF_4^{2-} in this solution.

12. Calculate the solubility of AgCN(s) ($K_{sp} = 2.2 \times 10^{-12}$) in a solution containing 1.0 M H^+. (The K_a for HCN is 6.2×10^{-10}.)

13. Calculate the solubility of HgS(s) ($K_{sp} = 1.0 \times 10^{-52}$) in a solution containing 10.0 M H^+. (For H_2S, $K_{a_1} = 1.02 \times 10^{-7}$, $K_{a_2} = 1.29 \times 10^{-13}$.)

14. Calculate the solubility of $Pb_3(PO_4)_2(s)$ $(K_{sp} = 1.0 \times 10^{-42})$ in $1.0\ M\ HNO_3$. For H_3PO_4, $K_{a_1} = 7.5 \times 10^{-3}$, $K_{a_2} = 6.2 \times 10^{-8}$, $K_{a_3} = 4.8 \times 10^{-13}$.

15. Calculate the solubility of $AgI(s)$ $(K_{sp} = 1.5 \times 10^{-16})$ in $5.0\ M\ NH_3$. Ag^+ reacts with NH_3 to form $Ag(NH_3)^+$, $K_1 = 2.1 \times 10^3$ and $Ag(NH_3)_2^+$, $K_2 = 8.2 \times 10^3$.

16. Calculate the solubility of $ZnS(s)$ $(K_{sp} = 1.2 \times 10^{-23})$ in $5.0\ M\ NH_3$. Zn^{2+} reacts with NH_3 to form $Zn(NH_3)^{2+}$, $K_1 = 1.5 \times 10^2$; $Zn(NH_3)_2^{2+}$, $K_2 = 1.8 \times 10^2$; $Zn(NH_3)_3^{2+}$, $K_3 = 2.0 \times 10^2$; $Zn(NH_3)_4^{2+}$, $K_4 = 1.0 \times 10^2$. Ignore all Brønsted acid-base reactions.

Multiple Choice Questions

17. What is the $[H^+]$ in a 1.00×10^{-3} M solution of phenol (C_6H_5OH, $K_a = 1.3 \times 10^{-10}$)?
    a) 1.00×10^{-7} M
    b) 4.74×10^{-7} M
    c) 1.00×10^{-3} M
    d) 3.74×10^{-7} M
    e) none of these

18. The pH in a solution of 1.0 M H_2X ($K_1 = 1.0 \times 10^{-6}$, $K_2 = 1.0 \times 10^{-10}$) is
    a) 5.0   b) 7.0   c) 6.0   d) 3.0   e) none of these

19. Calculate the solubility of MnS in 0.20 M H^+. For MnS(s), $K_{sp} = 1.4 \times 10^{-15}$, and for H_2S, $K_1 = 1.02 \times 10^{-7}$, $K_2 = 1.29 \times 10^{-13}$.
    a) 0.10 moles/ℓ
    b) 0.20 moles/ℓ
    c) 2.8×10^{-7} moles/ℓ
    d) 1.4×10^4 moles/ℓ
    e) none of these

20. The equilibrium $[H^+]$ in exercise 19 is
    a) 0
    b) 0.10 M
    c) 1.0×10^{-7} M
    d) 1.8×10^{-4} M
    e) 3.0×10^{-4} M

For exercises 21 and 22, consider a solution made up by mixing 50.0 mℓ of 2.0×10^{-4} M $CuNO_3$ and 50.0 mℓ of 4.0 M NaCN. Cu^+ reacts with CN^- to form the complex ion $Cu(CN)_3^{2-}$ where

$$Cu^+ + CN^- \rightleftharpoons CuCN \qquad K_1 = 1.0 \times 10^2$$
$$CuCN + CN^- \rightleftharpoons Cu(CN)_2^- \qquad K_2 = 1.0 \times 10^3$$
$$Cu(CN)_2^- + CN^- \rightleftharpoons Cu(CN)_3^{2-} \qquad K_3 = 1.0 \times 10^4$$

21. The concentration of Cu^+ at equilibrium is
    a) 2.0×10^{-4} M
    b) 1.0×10^{-4} M
    c) 1.3×10^{-14} M
    d) 5.0×10^{-14} M
    e) none of these

22. Calculate the solubility of CuBr(s) ($K_{sp} = 1.0 \times 10^{-5}$) in 1.0 ℓ of 1.0 M NaCN.
    a) 1.0 mole
    b) 1.0×10^{-6} mole
    c) 0.33 mole
    d) 1.0×10^3 moles
    e) none of these

23. 50.00 mℓ of a 1.00 M solution of a diprotic acid, H_2A ($K_1 = 1.0 \times 10^{-6}$ and $K_2 = 1.0 \times 10^{-10}$), is being titrated with 2.00 M NaOH. How many mℓ of 2.00 M NaOH must be added to reach a pH of 10?
    a) 0   b) 12.5 mℓ c) 25.0 mℓ d) 37.5 mℓ e) none of these

175

24. The $[H^+]$ in a solution containing 1.0×10^{-6} M HOCl ($K_a = 4.0 \times 10^{-8}$) is
    a) 3.0×10^{-7} M
    b) 1.0×10^{-7} M
    c) 2.0×10^{-7} M
    d) 2.1×10^{-7} M
    e) none of these

For exercises 25 to 28, consider the titration of 100.0 mℓ of 1.00 M H_2A ($K_{a1} = 1.50 \times 10^{-3}$, $K_{a2} = 2.00 \times 10^{-6}$) with 1.00 M NaOH. Calculate the $[H^+]$:

25. Before any NaOH is added:
    a) 3.87×10^{-2} M
    b) 1.50×10^{-3} M
    c) 5.48×10^{-5} M
    d) 2.00×10^{-6} M
    e) none of these

26. After 40.00 mℓ of 1.00 M NaOH has been added:
    a) 1.50×10^{-3} M
    b) 1.00×10^{-3} M
    c) 5.47×10^{-5} M
    d) 2.25×10^{-3} M
    e) none of these

27. After 100.0 mℓ of 1.00 M NaOH has been added:
    a) 1.00×10^{-7} M
    b) 1.41×10^{-10} M
    c) 1.50×10^{-3} M
    d) 5.48×10^{-5} M
    e) none of these

28. After 300.0 mℓ of 1.00 M NaOH has been added:
    a) 4.00×10^{-14} M
    b) 1.00 M
    c) 1.00×10^{-7} M
    d) 1.41×10^{-10} M
    e) none of these

6

SPONTANEITY, ENTROPY, AND FREE ENERGY

Chapter Objectives

1. Define potential energy, kinetic energy, temperature, heat, system, surroundings, endothermic, exothermic, entropy, free energy, and free energy of formation.

2. Learn to predict the sign and calculate $\Delta S_{surroundings}$ for processes which occur at constant T and P.

3. Learn to predict the sign of ΔS.

4. Learn to calculate ΔS from absolute entropies.

5. Learn to calculate ΔG^0 for a reaction from standard free energies of formation.

6. Learn to calculate ΔH^0 from values of ΔG^0, ΔS^0, and T.

7. Understand the temperature dependence of spontaneity.

8. Learn to calculate ΔS for a phase change.

9. Learn to calculate the value of K from ΔG^0.

6.1 REVIEW OF THE FIRST LAW OF THERMODYNAMICS*

The First Law of Thermodynamics is a statement of the law of conservation of energy: energy can be neither created nor destroyed. Another way of saying this is that the *energy of the universe is constant*.

Although the energy of the universe is constant, there are various forms of energy, and these can be interchanged in physical and chemical processes. For example, if you

---

*This material is covered in much more detail in Chapter 6 of *General Chemistry Problem Solving I* by R. S. Drago, D.C. Heath and Company, Lexington, Massachusetts.

drop a book to the floor, the following energy conversions occur. The book initially has **potential energy** (energy due to position or the potential to do work) because of its position above the floor. As the book travels from your hand to the floor, it exhibits **kinetic energy** (energy of motion). When the book hits the floor, this kinetic energy is transferred to the atoms in the floor, which increases their random kinetic energy. The **temperature** of an object is associated with the random motions of its component atoms or molecules. Thus when the book hits the floor, the temperature of the floor is slightly increased. This is an example of "frictional heating." (Note that in this example, the frictional heating of the air is being neglected.)

In summary, during this process, the following energy conversions occur: the initial potential energy of the book is changed to kinetic energy of the book which is transferred to the atoms in the floor as random motion. The net effect of this process is to change a given quantity of potential energy to exactly the same quantity of thermal energy. Thus, although energy has been converted from one form to another, the same quantity of energy exists before and after the process.

Now consider a chemical example. When natural gas is burned in excess oxygen, the major reaction is

$$CH_4(g) + 2O_2(g) \rightarrow CO_2(g) + 2H_2O(g) + \text{heat}$$

This reaction produces a significant quantity of heat and is said to be **exothermic**. **Heat** is a flow of energy due to a temperature differential between two objects. In this case the heat results from a lowering of the potential energy stored in the bonds of CH_4 and O_2 as they react to form CO_2 and H_2O.

Potential energy | $CH_4, 2O_2$
                 | ↘
                 | $CO_2, 2H_2O$ } Change in energy → Heat

This exothermic reaction is an example of a chemical process in which a given quantity of potential energy is changed to an equivalent quantity of thermal energy through heat.

To summarize: Problems involving the First Law of Thermodynamics are mainly bookkeeping problems. Typical questions are: How much energy is involved in the change? Does energy flow into or out of the sytem? What form does the energy finally assume?

6.2   UNITS OF ENERGY

Although many units are used in describing energy, the two most common are calories (cal) and joules (J). A **calorie** is defined as the energy required to change the temperature of exactly one gram of water from 14°C to 15°C. The calorie has been widely used in chemistry for many years. However, we are now switching to a new set of units (SI units) agreed upon in the scientific community. The fundamental unit of energy in the SI system is the **joule**, where

$$1 \text{ calorie} = 4.184 \text{ joules}$$

In this book, all of the problems will be solved in terms of joules. However, you should be able to work with both calories and joules. To change from calories to joules, use the factor

$$\frac{4.184 \text{ J}}{1 \text{ cal}}$$

Sample Problem 6–1

Convert 158 cal to joules.

Solution

$$(158 \text{ cal}) \left(\frac{4.184 \text{ J}}{1 \text{ cal}} \right) = 661 \text{ J} \qquad \text{(Note that the units of calories cancel.)}$$

To convert from joules to calories, use the factor

$$\frac{1 \text{ cal}}{4.184 \text{ J}}$$

TEST 6–1

A. Convert 568 cal to joules.

B. Convert 135 J to calories.

Where the energy change is large, it is convenient to use kilojoules (kJ) and kilocalories (kcal), where

$$1 \text{ kJ} = 10^3 \text{ J}$$
$$1 \text{ kcal} = 10^3 \text{ cal}$$

TEST 6–2

A. Express the following in J and kJ.
   1. 136 J
   2. 1868 cal

B. Express the following in cal and kcal.
   1. 28 cal
   2. 1325 J

6.3   SPONTANEOUS PROCESSES

As discussed in Section 6–1, the First Law of Thermodynamics provides the means for dealing with energy accounting problems. The First Law helps to keep track of energy changes, but it gives no hint as to why a particular process occurs in a given direction. The main question to be considered in this chapter concerns the spontaneity of a process.

First we need to define what spontaneous means. A process is said to be **spontaneous** if it occurs without outside intervention. Spontaneous processes may be fast or slow. It is the direction in which a process occurs—not the speed—which is treated by Thermodynamics. (The study of kinetics concerns the speed of chemical reactions.)

To explore the idea of spontaneity, consider several physical and chemical processes:
1.   A ball on a hill.

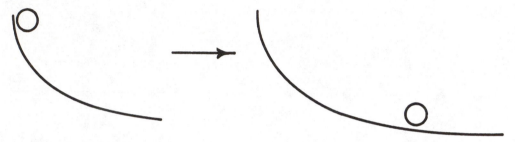

A ball rolls down a hill but never spontaneously rolls back up the hill.
2.   Rusting of steel

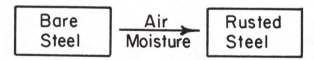

Exposed to air and moisture, steel rusts spontaneously. However, the reverse process is not spontaneous.
3.   Expansion of a gas into an evacuated container

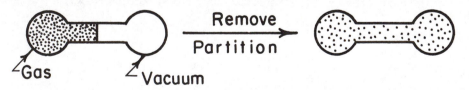

The gas spontaneously expands to fill the container. The reverse process (spontaneous collection of the gas in one end of the flask) never occurs spontaneously.
4.   Transfer of thermal energy

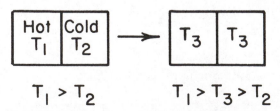

Energy flow via heat always occurs from the hot object to the cooler object. The reverse process never occurs spontaneously.

5. Burning of wood

$$Wood + O_2 \rightarrow CO_2(g) + H_2O(g) + heat$$

Wood burns to produce CO_2, H_2O, and heat. However, wood does not form when CO_2 and H_2O are heated together.

6. Melting and freezing of water

A. $T < 0°C$

$$H_2O(\ell) \rightarrow H_2O(s)$$

B. $T > 0°C$

$$H_2O(s) \rightarrow H_2O(\ell)$$

Note that whether liquid water spontaneously freezes or whether ice spontaneously melts depends upon the temperature.

What do these diverse processes have in common? What thermodynamic principle will provide an explanation of why each process, under a given set of conditions, occurs in one direction and never in the reverse?

In searching for an answer, note, for example, that the behavior of the ball on the hill can be explained in terms of gravity. But what does gravity have to do with the rusting of a nail or the freezing of water?

In the early days of thermodynamics it was thought that exothermicity might be the key, that a process is spontaneous in the direction in which it is exothermic. This does appear to be important, since many spontaneous processes are exothermic. However, exothermicity cannot be the total answer. For example, the melting of ice, which occurs spontaneously at $T > 0°C$, is an endothermic process.

Do these processes have a common characteristic which causes them to be spontaneous in one direction only? After many years of observation and conjecture about these and many other processes, scientists have concluded that the answer is "Yes." The characteristic common to all spontaneous process is an increase in a property which has been named **entropy**. *The driving force for a spontaneous process is an increase in the entropy of the universe*.

What is entropy? Although there is no simple answer which is completely accurate, entropy (designated by "S") can be viewed as a measure of randomness or disorder. The natural progression of things is from order to disorder, from lower to higher entropy.

To be more precise, entropy is a thermodynamic function which describes the number of arrangements (positions and/or energy levels) that are available to a system existing in a given state. Entropy is closely associated with probability. The key concept is that the more ways there are to achieve a particular state, the greater the likelihood (probability) of finding that state. In other words, *nature spontaneously proceeds toward the states which have the highest probability of occurring*. This is not a surprising conclusion at all. The difficulty with this concept is connecting it to real-life processes. For example, what does the spontaneous rusting of steel have to do with probability?

In this chapter we explore the connection between entropy and spontaneity which will allow us to answer the questions raised above.

System and Surroundings

To assist in the accounting process of energy and entropy, for each problem we divide the universe into two parts: a **system** (the part of the universe on which attention will be focused) and the **surroundings** (everything else). The total entropy change ($\Delta S_{universe}$) accompanying a particular process may be represented as

$$\Delta S_{universe} = \Delta S_{system} + \Delta S_{surroundings}$$

Because thermodynamic quantities most often refer to the system, the subscript is usually omitted. Thus ΔH and ΔS are assumed to refer to enthalpy and entropy changes in the system unless otherwise specified.

At this point it is important to realize that it is the entropy of the *universe* which must increase for a process to be spontaneous. A process can be spontaneous even though the entropy of the system decreases (unfavorable) as long as the accompanying entropy change in the surroundings is favorable and large enough. Thus water freezes spontaneously below 0°C, even though ΔS is negative for this process because other effects (which will be discussed in detail) cause $\Delta S_{universe}$ to be positive.

Thus, to understand why a given process is spontaneous, we must look at the changes that occur in the surroundings as well as those in the system. We will explore the factors that control $\Delta S_{surroundings}$ and ΔS_{system} in the next two sections.

6.4   ENTROPY CHANGES IN THE SURROUNDINGS

Consider a chemical reaction that occurs in a system at constant temperature. If the reaction is exothermic, heat must flow out of the system to maintain a constant temperature. On the other hand, heat must flow into the system to maintain constant temperature for an endothermic process.

Although it will not be proved here, it is this flow of heat that determines $\Delta S_{surroundings}$. To understand how this arises, consider an exothermic process that dumps 50 J of energy into the surroundings as heat. What happens to this energy?

The answer is that it becomes random kinetic energy distributed among the atoms in the surroundings. We have learned to associate this increase in the random motions with an increase in entropy. Thus, heat flowing into the surroundings increases the entropy of the surroundings. This is a positive contribution to $\Delta S_{universe}$ and thus favors the process.

When an endothermic process occurs in the system, the opposite effect occurs. In this case heat flows from the surroundings to the system, and the random motions (and thus the entropy) of the surroundings decrease. This has an unfavorable effect on the tendency of the process to occur spontaneously.

The principle being discussed here is often stated as follows: An important driving force in nature results from the tendency of a system to lower its energy. In this section we are emphasizing the *reason* that this is an important driving force: the energy released by the system as heat increases the random motions of the surroundings and thus makes a favorable contribution to $\Delta S_{universe}$. Thus we have switched the emphasis of this driving force from energy to entropy. It is the effect that the energy flow has on the entropy of the universe that is significant.

A very important property of this driving force is that *its significance depends upon the temperature at which the process occurs*. That this, the magnitude of $\Delta S_{surroundings}$ depends on the temperature at which the heat is transferred. We will not attempt to prove this fact here. Rather we will consider an illustration that should make you more comfortable with the idea.

Assume that you have \$50 to give away. Giving it to a millionaire would not create much of an impression. The millionaire has money to spare. However, to a poor college student \$50 would represent a significant sum and would be received with considerable joy.

The same principle can be applied to energy transfer via flow of heat. If 50 J of energy is transferred to the surroundings, the impact of that event depends greatly on the temperature. If the temperature of the surroundings is very high (frantic motions), the 50 joules will not make a large percentage change in these motions. On the other hand, if 50 joules is transferred to the surroundings at a very low temperature (sluggish motion), a large percentage change in the motions will occur. The point here is that the importance of the transfer of a given quantity of heat to or from the surroundings will be greatest at low temperatures.

Two very important points have been made and need to be re-emphasized:

1) *the sign of $\Delta S_{surroundings}$ depends on the direction of the heat flow*: when an exothermic process occurs in the system (at constant T), heat flows into the surroundings, increasing the random motions of the atoms and thereby increasing the entropy of the surroundings. For this case $\Delta S_{surroundings}$ is positive. The opposite is true for an endothermic process in the system. This principle is often stated in terms of energy: An important driving force in nature results from the tendency of the system to achieve the lowest possible energy.

2) *the magnitude of $\Delta S_{surroundings}$ depends on the temperature*. A given quantity of heat produces a much greater percentage change in the "randomness" of the surroundings when transferred to the surroundings at a low temperature than at a high temperature. Thus $\Delta S_{surroundings}$ depends directly upon the quantity of heat transferred and inversely upon temperature. In other words, the tendency for the system to lower its energy becomes a more important driving force at lower temperatures.

$$\begin{matrix} \text{driving force} \\ \text{provided by the} \\ \text{energy flow} \\ \text{(heat)} \end{matrix} = \begin{matrix} \text{magnitude of the} \\ \text{entropy change of} \\ \text{the surroundings} \end{matrix} = \frac{\text{quantity of heat}}{\text{temperature (K)}}$$

To summarize these two points: For an exothermic reaction the entropy of the surroundings increases:

$$\Delta S_{surroundings} = + \frac{\text{quantity of heat}}{\text{temperature}}$$

On the other hand, when an endothermic rection occurs in the system

$$\Delta S_{surroundings} = - \frac{\text{quantity of heat}}{\text{temperature}}$$

For a process carried out at constant pressure, the heat can be described in terms of a change in enthalpy:

$$\text{heat (constant } P) = \text{change in enthalpy} = \Delta H$$

Recall that ΔH consists of two parts: a sign and a number. The *sign* indicates the *direction* of heat flow, where $+$ means into the system (endothermic) and $-$ means out of the system (exothermic). The *number* indicates the *amount* of energy.

Combining all of these concepts produces the following definition of $\Delta S_{surroundings}$ for a reaction that takes place under conditions of constant T and P (where only pressure-volume work occurs):

$$\Delta S_{surroundings} = -\frac{\Delta H}{T}$$

The minus sign is necessary because the sign of ΔH is determined with respect to the system and the calculation is for a property of the surroundings. Thus if the reaction is exothermic, ΔH has a negative sign, but since heat flows into the surroundings, $\Delta S_{surroundings}$ is positive.

Sample Problem 6–2

Predict the sign of $\Delta S_{surroundings}$ for the following processes carried out at constant T and P:

A. $CH_4(g) + 2O_2(g) \rightarrow CO_2(g) + 2H_2O(g)$ Exothermic

Solution

To maintain a constant temperature, heat must flow into the surroundings. This increaes the random kinetic energy of the surroundings. Thus ΔS_{surr} is positive.

B. $H_2O(\ell) \rightarrow H_2O(g)$ Endothermic

Solution

This case is the opposite of A. To maintain a constant temperature, heat must flow from the surroundings into the system to furnish the energy to vaporize the water. Thus ΔS_{surr} is negative.

Sample Problem 6–3

Consider the reaction

$$2NiS(s) + 3O_2(g) \rightarrow 2SO_2(g) + 2NiO(s)$$

where the heats for formation are

Substance	ΔH_f^0
NiS(s)	-93 kJ/mole
O_2(g)	0
SO_2(g)	-297 kJ/mole
NiO(s)	-241 kJ/mole

Calculate ΔS_{surr} for this reaction carried out at a constant temperature of 25°C and a constant pressure of 1 atm.

Solution

Since $\Delta S_{surr} = -\dfrac{\Delta H}{T}$, ΔH for this reaction must first be calculated:

(See Drago, *General Chemistry Problem Solving I*, Chapter 6, Section 3 to review this procedure.)

$$\Delta H^0 = 2\Delta H_f^0(\text{NiO}) + 2\Delta H_f^0(\text{SO}_2) - 2\Delta H_f^0(\text{NiS}) - 3\Delta H_f^0(\text{O}_2)$$
$$= 2 \text{ moles}(-241 \text{ kJ/mole}) + 2 \text{ moles}(-297 \text{ kJ/moles}) -$$
$$2 \text{ moles}(-93 \text{ kJ/mole}) - 0$$
$$= -890 \text{ kJ}$$
$$T = 25 + 273 = 298$$

$$\Delta S_{surr} = -\frac{\Delta H}{T} = -\frac{-890 \text{ kJ}}{298 \text{ K}} = 2.99 \frac{\text{kJ}}{\text{K}}$$

TEST 6–3

Consider the following reaction:

$$\text{XeF}_6(g) \rightarrow \text{XeF}_4(s) + \text{F}_2(g)$$

where the enthalpies of formation for XeF_6(g) and XeF_4(s) are -294 kJ/mole and -251 kJ/mole, respectively.

A. Calculate ΔH for this reaction.

B. Calculate $\Delta S_{surroundings}$ for this reaction at 25°C.

Summary

Several key points have been made in this section:
1. After observing many spontaneous processes, investigators have concluded that the crucial property that drives a process is entropy.
2. Entropy is a measure of probability. Nature tends toward the most probable state. As randomness (disorder) increases, entropy increases.

3.   The flow of heat between the system and the surroundings determines $\Delta S_{\text{surroundings}}$, the change in entropy of the surroundings. For a process that occurs at constant T and P in the system,

$$\Delta S_{\text{surr}} = -\frac{\Delta H}{T}$$

Thus, when energy (heat) flows into the surroundings, the random kinetic energy, and the entropy, increases. *It is this event that drives the system toward lower energy and thus favors an exothermic process.*

6.5   ENTROPY CHANGES IN THE SYSTEM

Although ΔS_{system} (usually denoted ΔS) reflects all of the entropy changes that occur in the system during a particular process, ΔS is dominated, at least for processes at constant T and P, by something we will call **positional probability.**

As an illustration of this concept, consider the expansion of a gas into a vacuum:

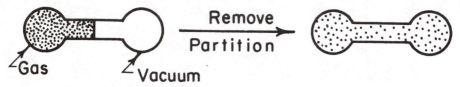

For an ideal gas this process involves no energy changes, since it is assumed that no forces exist among the gas molecules. However, when a real gas expands in an insulated container, the temperature of the gas decreases, because thermal energy is used to overcome the attractive forces existing among the molecules.

TEST 6–4

Consider a *real* gas expanding as above in a container where heat flow to or from the surroundings can occur.

A.   Is this expansion an endothermic or an exothermic process?

B.   What is the sign of $\Delta S_{\text{surroundings}}$?

To summarize, for the expansion of a gas into a vacuum:
1.   For an ideal gas, no heat flow occurs and $\Delta S_{\text{surr}} = 0$.
2.   For a real gas, heat flows into the system and ΔS_{surr} is negative (unfavorable).
We have previously stated that the spontaneity of a process depends upon an increase in entropy. However, as shown above, this process is not driven by an increase in the entropy of the surroundings. What makes this process spontaneous? The driving force still

results from an increase in entropy, but in this case the increase occurs in the system and is due to an increase in positional probability. To understand this concept, consider some of the possible arrangements of four gas molecules in a two-bulbed container.

Arrangement 1

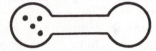

There is one way to achieve this arrangement.

Arrangement 2

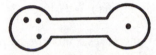

There are four ways to achieve this arrangement (molecule 1 in the right bulb with 2, 3, and 4 in the left; molecule 2 in the right bulb with 1, 3, and 4 on the left; etc.).

Arrangement 3

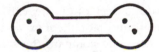

TEST 6–5

Write down the various configurations of gas molecules which lead to arrangement 3. For example,

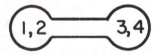

The key question is: Which arrangement is most likely to occur? The answer is the one that can be achieved in the greatest number of ways. Thus, arrangement 3 is most probable; the relative probabilities of arrangements 3, 2, and 1 are 6:4:1.

We have discovered an important principle: the probability of occurrence of a particular arrangement (state) depends on the number of ways (configurations) in which that arrangement can be achieved. Thus when a gas is placed in a flask such as the one we have been considering, it will spontaneously expand to fill the entire vessel evenly. For a large number of gas molecules, there are a huge number of specific configurations which lead to equal numbers of molecules in both ends. On the other hand, the opposite process,

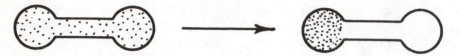

although not impossible, is highly improbable, since only one configuration leads to this arrangement. The process does not occur spontaneously in the direction shown above because of unfavorable probability.

To illustrate this principle further, consider the evaporation of one mole of liquid water at a pressure of one atmosphere. One mole of liquid water (18 g) has a volume of approximately 18 ml. When this water is changed to a gas at one atmosphere at 100°C, it occupies a volume of approximately 31 liters. Clearly there are many more positions available to the water molecules in a volume of 31 ℓ than in 18 mℓ. Thus for the process

$$H_2O(\ell) \rightarrow H_2O(g)$$

positional disorder (probability) increases, and the vaporization of water is favored by positional probability.

TEST 6–6

Assume that you order a deck of playing cards in a particular way. Then you throw the cards into the air and pick them up at random. After picking up all of the cards, you look at them and compare the sequence of cards to the original ordered deck. Would you be surprised to find them in the original order? Explain in terms of probabilities.

Positional Probability and Chemical Reactions

How can we relate positional probability to chemical reactions? Consider the reaction between H_2 and N_2 to form NH_3:

$$N_2(g) + 3H_2(g) \rightarrow 2NH_3(g)$$

In this reaction four molecules become two molecules, thus lowering the number of independent "particles," which leads to less positional disorder: *fewer molecules means fewer possible configurations*.

To help clarify this important principle, consider a special container with a million compartments, each large enough to hold a hydrogen molecule, H_2. Thus, there are one million ways one H_2 molecule can be placed into this container. Now break the H–H bond to produce two H atoms, and consider the number of ways these independent H atoms can be placed in the container. A little thought will convince you that there are many more than a million ways to place the two separate atoms into the container. The number of arrangements of the two independent atoms in the container is much greater than for the molecule where the atoms are bound together. Thus for the process

$$H_2 \rightarrow 2H$$

positional probability increases.

Sample Problem 6–4

Consider the following reaction of NH_3 with O_2:

$$4NH_3(g) + 5O_2(g) \rightarrow 4NO(g) + 6H_2O(g)$$

Does positional randomness increase or decrease when this reaction takes place?

Solution

In this case, 9 gaseous molecules are changed to 10 gaseous molecules and the positional randomness increases. There are more independent units as products than as reactants. In general, when a reaction involves gaseous molecules, the *change in positional randomness is dominated by the relative number of gaseous reactants and products*. If the number of molecules of gaseous product is greater than the number of molecules of gaseous reactant, positional randomness typically increases.

Positional Probability and Phases of Matter

Another important general principle involves changes of phase (solid $\rightleftarrows$ liquid, liquid $\rightleftarrows$ gas). In general, positional disorder decreases as follows:

$$gas > liquid > solid$$

In a gas, the molecules are far apart and move quite independently of one another. At the other extreme is the solid, in which the molecules are close together and highly ordered. The liquid state is intermediate in terms of positional randomness.

Summary—Positional Probability and ΔS_{system}

Although ΔS reflects all of the entropy changes that occur in the system during a particular process, ΔS is dominated by positional effects for processes that occur at constant temperature and pressure. In the examples covered in this book we will assume that ΔS primarily reflects changes in positional probability occurring in the system.

Sample Problem 6–5

Predict the sign of ΔS for the following processes:

A. $4NH_3(g) + 5O_2(g) \rightarrow 4NO(g) + 6H_2O(g)$

Solution

ΔS should be positive, since the number of molecules of gas increases.

B. $H_2O(s) \rightarrow H_2O(\ell)$

Solution

ΔS is positive, since liquid water has more positional disorder than solid water.

C. Sugar plus water → solution

Solution

ΔS is positive. The ordered solid sugar is dispersed randomly in the water.

TEST 6–7

A. Assume that you have two small rubber balls and a box with 10 compartments (each compartment is large enough to hold both balls at the same time). For which of the following cases do the greatest number of arrangements exist?
1. The two balls placed independently into the 10 compartments.
2. The two balls glued together and then placed into the compartments.
3. Explain how this situation is related to the change in positional randomness for the process

$$2Cl(g) \rightarrow Cl_2(g)$$

4. What will be the sign of ΔS for the process in 3?

B. For each of the following processes predict whether positional disorder increases or decreases, and predict the sign of ΔS.
1. $2SO_2(g) + O_2(g) \rightarrow 2SO_3(g)$
2. $CaCO_3(s) \rightarrow CaO(s) + CO_2(g)$
3. $S(s) + O_2(g) \rightarrow SO_2(g)$
4. $H_2O(g) \rightarrow H_2O(\ell)$
5. $H_2(g) + F_2(g) \rightarrow 2HF(g)$

6.6 ENTROPY CHANGES AND SPONTANEITY— A SUMMARY

At this point it is necessary to summarize and systematize the various concepts considered up to now.

By observing many types of processes, scientists have concluded that a process occurs spontaneously only if the total entropy change, ΔS_{univ}, associated with that process is positive. This leads to the *Second Law of Thermodynamics*: The *entropy* of the universe is always increasing. Remember that the First Law of Thermodynamics is: The *energy* of the universe is constant.

To predict whether a process is spontaneous, $\Delta S_{universe}$ must be considered, where

$$\Delta S_{universe} = \Delta S_{surroundings} + \Delta S_{system}$$

If ΔS_{univ} is positive for a given process, the process is spontaneous. If ΔS_{univ} is *negative*, the process is spontaneous in the *opposite* direction. For a process that occurs at constant temperature and pressure:

$\Delta S_{surroundings}$ is associated with the flow of energy (heat) between the system and surroundings. This is the term that reflects the changes in random motions in the surroundings and thus depends on whether the reaction is exothermic or endothermic.

ΔS_{system} can be associated with changes in "positional randomness." Although in general ΔS reflects both energy and positional changes that occur in the system, under conditions of constant temperature and pressure it is dominated by positional effects.

TEST 6–8

A. Predict the sign of ΔS and ΔS_{surr} for each of the following processes (at 25°C).
1. $CaCO_3(s) \rightarrow CaO(s) + CO_2(g)$ (1 atm) $\Delta H = 178$ kJ
2. $NH_3(g) + \frac{7}{4}O_2(g) \rightarrow NO_2(g) + \frac{3}{2}H_2O(g)$ (all gases at 1 atm)
$\Delta H = -283$ kJ

B. For each pair, choose the substance with the highest entropy.
1. $CO_2(s)$, $CO_2(g)$
2. 1 mole of $N_2(g)$ at 1 atm, 1 mole of $N_2(g)$ at 1.0×10^{-2} atm.
3. $Na(s)$, $Na(\ell)$

C. Consider a living cell. This is a system where large molecules are assembled from simple ones. Is this process consistent with the Second Law of Thermodynamics?

6.7   STANDARD STATES

Because changes in thermodynamic functions, such as enthalpy and and entropy, depend on the concentration (or pressure) of the substances involved, standard states have been defined. We will assume the following definitions for standard states:

For a gas, the standard state is a pressure of exactly one atmosphere.

For a substance present in a solution, the standard state is a concentration of exactly one molar.

For a pure substance in a condensed state (liquid or solid), the standard state is the pure liquid or solid.

The temperature is assumed to be 25°C unless otherwise stated.

A superscript zero on a thermodynamic function, e.g., ΔH^0, ΔS^0, indicates that the process has been carried out under standard conditions.

6.8 ABSOLUTE ENTROPIES

So far in the treatment of entropy, only relative entropies and changes in entropy have been considered. Absolute values for entropy are based on the *Third Law of Thermodynamics*: The entropy of a perfect crystal at 0 K is zero.

Using this reference state and the temperature dependence of entropy (which will not be considered here), an entropy value can be calculated for a particular substance at a particular temperature. Absolute entropy values can be used to calculate ΔS values for particular reactions.

Sample Problem 6–6

Calculate ΔS^0 at 25°C for the reaction

$$Al_2O_3(s) + 3H_2(g) \rightarrow 2Al(s) + 3H_2O(g)$$

using the following standard entropies:

Substance	S^0(J/K·mole)
$Al_2O_3(s)$	51
$H_2(g)$	131
$Al(s)$	28
$H_2O(g)$	189

Solution

$\Delta S^0 = \Sigma S^0(\text{products}) - \Sigma S^0(\text{reactants})$

$\Delta S^0 = 2S^0_{Al(s)} + 3S^0_{H_2O(g)} - 3S^0_{H_2(g)} - S^0_{Al_2O_3(s)}$

$$= 2 \text{ moles}\left(28 \frac{J}{K \cdot mole}\right) + 3 \text{ moles}\left(189 \frac{J}{K \cdot mole}\right) - 3 \text{ moles}\left(131 \frac{J}{K \cdot mole}\right)$$
$$- 1 \text{ mole}\left(51 \frac{J}{K \cdot mole}\right)$$

$\Delta S^0 = 56\dfrac{J}{K} + 567\dfrac{J}{K} - 393\dfrac{J}{K} - 51\dfrac{J}{K}$

$= 179\dfrac{J}{K}$

Before leaving this problem, consider one more point. Notice that this reaction involves three moles of gas on both the reactant and the product sides. Would you expect ΔS to be large or small for such a case? It has previously been assumed that ΔS depends on the relative number of molecules of gaseous reactants and products. Based on that assumption, ΔS should be near zero for the present reaction. However, ΔS is large and positive. Why is this so?

Examination of the entropies used to solve this problem shows that the large ΔS results from the difference in the entropies of $H_2O(g)$ and $H_2(g)$. The reason for this difference can be traced to the difference in structure. Because it is a non-linear, triatomic molecule, H_2O has more associated rotational and vibrational motions (called *degrees of freedom*) than does the diatomic H_2 molecule. Thus the absolute entropy of $H_2O(g)$ is greater than that of $H_2(g)$.

This is a useful principle: generally, *the more complex the molecule, the higher the absolute entropy*.

TEST 6–9

Consider the reaction

$$2NO(g) + O_2(g) \rightarrow 2NO_2(g)$$

where the standard entropies are:

Substance	S^0(J/K·mole)
NO(g)	211
O_2(g)	205
NO_2(g)	240

A. Predict the sign of ΔS^0. Explain your reasoning.

B. Calculate ΔS^0 using the S^0 values given.

C. Does the sign of the calculated value of ΔS^0 agree with your prediction in A?

D. Account for the fact that $S^0_{NO_2(g)} > S^0_{NO(g)}$.

6.9   FREE ENERGY

It has been established that the prediction of the spontaneity of a given process requires the calculation of ΔS_{univ} for that process. Since the universe is large and complicated, this could present considerable difficulties. It would be very convenient to find a more manageable function associated with the system which could be used to predict spontaneity.

Such a function has been defined. It is called **free energy**, and is defined by the relationship:

$$\text{free energy} = G = H - TS$$

For a process that occurs at constant temperature, the free energy change (ΔG) is given by

$$\Delta G = \Delta H - T\Delta S$$

This expression has many applications, and you should memorize it. To see how this equation relates to spontaneity, divide both sides by $-T$ to produce

$$-\frac{\Delta G}{T} = -\frac{\Delta H}{T} + \Delta S$$

Remember that at constant temperature and pressure (where only pressure-volume work occurs):

$$\Delta S_{surr} = -\frac{\Delta H}{T}$$

Thus at constant T and P

$$-\frac{\Delta G}{T} = -\frac{\Delta H}{T} + \Delta S = \Delta S_{surr} + \Delta S = \Delta S_{univ}$$

We have shown that

$$\Delta S_{univ} = -\frac{\Delta G}{T} \text{ at constant } T \text{ and } P.$$

This is a very important result. It means that a process carried out at constant T and P will be spontaneous only if ΔG is negative.

   Thus, at constant T and P, a *process is spontaneous in the direction in which the free energy decreases.*

Sample Problem 6–7

Calculate ΔG, ΔS_{surr} and ΔS_{univ} at 25°C for the reaction

$$C(s) + O_2(g) \text{ (1 atm)} \rightarrow CO_2(g) \text{ (1 atm)}$$

$$\Delta H^0 = -393.5 \text{ kJ}$$
$$\Delta S^0 = 3.05 \text{ J/K}$$

Is this process spontaneous?

Solution

$$\Delta G^0 = \Delta H^0 - T\Delta S^0$$
$$T = 25 + 273 = 298 \text{ K}$$
$$\Delta G^0 = -393,500 \text{ J} - (298 \text{ K}) \left(\frac{3.05 \text{ J}}{K}\right)$$
$$= -394,400 \text{ J} = -394.4 \text{ kJ}$$

$$\Delta S_{surr} = -\frac{\Delta H}{T} = -\frac{-393,500 \text{ J}}{298 \text{ K}} = 1320 \text{ J/K}$$
$$\Delta S_{univ} = \Delta S_{surr} + \Delta S^0 = 1320 \text{ J/K} + 3.05 \text{ J/K}$$
$$= 1323 \text{ J/K}$$

Note that ΔS_{surr} clearly dominates ΔS_{univ} although both ΔS and ΔS_{surr} are favorable toward spontaneity. Also note that

$$\Delta S_{univ} = - \frac{\Delta G^0}{T} = - \frac{-394.4 \text{ kJ}}{298 \text{ K}} = 1.323 \text{ kJ/K}$$
$$= 1323 \text{ J/K}$$

Since ΔG^0 is negative (and thus ΔS_{univ} is positive), the process is spontaneous.

Sample Problem 6–8

For the reaction

$$2NiS(s) + 3O_2(g) \rightarrow 2SO_2(g) + 2NiO(s)$$

$$\Delta H^0 = -890 \text{ kJ}$$
$$S^0_{SO_2} = 248 \text{ J/K·mole}$$
$$S^0_{NiO(s)} = 38 \text{ J/K·mole}$$
$$S^0_{O_2(g)} = 205 \text{ J/K·mole}$$
$$S^0_{NiS} = 53 \text{ J/K·mole}$$

A. Calculate (at 25°C):
   1. ΔS^0
   2. ΔS_{surr}
   3. ΔG^0
   4. ΔS_{univ}

Solution

1. $\Delta S^0 = 2S^0_{SO_2} + 2S^0_{NiO(s)} - 2S^0_{NiS(s)} - 3S^0_{O_2}$

$$= 2 \text{ moles}\left(248 \frac{J}{K \cdot mole}\right) + 2 \text{ moles}\left(38 \frac{J}{K \cdot mole}\right) -$$

$$2 \text{ moles}\left(53 \frac{J}{K \cdot mole}\right) - 3 \text{ moles}\left(205 \frac{J}{K \cdot mole}\right)$$

$$= -149 \text{ J/K}$$

Note that ΔS^0 has the expected sign since the number of gas molecules decreases from 3 to 2.

2. $\Delta S_{surr} = - \frac{\Delta H}{T} = - \frac{-890 \text{ kJ}}{298 \text{ K}} = 2.99 \frac{kJ}{K} = 2990 \frac{J}{K}$

3. $\Delta G^0 = \Delta H^0 - T\Delta S^0$
$\Delta G^0 = -890 \text{ kJ} - (298 \text{ K})(-147 \text{ J/K})$
$= -890 \text{ kJ} + 43800 \text{ J}$

To add these quantities, they must be in the same units.

$$(43800 \text{ J}) \left(\frac{1 \text{ kJ}}{10^3 \text{J}}\right) = 43.8 \text{ kJ} \approx 44 \text{ kJ}$$

$$\Delta G^0 = -890 \text{ kJ} + 44 \text{ kJ} = -846 \text{ kJ}$$

4. $\Delta S_{univ} = \Delta S_{surr} + \Delta S^0$
    $= 2990 \text{ J/K} - 147 \text{ J/K} = 2843 \text{ J/K}$
    $= 2840 \text{ J/K}$ (to the correct number of significant figures)

Also,

$$\Delta S_{univ} = -\frac{\Delta G}{T} = -\frac{-846 \times 10^3 \text{ J}}{298 \text{ K}} = +2840 \text{ J/K}$$

B. Is this process spontaneous?

Solution

Yes. ΔG is negative (ΔS_{univ} is postive).

C. Discuss the effect of ΔS^0 and ΔH^0 on the spontaneity of the process.

Solution

ΔS^0 is negative. This opposes spontaneity for the process. However, since ΔH^0 is large in magnitude and has a negative sign, ΔS_{surr} is very large and positive and favors spontaneity. Thus the process is spontaneous because the large, favorable ΔS_{surr} due to the exothermicity of the process overwhelms the small, unfavorable ΔS^0. In this case, exothermicity (tendency of the system to lower its energy) dominates the unfavorable change in positional disorder.

Although we have paid a lot of attention to ΔS_{univ} and ΔS_{surr}, a chemist who is interested in predicting whether a given process (constant T and P) is spontaneous is usually concerned only with the sign of ΔG. If ΔG is negative, the process is spontaneous; if ΔG is positive, the process is not spontaneous. Note from the equation

$$\Delta G = \Delta H - T\Delta S$$

that negative ΔG is favored by a negative value for ΔH (exothermic reaction) and a positive value for ΔS (increase in positional randomness).

Assuming that you now understand why a negative sign for ΔG is essential for a process to be spontaneous (negative ΔG means positive ΔS_{univ}), we will focus on ΔG rather than ΔS_{univ} in the remainder of this chapter. Remember: For a process at constant temperature and pressure, the system will always run spontaneously in the direction which lowers its free energy.

TEST 6–10

Consider the reaction

$$2SO_2(g) + O_2(g) \rightarrow 2SO_3(g)$$

carried out at 25°C with all pressures at 1 atm. The following data are relevant:

Substance	ΔH_f^0(kJ/mole)	S^0(J/K·mole)
$SO_2(g)$	-297	248
$SO_3(g)$	-396	257
$O_2(g)$	0	205

A. Calculate (at 25°C):
  1. ΔH^0 (use the ΔH_f^0 values given above)
  2. ΔS^0 (predict the sign before you calculate it)
  3. ΔG^0

B. Is the process spontaneous?

C. Discuss how ΔS^0 and ΔH^0 contribute to the spontaneity.

6.10   THE THERMODYNAMICS OF PHASE CHANGES

In this section we will consider the thermodynamic properties of substances undergoing a change of phase. We will develop the general principles by examining a familiar process: the melting of ice.

Consider the process:

$$H_2O(s) \rightarrow H_2O(\ell)$$

This process is well known to virtually everyone. At one atmosphere pressure, it occurs spontaneously at temperatures greater than 0°C. At temperatures below 0°C, the reverse process is spontaneous. At 0°C, the solid and liquid phases coexist (the melting point/freezing point).

How can these observations be interpreted in terms of free energy?

First, consider the situation at 0°C. At this temperature, the liquid and solid phases are in equilibrium. There is no driving force toward either phase. What must be true about the free energies of liquid and solid water at 0°C? They must be equal, i.e.,

$$G_{H_2O(\ell)} = G_{H_2O(s)}$$

If they were not equal, nature would drive the system toward the one with the lower free energy. Thus, at 0°C, for the process

$$H_2O(s) \rightarrow H_2O(\ell)$$
$$\Delta G = G_{H_2O(\ell)} - G_{H_2O(s)} = 0$$

This is a general result. At constant T and P, for a system at equilibrium, $\Delta G = 0$.
Thus for a substance at its melting point $\Delta G = 0$ for the process

$$s \rightleftharpoons \ell$$

and for a substance at its boiling point $\Delta G = 0$ for the process

$$\ell \rightleftharpoons g$$

Next, we will consider ΔS for a phase change. Again consider the melting of water

$$H_2O(s) \rightarrow H_2O(\ell)$$

where ΔH (called the heat of fusion) is 6,025 J/mole.
There are two methods available to us for calculating ΔS for this process. One method involves use of the absolute entropies of $H_2O(s)$ and $H_2O(\ell)$ obtained from a reference table. The second method involves use of the equation

$$\Delta G = \Delta H - T\Delta S$$

The latter procedure is considered in Sample Problem 6–9.

Sample Problem 6–9

Calculate the value of ΔS for the process

$$H_2O(s) \rightarrow H_2O(\ell)$$

at 0°C. ΔH for this process is 6,025 J/mole.

Solution

To calculate ΔS, we will use the equation $\Delta G = \Delta H - T\Delta S$. Since the solid and liquid phases are at equilibrium at 0°C, $\Delta G = 0$. Then

$$0 = \Delta H - T\Delta S$$

and

$$\Delta S = \frac{\Delta H}{T} = \frac{6025 \text{ J/mole}}{273 \text{ K}} = 22.1 \text{ J/mole·K}$$

This problem leads to an important general result. For the melting of a solid

$$\Delta G_{s \rightarrow \ell} = \Delta H_{s \rightarrow \ell} - T(\Delta S_{s \rightarrow \ell})$$

At the melting point of the solid ($T_{\text{M.P.}}$), $\Delta G_{s \to \ell} = 0$. Substitution into the above equation gives

$$\Delta G_{s \to \ell} = 0 = \Delta H_{s \to \ell} = T_{\text{M.P.}} (\Delta S_{s \to \ell})$$

or

$$\Delta S_{s \to \ell} = \frac{\Delta H_{s \to \ell}}{T_{\text{M.P.}}}$$

where $\Delta H_{s \to \ell}$ is usually called the heat of fusion (ΔH_{fus}).

A similar situation holds at the boiling point of a liquid, where the liquid and vapor phases of a substance are at equilibrium ($\Delta G_{\ell \to g} = 0$), which leads to

$$\Delta S_{\ell \to g} = \frac{\Delta H_{\ell \to g}}{T_{\text{B.P.}}}$$

where $\Delta H_{\ell \to g}$ is called the heat of vaporization of the liquid (ΔH_{vap}).

TEST 6–11

Consider liquid hydrogen, $H_2(\ell)$, which has a boiling point of $-253°C$ and a heat of vaporization of 903 J/mole. Calculate ΔS for the process

$$H_2(\ell) \to H_2(g)$$

at $-253°C$.

So far we have considered phase changes only at the melting and boiling points, where the two phases are in equilibrium. Now we will consider phase change processes at other temperatures.

Consider again the melting of water

$$H_2O(s) \to H_2O(\ell)$$

We have established that at $T = 0°C$ and a pressure of 1 atmosphere, $\Delta G = 0$ for this process. Now consider this process at temperatures above the melting point.

At temperatures above $0°C$, the process occurs spontaneously. This means that ΔG must be negative or, in other words, at temperatures greater than $0°C$,

$$G_{H_2O(\ell)} < G_{H_2O(s)}$$

We can verify this since we know the values of ΔH and ΔS for this process.

Sample Problem 6–10

For the process

$$H_2O(s) \rightarrow H_2O(\ell)$$

ΔH = 6,025 J/mole and ΔS = 22.1 J/mole·K. Assuming these quantities to be temperature-independent, calculate ΔG for the melting of ice at 10°C.

Solution

We know that

$$\Delta G = \Delta H - T\Delta S$$

where

$$T = 10 + 273 = 283 \text{ K}$$
$$\Delta H = 6,025 \text{ J/mole}$$
$$\Delta S = 22.1 \text{ J/K·mole}$$

Substituting these values into the equation for ΔG gives

$$\Delta G = 6,025 \text{ J/mole} - (283 \text{ K})(22.1 \text{ J/K·mole})$$
$$= 6,025 \text{ J/mole} - 6,254 \text{ J/mole} = -229 \text{ J/mole}$$

Note that ΔG is negative, as expected from the knowledge that ice melts spontaneously above 0°C.

At temperatures below 0°C the process

$$H_2O(s) \rightarrow H_2O(\ell)$$

is known to occur spontaneously in the opposite direction. This means that at temperatures below 0°C, ΔG is positive for the process as written. This is verified in Test 6–12.

TEST 6–12

For the process

$$H_2O(s) \rightarrow H_2O(\ell)$$
$$\Delta H = 6,025 \text{ J/mole and } \Delta S = 22.1 \text{ J/K·mole}$$

Calculate ΔG for this process at $T = -20°C$.

To summarize, for the process

$$H_2O(s) \rightarrow H_2O(\ell)$$

$T > 0°C$	$\Delta G < 0$	spontaneous
$T = 0°C$	$\Delta G = 0$	equilibrium
$T < 0°C$	$\Delta G > 0$	reverse process is spontaneous

Consideration of the phase changes of water has led us to a very important result: spontaneity can be temperature-dependent. We will explore this idea in the next section.

6.11   THE TEMPERATURE DEPENDENCE OF SPONTANEITY

In the previous section we discovered that spontaneity can be temperature-dependent. That is, a given process can be spontaneous in one direction at high temperatures and spontaneous in the opposite direction at low temperatures. This is illustrated nicely by the temperature dependence of the freezing/melting of water.

Why is spontaneity sometimes temperature dependent? This question can be answered by looking at the relationship of ΔG, ΔH, ΔS and T:

$$\Delta G = \Delta H - T\Delta S$$

For a process to be spontaneous at constant T and P, ΔG must be negative. Spontaneity is favored by negative ΔH (remember this means positive ΔS_{surr}) and positive ΔS. However, for a given process one of these terms might oppose spontaneity. For example, ΔS might be negative. The process can still be spontaneous if ΔH is negative and large enough in magnitude to overwhelm the unfavorable ΔS term. For processes that have opposing ΔH and ΔS terms, temperature becomes important in determining in which direction the process will run, because temperature weights the two contributions (as can be seen in the above equation).

For the process $H_2O(s) \rightarrow H_2O(\ell)$, ΔH is positive and ΔS is positive. Thus the natural tendencies for systems to lower their energy and increase their positional randomness are in opposition for this process. At low T, ΔH dominates, and at high T, ΔS dominates.

Summary

The temperature dependence of ΔG is given by the equation

$$\Delta G = \Delta H - T\Delta S$$

If the ΔH and ΔS terms are in opposition, the spontaneous direction of the process depends upon the temperature.

The various cases are tabulated below:

	Case	Result
1.	ΔS positive, ΔH negative	spontaneous at all temperatures
2.	ΔS positive, ΔH positive	spontaneous at high temperatures (where exothermicity is relatively unimportant)

3. ΔS negative, ΔH negative — spontaneous at low temperatures (where exothermicity is dominant)

4. ΔS negative, ΔH positive — reverse process is spontaneous at all temperatures

---

TEST 6–13

    A. For the process $H_2O(\ell) \rightarrow H_2O(g)$ (1 atm), $\Delta H = 41.2$ kJ/mole at 100°C.

        1. Calculate, at 100°C:
            a) ΔS b) ΔG

        2. Discuss why this process is spontaneous at one atmosphere pressure and $T > 100°C$.

    B. Consider chloroform ($CHCl_3$).

        1. For the process $CHCl_3(s) \rightarrow CHCl_3(\ell)$

$$\Delta H = 9.2 \text{ kJ/mole}$$
$$\Delta S = 43.9 \text{ J/mole·K}$$

        a) What is the melting point of chloroform?

        b) Discuss how ΔH, ΔS, and T influence the spontaneous direction of the freezing and melting of chloroform.

6.12 PHYSICAL INTERPRETATION OF THE TEMPERATURE DEPENDENCE OF SPONTANEITY (optional)

How can the observations discussed in the previous section be interpreted in terms of the concepts of energy and positional disorder introduced earlier?

For the process $H_2O(s) \rightarrow H_2O(\ell)$,

$$\Delta H = 6.025 \text{ kJ/mole}$$

Thus the melting of water is an endothermic process, which means that ΔS_{surr} is negative:

$$\Delta S_{surr} = -\frac{6025 \text{ J/mole}}{T}$$

The randomness of the surroundings decreases, which is an unfavorable contribution to ΔS_{univ}. On the other hand, $\Delta S = 22.1$ J/K·mole. This term can be associated with a change in positional randomness. In going from $H_2O(s)$ to $H_2O(\ell)$, the positional randomness increases, which is expected in going from a highly ordered solid (molecules in lattice sites) to a less-ordered liquid (molecules with freedom to move around).

To summarize, for the process $H_2O(s) \rightarrow H_2O(\ell)$, ΔS_{surr} is unfavorable and ΔS is favorable.

Why is temperature important in determining in which direction this process is spontaneous? Note that ΔS_{surr} is temperature dependent $\left(\Delta S_{surr} = -\dfrac{\Delta H}{T} \right)$. At low temperatures, the magnitude of ΔS_{surr} becomes larger than that of ΔS. Thus at low temperatures the process runs in the direction for which ΔS_{surr} is favorable. At high temperatures, the magnitude of ΔS_{surr} is smaller than that of ΔS and the process runs in the direction for which ΔS is positive.

In other words, at low temperatures the energy change dominates (energy transferred to the surroundings has the most impact at low temperatures). At high temperatures, positional randomness dominates.

At 0°C, the two contributions are balanced, and the system exists at equilibrium. Note that at 0°C

$$\Delta S_{surr} = -\frac{\Delta H}{T} = -\frac{6025 \text{ J/mole}}{273 \text{ K}} = -22.1 \text{ J/K·mole}$$

and

$$\Delta S = 22.1 \text{ J/K·mole}$$

This means that

$$\Delta S_{univ} = \Delta S_{surr} + \Delta S = -22.1 \text{ J/mole·K} + 22.1 \text{ J/mole·K} = 0$$

This is a very important general result: For a system at equilibrium, $\Delta S_{univ} = 0$. This is the thermodynamic definition of equilibrium. (For a process at constant T and P this is equivalent to $\Delta G = 0$.)

6.13   CALCULATION OF THE CHANGE IN FREE ENERGY FOR A CHEMICAL REACTION

Free energy is a **state function**. That is, a change in free energy which accompanies a particular process *depends only upon the initial and final states*, not upon the pathway. This situation is identical to that for enthalpy changes, where Hess's Law is used to calculate enthalpies of reaction. (See Drago, *General Chemistry Problem Solving I*, Chapter 6, Section 4.)

Sample Problem 6–11

Use the following data:

	$\Delta G^0(kJ)$
1. $2CH_4(g) + 3O_2(g) \rightarrow 2CO(g) + 4H_2O(g)$	-1088
2. $CH_4(g) + 2O_2(g) \rightarrow CO_2(g) + 2H_2O(g)$	-801

to calculate ΔG^0 for the reaction

3. $2CO(g) + O_2(g) \rightarrow 2CO_2(g)$

Solution

The reaction of interest is

$$2CO(g) + O_2(g) \rightarrow 2CO_2(g)$$

To determine how reactions 1 and 2 can be combined to give 3, note that in reaction 3, $CO(g)$ is a reactant. Thus reaction 1 must be reversed, since $CO(g)$ is a product in that reaction. When a reaction is reversed, the sign of ΔG is reversed. Thus ΔG^0 for the reverse of 1 is $-(-1088 \text{ kJ}) = 1088 \text{ kJ}$.

In reaction 2, $CO_2(g)$ is a product, as needed, but only one $CO_2(g)$ is formed. Thus equation 2 must be multiplied by two, which means ΔG^0 for 2 must also be multiplied by two. This leads to:

	ΔG^0
$2CO(g) + 4H_2O(g) \rightarrow 2CH_4(g) + 3O_2(g)$	$-(-1088)$
$2CH_4(g) + 4O_2(g) \rightarrow 2CO_2(g) + 4H_2O(g)$	$2(-801)$

Adding these reactions and the corresponding free energy changes gives

$$2CO(g) + 4H_2O(g) + 2CH_4(g) + 4O_2(g) \rightarrow 2CH_4(g) + 4H_2O(g) + 3O_2(g) + 2CO_2(g)$$
$$\Delta G = -(-1088) + 2(-801) = 1088 - 1602 = -514 \text{ kJ}$$

Cancelling identical species on both sides of the equation gives

$$2CO(g) + O_2(g) \rightarrow 2CO_2(g) \qquad \Delta G^0 = -514 \text{ kJ}$$

This is the required result.

In doing problems of this type, use the following steps:

1) By observing the reactants and products in the final equation, determine which (if any) of the reactions must be reversed.
2) Write the reaction(s) that must be reversed and change the sign of their ΔG values.
3) Multiply each equation by an integer as needed to achieve the final equation. ΔG is multiplied by the same integer.
4) Add the equations and cancel identical species.

TEST 6–14

Use the following data

$$\Delta G^0 (\text{kJ})$$

1) $C_{(s)}^{\text{diamond}} + O_2(g) \rightarrow CO_2(g)$ -397

2) $C_{(s)}^{\text{graphite}} + O_2(g) \rightarrow CO_2(g)$ -394

to calculate ΔG^0 for the reaction

3) $C_{(s)}^{\text{graphite}} \rightarrow C_{(s)}^{\text{diamond}}$

To summarize the main points:
1) Free energy is a state function.
2) Because free energy is a state function, ΔG values for reactions can be summed to find ΔG values for other reactions.
3) When a reaction is reversed, the sign of ΔG is reversed.
4) When a reaction is multiplied by an integer, ΔG must be multiplied by that same integer.

Free Energy of Formation

The **standard free energy of formation** of a substance is defined as the *change in free energy which accompanies the formation of one mole of that substance from its constituent elements* with all reactants and products in their standard states. (The form of the element used is assumed to be the form most stable at 25°C and a pressure of one atmosphere.) For example, for glucose ($C_6H_{12}O_6$), the appropriate reaction is

$$6C(s) + 6H_2(g) + 3O_2(g) \rightarrow C_6H_{12}O_6(s)$$

The standard free energy associated with this process is called the free energy of formation of glucose and is designated by ΔG_f^0. Values of the standard free energy of formation of most common substances are found in reference tables and are useful in calculating ΔG^0 for specific chemical reactions. (See Drago, *General Chemistry Problem Solving I*, Chapter 6 for similar calculations involving enthalpies of formation.)

Sample Problem 6–12

Consider the reaction

$$2CH_3OH(g) + 3O_2(g) \rightarrow 2CO_2(g) + 4H_2O(g)$$

This reaction is relevant to the present search for alternate fuels. Methyl alcohol (CH_3OH) has long been used in races such as the Indianapolis 500, and is being evaluated as a replacement for gasoline in certain situations.

Calculate ΔG^0 for this reaction, given the following free energies of formation:

Substance	G_f^0 (kJ/mole)
$CH_3OH(g)$	-163
$O_2(g)$	0
$CO_2(g)$	-394
$H_2O(g)$	-229

Solution

Note that ΔG_f^0 for $O_2(g)$ is zero. The *free energy of formation for any element in its standard state is defined to be zero*.

To solve this problem, use the relationship

$$\Delta G_{reaction}^0 = \Sigma \Delta G_f^0(\text{products}) - \Sigma \Delta G_f^0(\text{reactants})$$

where Σ represents the sum of the ΔG_f^0 values for the products and the reactants, respectively.

$$\Delta G^0 = 2\Delta G_f^0(CO_2) + 4\Delta G_f^0(H_2O) - 3\Delta G_f^0(O_2) - 2\Delta G_f^0(CH_3OH)$$
$$\Delta G^0 = 2 \text{ moles}(-394 \text{ kJ/mole}) + 4 \text{ moles}(-229 \text{ kJ/mole})$$
$$- 3\,(0) - 2 \text{ moles}(-163 \text{ kJ/mole})$$
$$= -1378 \text{ kJ}$$

TEST 6–15

A. Calculate ΔG^0 for the reaction

$$4PH_3(g) + 8O_2(g) \rightarrow P_4O_{10}(s) + 6H_2O(\ell)$$

given the following:

Substance	ΔG_f^0 (kJ/mole)
$PH_3(g)$	13.4
$O_2(g)$	0
$P_4O_{10}(s)$	-2697.8
$H_2O(\ell)$	-237.2

B. For glucose $(C_6H_{12}O_6)$, the standard free energy of combustion (reaction with oxygen) is -2830 kJ/mole. For $CO_2(g)$ and $H_2O(g)$, the standard free energies of formation are -394 kJ/mole and -229 kJ/mole, respectively. Calculate the standard free energy of formation of glucose.

6.14 THE DEPENDENCE OF FREE ENERGY ON PRESSURE AND CONCENTRATION (optional)

In this section we will consider how the free energy of a substance depends upon its pressure (if gaseous) or its concentration (if present in solution). The free energy of an ideal gas will be considered in developing this relationship.

Recall that free energy is defined as $G = H - TS$. For an ideal gas, enthalpy is not pressure-dependent. However, entropy does depend on pressure because of its dependence on volume. Consider one mole of an ideal gas at a given temperature. If this gas has a volume of 10.0 ℓ, it has many more positions available for the molecules than if its volume is 1.0 ℓ. Entropy is proportional to volume for a gas at constant temperature.

To summarize, at a given temperature for a mole of ideal gas

$$S_{\text{large volume}} > S_{\text{small volume}}$$

or, since pressure and volume are inversely related:

$$S_{\text{low pressure}} > S_{\text{high pressure}}$$

This means that the entropy, and thus the free energy, of an ideal gas depends on its pressure. Using a more detailed argument, it can be shown that

$$G = G^0 + RT \ln P$$

where G^0 is the free energy of the gas at a pressure of one atmosphere and G is the free energy of the gas at a pressure of P atmospheres. Using this equation, it can be shown for a chemical reaction involving gases that

$$\Delta G = \Delta G^0 + RT \ln Q = \Delta G^0 + 2.303 RT \log Q$$

where

$\ln Q = 2.303 \log Q$ (Recall that ln means natural logarithm and log means logarithm to the base 10.)

Q is the reaction quotient (from the Law of Mass Action). This will be illustrated below.

T is the temperature (K)

R is the gas law constant: $R = 8.315$ J/K·mole

ΔG^0 is the free energy change for the reaction with all reactants and products at a pressure of one atmosphere.

ΔG is the free energy change for the reaction for the pressures of reactants and products specified.

Sample Problem 6–13

For the reaction

$$N_2(g) + 3H_2(g) \rightarrow 2NH_3(g)$$

ΔG^0 at 25°C is -33.3 kJ. Calculate ΔG at 25°C for the process in which 1 mole of $N_2(g)$ at 3.0 atm reacts with 3 moles of $H_2(g)$ at 5.0 atm to form 2 moles of $NH_3(g)$ at 4.0 atm.

Solution

For this reaction,

$$Q = \frac{P_{NH_3}{}^2}{P_{N_2}P_{H_2}{}^3}$$

Under the conditions specified in the problem, $P_{N_2} = 3.0$ atm, $P_{H_2} = 5.0$ atm, and $P_{NH_3} = 4.0$ atm. Thus

$$Q = \frac{(4.0)^2}{(3.0)\,(5.0)^3} = 4.3 \times 10^{-2}$$

$$\begin{aligned}
\Delta G &= \Delta G^0 + 2.303RT \log Q \\
&= -33.3 \text{ kJ} + 2.303\left(8.315 \frac{J}{K}\right)(298 \text{ K}) \log(4.3 \times 10^{-2}) \\
&= -33.3 \text{ kJ} - 7820 \text{ J}
\end{aligned}$$

Now the first term has the units kJ and the second, J. Converting to the same units:

$$\begin{aligned}
\Delta G &= 33.3 \text{ kJ} - (7820 \text{ J})\left(\frac{1 \text{ kJ}}{10^3 \text{ J}}\right) \\
&= -33.3 \text{ kJ} - 7.8 \text{ kJ} = -41.1 \text{ kJ}
\end{aligned}$$

Thus ΔG for this reaction is more negative for the pressures specified than for the standard pressure (1 atm).

TEST 6–16

Consider the reaction (25°C)

$$2NO(g) + O_2(g) \rightarrow 2NO_2(g)$$

where $\Delta H^0 = -112$ kJ and $\Delta S^0 = -147$ J/K.

A. Calculate ΔG^0 at 25°C.

B. Calculate ΔG at 25°C under conditions where $P_{NO} = 2.5$ atm, $P_{O_2} = 1.3$ atm, and $P_{NO_2} = 3.8$ atm.

C. Calculate ΔG^0 at 65°C.

6.15   FREE ENERGY AND EQUILIBRIUM
(optional)

It has been established that a system moves spontaneously to lower its free energy. The concentrations or pressures in a system where a chemical reaction is occurring will continue to change until a minimum in total free energy is achieved.

To understand the relationship of free energy to equilibrium, consider the following hypothetical reaction

$$A(g) \rightarrow B(g)$$

where 1.0 mole of A(g) is initially placed in a reaction vessel at a pressure of 2.0 atm. As A reacts to form B, the total free energy of the system changes, where

$$\text{free energy of A} = G_A = G_A{}^0 + RT \ln P_A$$
$$\text{free energy of B} = G_B = G_B{}^0 + RT \ln P_B$$
$$\text{total free energy of system} = G = G_A + G_B$$

Note that as A is changed to B, G_A will decrease (P_A is decreasing) and G_B will increase (P_B is increasing). The system will proceed to the right (A changing to B) as long as the total free energy of the system decreases (as long as $G_B < G_A$). At some point the pressures of A and B reach values $P_A{}^e$ and $P_B{}^e$ which make $G_A = G_B$. The system has reached *equilibrium*. Since A (at pressure $P_A{}^e$) and B (at pressure $P_B{}^e$) have the same free energy ($G_A = G_B$), $\Delta G = 0$ for A at pressure $P_A{}^e$ changing to B at pressure $P_B{}^e$. The system has reached minimum free energy. There is no longer any driving force to change A to B or B to A so the system remains at this position (the pressures of A and B remain constant).

The experiment described above might have a graph of free energy versus fraction of A reacted as follows:

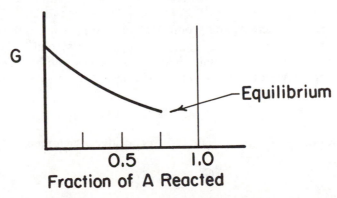

In this experiment, minimum free energy is reached when 75% of A has been changed to B. At this point, the pressure of A is 0.25 of the original pressure, or (0.25) (2.0 atm) = 0.50 atm. The pressure of B is (0.75) (2.0 atm) = 1.5 atm. This is the equilibrium position so

$$K = \frac{P_B^e}{P_A^e} = \frac{1.5}{0.5} = 3.0$$

for A $\rightleftharpoons$ B at this temperature.

In summary, when substances are mixed which undergo a chemical reaction, the reaction proceeds to minimum free energy (equilibrium). This corresponds to the point where $G_{products} = G_{reactants}$ or where

$$\Delta G = G_{products} - G_{reactants} = 0$$

Next we will establish a quantitative relationship between free energy and the value of the equilibrium constant. Consider the equation that shows how ΔG depends on pressure:

$$\Delta G = \Delta G^0 + RT \ln Q$$

At equilibrium $\Delta G = 0$ and $Q = K$. Thus

$$\Delta G = 0 = \Delta G^0 + RT \ln K$$

or

$$\Delta G^0 = -RT \ln K = -2.303RT \log K$$

This is a very important equation because it shows how K and ΔG^0 are related.
Note the following characteristics of this equation:

Case 1 $\Delta G^0 = 0$
This means that for a particular reaction the free energies of the reactants and products are equal with all components in the standard states (1 atm for gases). The system is at equilibrium with the pressures of all reactants and products at 1 atm. This means that $K = 1$.

Case 2 $\Delta G^0 < 0$
In this case $\Delta G^0 = G^0_{products} - G^0_{reactants}$ is negative, which means that

$$G^0_{products} < G^0_{reactants}$$

If a flask contains the reactants and products all at 1 atm pressure, the system will *not* be at equilibrium. In this case since $G^0_{products} < G^0_{reactants}$ the system will adjust to the right (reactants $\rightarrow$ products) to reach equilibrium. In this case K will be *greater than one*, since at equilibrium the pressures of the products will be greater than 1 atm and the pressures of reactants will be less than 1 atm.

Case 3 $\Delta G^0 > 0$
In this case $\Delta G^0 = G^0_{products} - G^0_{reactants}$ is positive which means that

$$G^0_{reactants} < G^0_{products}$$

If a flask contains the reactants and products all at 1 atm pressure, the system will *not* be at equilibrium. In this case the system will adjust to the left (toward the reactants, which have lower free energy) to reach equilibrium. In this case K will be *less than one* since at equilibrium the pressures of the reactants will be greater than 1 atm and the pressure of the products will be less than 1 atm.

Summary

Case 1 $\Delta G^0 = 0$ $K = 1$
Case 2 $\Delta G^0 < 0$ $K > 1$
Case 3 $\Delta G^0 > 0$ $K < 1$

The quantitative relationship between ΔG^0 and K is given by the equation

$$\Delta G^0 = - RT \ln K$$

Sample Problem 6–14

Consider the reaction

$$4Fe(s) + 3O_2(g) \rightarrow 2Fe_2O_3(s)$$

where ΔH_f^0 for $Fe_2O_3(s)$ is -826 kJ/mole, $S^0{}_{Fe_2O_3(s)}$ is 90 J/K·mole, $S^0{}_{Fe(s)}$ is 27 J/K·mole, and $S^0{}_{O_2(g)}$ is 205 J/K·mole.

Calculate the following quantities:

A. ΔH^0

Solution

Note that this reaction involves 2 moles of $Fe_2O_3(s)$ being formed from the elements. Thus

$$\Delta H^0 = 2\Delta H_f^0(Fe_2O_3(s)) = 2 \text{ moles}(-826 \text{ kJ/mole}) = -1652 \text{ kJ}$$

B. ΔS^0

Solution

$$
\begin{aligned}
\Delta S^0 &= 2S^0{}_{Fe_2O_3(s)} - 4S^0{}_{Fe(s)} - 3S^0{}_{O_2(g)} \\
&= 2 \text{ moles}(90 \text{ J/K·mole}) - 4 \text{ moles}(27 \text{ J/K·mole}) - 3 \text{ moles}(205 \text{ J/K·mole}) \\
&= 180 \text{ J/K} - 108 \text{ J/K} - 615 \text{ J/K} \\
&= -543 \text{ J/K}
\end{aligned}
$$

C. ΔG^0 at 25°C

Solution

$$\Delta G^0 = \Delta H^0 - T\Delta S^0$$
$$T = 25 + 273 = 298 \text{ K}$$
$$\Delta G^0 = -1652 \text{ kJ} - (298)(-543 \text{ J/K})\left(\frac{1 \text{ kJ}}{10^3 \text{ J}}\right)$$
$$= -1652 \text{ kJ} + 161.8 \text{ kJ}$$
$$= -1490 \text{ kJ}$$

D. K at 25°C

Solution

$\Delta G^0 = -RT \ln K = -2.303RT \log K$

$-1490 \text{ kJ} = -\left(8.315 \frac{J}{K}\right) \left(\frac{1 \text{ kJ}}{10^3 \text{ J}}\right) (298 \text{ K}) (2.303) \log K$

$-1490 \text{ kJ} = (-5.71 \text{ kJ}) \log K$

$$\log K = \frac{1490}{5.71} = 261$$

This is a huge equilibrium constant (too large for ordinary hand calculators):

$$K = 10^{261}$$

Notice that the reaction considered in this example is the one that describes formation of rust. Rusting is clearly a very favorable process from a thermodynamic standpoint.

TEST 6–17

A.   Consider the reaction

$$H_2(g) + Cl_2(g) \rightleftarrows 2HCl(g)$$

where

$$\Delta H_f^0 \text{ for HCl(g)} = -92 \text{ kJ/mole}$$
$$S^0 \text{ for } H_2(g) = 131 \text{ J/K·mole}$$
$$S^0 \text{ for } Cl_2(g) = 223 \text{ J/K·mole}$$
$$S^0 \text{ for HCl(g)} = 187 \text{ J/K·mole}$$

1.   Calculate
a. ΔH^0
b. ΔS^0
c. ΔG^0 (at 25°C)
2.   If $H_2(g)$, $Cl_2(g)$, and HCl(g) are placed in a flask such that the pressure of each gas is 1 atm, in which direction will the system shift to come to equilibrium?
3.   Calculate K for this reaction at 25°C.

B.   Consider the reaction

$$H_2S(aq) \rightleftarrows H^+(aq) + HS^-(aq)$$

where

$$\Delta H_f^0 \text{ for } H_2S(aq) = -21 \text{ kJ/mole}$$
$$\Delta H_f^0 \text{ for } HS^-(aq) = -18 \text{ kJ/mole}$$
$$\Delta H_f^0 \text{ for } H^+(aq) = 0$$

and

$$S^0_{H_2S(aq)} = 206 \text{ J/K·mole}$$
$$S^0_{HS^-(aq)} = 63 \text{ J/K·mole}$$
$$S^0_{H^+(aq)} = 0$$

1. For this reaction, calculate
   a. ΔH^0
   b. ΔS^0
   c. ΔG^0 at 25°C
   d. K at 25°C
2. Discuss the value of ΔS^0 obtained for this process. Does it seem reasonable?

Exercises

DATA TABLE

Substance	ΔG_f^0 (kJ/mole)	S^0 (J/K·mole)	Substance	ΔG_f^0 (kJ/mole)	S^0 (J/K·mole)
$H_2O(\ell)$	-237	70	$SO_3(g)$	-371	257
$H_2O(g)$	-229	189	$Xe(g)$	0	170
$H_2(g)$	0	131	$XeF_2(g)$	-48	254
$N_2(g)$	0	192	$F_2(g)$	0	203
$O_2(g)$	0	205	$Cr(s)$	0	24
$NH_3(g)$	-16	193	$Cr_2O_3(s)$	-1047	81
$NO(g)$	87	211	$Sn(s)$	0	52
$NO_2(g)$	52	240	$SnO_2(s)$	-520	52
$N_2O_4(g)$	98	304	$Fe(s)$	0	27
$C^{diamond}_{(s)}$	3	2	$Fe_2O_3(s)$	-740	90
$C^{graphite}_{(s)}$	0	6	$CaO(s)$	-604	40
$CO_2(g)$	-394	214	$CaSO_4(s)$	-1320	107
$CH_4(g)$	-51	186	$NaBr(s)$	-347	84
$Cl_2(g)$	0	223	$Na^+(aq)$	-262	59
$S_8(g)$	50	431	$Br^-(aq)$	-104	82
$SF_6(g)$	-1105	292			

For exercises 1 to 6, first predict the sign of ΔS_{surr} and then calculate ΔS_{surr} for each of the following processes carried out at constant temperature and pressure (assume $T = 298$ K):

1. $C_2H_5OH(\ell) \rightarrow C_2H_5OH(g)$ $\Delta H = 38.6$ kJ/mole
2. $NaCl(s) \rightarrow Na^+(aq) + Cl^-(aq)$ $\Delta H = 4$ kJ/mole
3. $H_2(g) \rightarrow 2H(g)$ $\Delta H = 436$ kJ/mole H_2
4. $H_2O(g) \rightarrow H_2O(\ell)$ $\Delta H = -43.9$ kJ/mole
5. $N_2(g) + 3H_2(g) \rightarrow 2NH_3(g)$ $\Delta H = -92$ kJ/mole
6. $2H_2(g) + O_2(g) \rightarrow 2H_2O(g)$ $\Delta H = -484$ kJ/mole

For exercises 7 to 16, predict the sign of ΔS for each of the following processes carried out at constant temperature and pressure:

7. $2NO(g) + O_2(g) \rightarrow 2NO_2$

8. $H_2O(\ell) \rightarrow H_2O(g)$

9. $Fe_2O_3(s) + 3H_2(g) \rightarrow 2Fe(s) + 3H_2O(g)$

10. $N_2H_4(\ell) + O_2(g) \rightarrow N_2(g) + 2H_2O(\ell)$

11. $SnO_2(s) + 2H_2(g) \rightarrow Sn(s) + 2H_2O(g)$

12. $PCl_5(g) \rightarrow PCl_3(g) + Cl_2(g)$

13. $2NO_2(g) \rightarrow N_2O_4(g)$

14. $4NH_3(g) + 7O_2(g) \rightarrow 4NO_2(g) + 6H_2O(g)$

15. $H_2O(\ell) \rightarrow H_2O(s)$

16. $Alcohol + H_2O \rightarrow Solution$

For exercises 17 to 24, predict the sign of ΔS^0, then calculate ΔS^0 for each of the following reactions (see data table for pertinent information).

17. $Xe(g) + F_2(g) \rightarrow XeF_2(g)$

18. $C_{(s)}^{diamond} \rightarrow C_{(s)}^{graphite}$

19. $SnO_2(s) + 2H_2(g) \rightarrow Sn(s) + 2H_2O(g)$

20. $CH_4(g) + 2O_2(g) \rightarrow CO_2(g) + 2H_2O(\ell)$

21. $CaSO_4(s) \rightarrow CaO(s) + SO_3(g)$

22. $4NH_3(g) + 7O_2(g) \rightarrow 4NO_2(g) + 6H_2O(g)$

23. $H_2O(\ell) \rightarrow H_2O(g)$

24. $NaBr(s) \rightarrow Na^+(aq) + Br^-(aq)$

25. Consider the reaction

$$N_2H_4(\ell) + O_2(g) \rightarrow N_2(g) + 2H_2O(\ell)$$

ΔG^0 for this reaction is -623 kJ. Using information from the data table, calculate ΔG_f^0 for $N_2H_4(\ell)$.

For exercises 26 to 30, use the information in the data table to calculate ΔG^0, ΔS^0, ΔH^0, and K at 298 K for each reaction:

26. $2H_2(g) + O_2(g) \rightarrow 2H_2O(g)$

27. $Cr_2O_3(s) + 3H_2(g) \rightarrow 2Cr(s) + 3H_2O(g)$

28. $N_2O_4(g) \rightarrow 2NO_2(g)$

29. $S_8(g) + 24F_2(g) \rightarrow 8SF_6(g)$

30. $4NH_3(g) + 5O_2(g) \rightarrow 4NO(g) + 6H_2O(g)$

31. For the reaction

$$N_2(g) + 3H_2(g) \rightleftarrows 2NH_3(g)$$

the equilibrium constant is 6.0×10^{-2} ℓ/mole at 500°C. Calculate ΔG^0 at 500°C.

32. Consider the reaction

$$Fe_2O_3(s) + 3H_2(g) \rightarrow 2Fe(s) + 3H_2O(g)$$

a. Use information in the data table to calculate ΔG^0.
b. Is this reaction spontaneous under standard conditions at 298 K?
c. ΔH^0 for this reaction is 100 kJ. Beyond what temperature is the reaction spontaneous under standard conditions?

33. When 1.0 mole of NaCl(s) dissolves in water at constant temperature, 4 kJ of heat is absorbed by the solution.
a. What must be the sign of ΔS for this process?
b. Will the solubility of NaCl(s) increase or decrease as the temperature is raised?

34. Consider the dissociation of hydrogen:

$$H_2(g) \rightleftarrows 2H(g) \qquad \Delta H^0_{300\ K} = 435.6\ kJ$$
$$\Delta S^0_{300\ K} = 98.5\ J/K$$

Assuming ΔH^0 and ΔS^0 are temperature-independent, would you expect this process to proceed spontaneously on the surface of the sun where the temperature is approximately 6000 K?

TRUE-FALSE
35. The energy of the universe is constant.

36. The entropy of the universe is constant.

37. If a process has a positive value of ΔS and is endothermic, it will be spontaneous at all temperatures.

38. If ΔG^0 for a reaction is negative, the value of K for that reaction will be greater than 1.

39. For an exothermic reaction carried out at constant T and P, ΔS_{surr} will be positive.

40. For a proces to be spontaneous at constant T and P, the sign of ΔG must be positive.

41. Exothermicity is most important as a driving force for spontaneity at low temperatures.

Verbalizing General Concepts

Answer the following in your own words:

42. State the Second Law of Thermodynamics.

43. What is the significance of the Second Law of Thermodynamics?

44. Define entropy.

45. Define free energy.

46. How is the change in free energy in a system related to the change in entropy of the universe?

47. In terms of entropy, explain why the tendency of a system to lower its potential energy is a driving force for a spontaneous process.

48. Why is exothermicity most important as a driving force for spontaneity at low temperatures?

49. Under what conditions can a process for which ΔS is negative be spontaneous?

50. Under what conditions can an endothermic process be spontaneous?

51. How is the melting point of a substance defined in terms of the free energies of the two phases?

52. Define standard free energy of formation.

53. Define equilibrium in thermodynamic terms.

54. How is the equilibrium constant for a reaction related to ΔG^0 for that reaction?

Multiple Choice Questions

From the following pairs of substances (55 to 59), predict which one will have the largest absolute entropy:

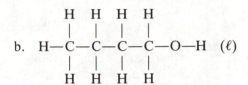

55. a. $H-C-O-H$ (ℓ)   b. $H-C-C-C-C-O-H$ (ℓ)

56. a. 1 mole of $N_2(g)$ at 25°C and 1 atm   b. 1 mole of $N_2(g)$ at 25°C and 10 atm

57. a. $CO_2(s)$ b. $CO_2(g)$

58. a. $F^-(g)$ b. $F^-(aq)$

59. a. $NO_2(g)$ b. $N_2O_4(g)$

60. Pick the correct statement.
    a. Exothermic reactions must always be spontaneous.
    b. Free energy is independent of temperature.
    c. A reaction which exhibits a negative value of ΔS cannot be spontaneous.
    d. At constant temperature and pressure, a decrease in free energy insures an increase in the entropy of the universe.
    e. None of these statements is true.

61. Which process will probably show the largest increase in entropy?
    a. $H_2O(\ell) \rightarrow H_2O(s)$
    b. $H_2(g) + F_2(g) \rightarrow 2HF(g)$
    c. $H_2O(s) \rightarrow H_2O(g)$
    d. $H_2O(\ell) \rightarrow H_2O(g)$
    e. $Ag^+(aq) + Cl^-(aq) \rightarrow AgCl(s)$

62. The standard free energy of formation of $AgCl(s)$ is -110 kJ/mole. Calculate ΔG^0 for the reaction

$$2AgCl(s) \rightarrow 2Ag(s) + Cl_2(g)$$

    a. 110 kJ   d. -220 kJ
    b. 220 kJ   e. none of these
    c. -110 kJ

63. Vaporization of a liquid ($A(\ell) \rightarrow A(g)$) is a process for which:
    a. ΔH, ΔS, and ΔG are positive at all temperatures.
    b. ΔH and ΔS are positive at all temperatures.

   c. ΔG is negative at low temperatures but positive at high temperatures.
   d. ΔG is negative at all temperatures.
   e. ΔH and ΔS are negative at all temperatures.

For exercises 64 and 65 consider the process

$$\text{benzene}(\ell) \rightarrow \text{benzene}(g)$$

where ΔH = 30.5 kJ/mole
            ΔS = 86.4 J/mole·K

64. What is the boiling point of benzene?
   a. 353°C   c. −353 K
   b. 80°C   d. not enough data to calculate

65. ΔS for the process benzene(g) $\rightarrow$ benzene(ℓ) is
   a. −86.4 J/mole·K   b. −30.5 kJ/mole   c. 86.4 J/mole·K

66. The Second Law of Thermodynamics states that
   a. exothermic reactions are always spontaneous.
   b. endothermic reactions are never spontaneous.
   c. the entropy change within a given system must be positive for a process to be spontaneous.
   d. none of these

For exercise 67 and 68 consider the dimerization of NO_2:

$$2NO_2(g) \rightleftarrows N_2O_4(g)$$

where ΔH^0 = −56.8 kJ and ΔS^0 = −175 J/K.

67. ΔG^0 at T = 298 K is
   a. 52.3 kJ   d. 109 kJ
   b. −56.8 kJ   e. none of these
   c. −4.6 kJ

68. The value of K $\left(\text{where } K = \dfrac{P_{N_2O_4}}{P_{NO_2^2}}\right)$ at T = 298 K is

   a. 1.0 atm^{-1} d. 76 atm^{-1}
   b. 6.4 atm^{-1} e. none of these
   c. 1.6×10^{-1} atm^{-1}

69. A change of state occurs within a system that produces 15.3 kJ of heat, which is transferred to the surroundings at a constant temperature of 300 K. For this process, $\Delta S_{\text{surroundings}}$ is
   a. 15,300 J   d. −51.0 J/K
   b. −15,300 J   e. none of these
   c. 51.0 J/K

For exercises 70 to 72, consider the melting of anthracene:

$$anthracene(s) \rightarrow anthracene(\ell)$$

where $\Delta H = 21.0$ kJ/mole. The melting point of anthracene is 218°C.

70. Calculate ΔS for this process.
    a. 96.3 J/K·mole
    b. 42.8 J/K·mole
    c. 10,300 J/K·mole
    d. 2.34×10^{-2} J/K·mole
    e. none of these

71. Calculate ΔG for this process at 218°C.
    a. 0
    b. -26.3 kJ/mole
    c. 21.0 kJ/mole
    d. 11.7 kJ/mole
    e. none of these

72. Calculate ΔG for this process at 150°C (assume ΔH and ΔS are not temperature-dependent).
    a. 0
    b. 14.6 kJ/mole
    c. 2.9 kJ/mole
    d. -1.4×10^{-2} kJ/mole
    e. none of these

73. Consider the reaction

$$CO(g) + H_2O(g) \rightleftharpoons CO_2(g) + H_2(g)$$

At 700 K the equilibrium constant for this reaction has the value 5.10. Calculate ΔG^0 for this reaction at 700 K.
    a) 0
    b) 29.7 kJ
    c) 9.48 kJ
    d) -9.48 kJ
    e) none of these

7

ELECTROCHEMISTRY

Chapter Objectives

1. Define oxidation, reduction, oxidizing agent, reducing agent, electrochemistry, galvanic cell, electrolytic cell, electrical potential, maximum cell potential, electrical work, the Faraday, reduction potential, anode and cathode.

2. Learn to manipulate half-cell potentials to calculate $\mathscr{E}^0$ values for redox reactions.

3. Learn to describe galvanic cells, given the half-reactions involved.

4. Learn to calculate the amount of product produced in an electrolytic cell, given the current and the time.

5. Learn to calculate electrical work, given the potential difference and the charge transferred.

6. Learn to calculate the change in free energy, given the potential difference and the charge transferred.

7. Learn to use the Nernst equation to calculate the potential of a cell.

8. Learn to calculate the value of the equilibrium constant for a redox reaction from $\mathscr{E}^0$.

7.1   INTRODUCTION

In this chapter we will consider several aspects of electrochemistry. Before this can be done, however, a few definitions involving oxidation-reduction reactions must be reviewed.*

An oxidation-reduction (redox) reaction is one that involves a transfer of electrons. **Oxidation** is defined as a loss of electrons (increase in oxidation state) and **reduction** as a gain of electrons (decrease in oxidation state). In a redox reaction the **oxidizing agent** takes electrons from the **reducing agent.**

_____

*See R.S. Drago, *General Chemistry Problem Solving I,* Chapter 9 for a more detailed treatment.

It is often useful to divide a redox reaction into **half-reactions**, one involving oxidation (the electrons appear on the product side) and one involving reduction (the electrons appear as reactants). These half-reactions can be balanced separately, multiplied by appropriate integers to make the numbers of electrons equal, and then summed to produce the balanced redox reaction.

7.2 ELECTROCHEMISTRY

Electrochemistry involves the study of the interchange of chemical and electrical energy. It is primarily concerned with two situations: the generation of an electric current from a chemical reaction, or the opposite process, the use of a current to produce chemical change. As might be expected, both applications involve oxidation-reduction reactions.

Galvanic Cells

To understand how a redox reaction can be used to generate a current, consider the reaction between MnO_4^- and Fe^{2+}:

$$8H^+ + MnO_4^- + 5Fe^{2+} \rightarrow Mn^{2+} + 5Fe^{3+} + 4H_2O$$

In this reaction Fe^{2+} is oxidized and MnO_4^- is reduced (electrons are transferred from Fe^{2+} [the reducing agent] to MnO_4^- [the oxidizing agent]). The balanced half-reactions are

1) $8H^+ + MnO_4^- + 5e^- \rightarrow Mn^{2+} + 4H_2O$
2) $5(Fe^{2+} \rightarrow Fe^{3+} + e^-)$

The 5 beside the second half-reaction indicates that it must occur five times for each time the first reaction occurs.

In solution the electrons are transferred directly between the reactants when they collide. In this situation no work is obtained from the chemical energy that is expended when the transfer of the electrons occurs.

What type of device would allow this energy to be harnessed? The essential characteristic of such a device is that it physically separates the oxidizing agent from the reducing agent and requires that the electrons flow through a wire from the substance being oxidized to the substance being reduced. The current in this wire can then be directed through a device such as an electric motor, and thus produce useful work.

Consider the set-up shown in Figure 7–1. If the above reasoning is correct, electrons should flow from the Fe^{2+} through the wire toward the MnO_4^-. However, when the apparatus is constructed, no flow of electrons occurs. Something must be wrong. What is it?

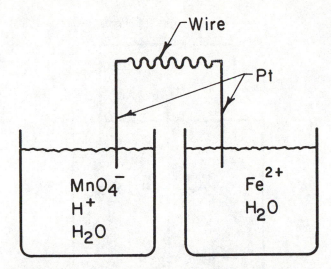

Figure 7–1   Note: Both solutions contain appropriate counter ions to make the overall charge zero.

The problem is that if electrons flow from the right to the left compartment, the left compartment will become negatively charged (due to the incoming electrons) and the right compartment will experience a build-up of positive charge (Fe^{2+} is being changed to Fe^{3+} but with no increase in the number of anions). Nature will not operate this way. A charge separation of this type requires large amounts of energy, and the electron flow cannot occur.

This problem can, however, be solved very simply. The solutions must be connected so that ion flow can occur to keep the net charge in each cell zero, but without allowing the two solutions to mix (MnO_4^- and Fe^{2+} cannot be in same solution or they will transfer electrons directly instead of through the wire). This can be accomplished using a salt-bridge (a U-tube filled with an electrolyte) or a porous disk in a tube connecting the two solutions. Either of these devices allows ion flow without extensive mixing of the solutions.

In this book the ion connection will be represented as a dotted line between the two compartments, as shown in Figure 7–2.

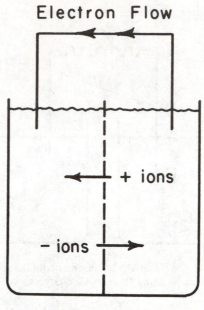

Figure 7–2

When provision for ion flow is made, the circuit is complete. Electrons flow through the wire from reducing agent to oxidizing agent, and ions flow from one compartment to the other to keep the net charge zero.

We have now discussed all of the essential characteristics of a galvanic cell, a device in which chemical energy is changed to electrical energy.

Electrolytic Cells

The opposite process can be accomplished with a very similar device. In this case, however, current is forced through the cell, using electrical energy to produce chemical change. That is, a nonspontaneous chemical reaction is caused to occur through use of electrical work. This process is called electrolysis. We will consider the details in a later section.

7.3   ELECTRICAL POTENTIAL

Consider a galvanic cell of the type discussed earlier. There is an oxidizing agent which has the power to pull electrons through a wire from a reducing agent in the other compartment. The "pull" is the potential of the cell (usually given in units of volts). How can this potential be measured? One possible device for doing this is a voltmeter, which works by drawing current through a known resistance. However, when current flows through a wire, frictional heating occurs. This wastes some of the potentially useful energy of the cell. Thus the potential measured by such a device will be less than the maximum potential.

How can the maximum potential be measured? The key is to do the measurement under zero current conditions. This can be accomplished by inserting a variable voltage device (powered by plugging into the power company) in *opposition* to the cell voltage, as shown in Figure 7–3.

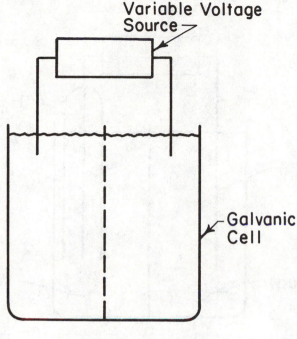

Figure 7–3

The variable voltage is adjusted until no current flows in the cell circuit. Under this condition the cell voltage is equal in magnitude and opposite in sign to the setting on the variable voltage device. In this way the maximum cell potential can be measured (no energy is wasted through heating the wires).

7.4   STANDARD REDUCTION POTENTIALS

The reaction in a galvanic cell is an oxidation-reduction reaction which can be broken down into two half-reactions. It would be convenient to assign a potential to each half-reaction, so that when a cell is constructed from a given pair of half-reactions the cell voltage could be obtained by summing the half-cell potentials (commonly called standard reduction potentials or $\mathscr{E}^0$). For example, consider the cell illustrated in Figure 7–4.

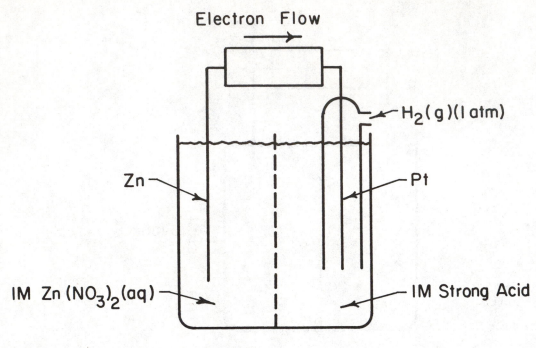

Figure 7–4

The observed potential for this cell is 0.76 volts. The cell reaction in this case is

$$2H^+(aq) + Zn(s) \rightarrow Zn^{2+}(aq) + H_2(g)$$

which can be divided into the two half-reactions

$$2H^+ + 2e^- \rightarrow H_2$$
$$Zn \rightarrow Zn^{2+} + 2e^-$$

The electrons thus travel from the Zn electrode to the H^+ ions in solution through the Pt conductor.

We want to determine the potential of each half-cell. However, there is no way to measure a half-cell potential directly. Only the total potential of a cell can be measured. If we want half-cell potentials, we must arbitrarily divide the total cell potential. For example, if we arbitrarily assign the reaction

$$2H^+ + 2e^- \rightarrow H_2$$

a potential of exactly zero volts, then the $Zn \rightarrow Zn^{2+} + 2e^-$ reaction would have a potential of 0.76 volts ($\mathscr{E}_{cell} = \mathscr{E}_{H^+ \rightarrow H_2} + \mathscr{E}_{Zn \rightarrow Zn^{2+}} = 0.76 \text{ V} = 0 + 0.76 \text{ V}$).

Thus the arbitrary assignment of one half-cell potential allows assignment of values to all other half-cell potentials.

To further understand this process, consider the cell illustrated in Figure 7–5. The measured potential is 1.10 volts and the cell reaction is

$$Zn(s) + Cu^{2+}(aq) \rightarrow Zn^{2+}(aq) + Cu(s)$$

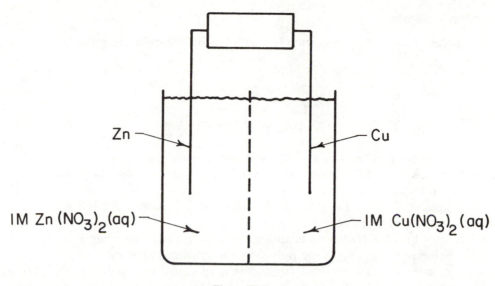

Figure 7–5

This can be divided into the half-reactions

$$Zn \rightarrow Zn^{2+} + 2e^-$$
$$Cu^{2+} + 2e^- \rightarrow Cu$$

where

$$\mathscr{E}_{cell} = \mathscr{E}_{Zn \rightarrow Zn^{2+}} + \mathscr{E}_{Cu^{2+} \rightarrow Cu}$$

From the above cell involving Zn and H^+, the Zn half-cell potential was assigned the value 0.76 V. Thus 1.10 V = 0.76 V + $\mathscr{E}_{Cu^{2+} \rightarrow Cu}$ and

$$\mathscr{E}_{Cu^{2+} \rightarrow Cu} = 1.10 - 0.76 = 0.34 \text{ V}$$

The half-cell potentials based on the assumption that the process $2H^+ + 2e^- \rightarrow H_2$ has a potential of zero volts are universally accepted by the scientific community and are commonly tabulated in chemistry textbooks and reference books. However, before these values can be used to calculate cell potentials, a few characteristics of half-cell potentials must be understood. These will be discussed below.

Standard States

As discussed in Chapter 6, many thermodynamic properties depend on concentration or pressure. Because galvanic cell potentials are among these properties, reference half-cell potentials have been established for cells in which all substances are in their standard states (1 atm for gases, 1 M for solutions). These potentials are denoted by a superscript zero, $\mathscr{E}^0$.

Reduction Potentials

The currently accepted convention is to tabulate half-reactions as reduction processes. For example,

$$2H^+ + 2e^- \rightarrow H_2$$
$$Cu^{2+} + 2e^- \rightarrow Cu$$
$$Zn^{2+} + 2e^- \rightarrow Zn$$

The $\mathscr{E}^0$ values corresponding to these half-reactions are called **standard reduction potentials**. In this book the $\mathscr{E}^0$ value for a given half-reaction will always be assumed to be for the reduction process.

In combining half-reactions to obtain balanced oxidation-reduction reactions, two common manipulations are necessary.

First, since electron transfer reactions must involve a substance being oxidized and a substance being reduced, one of the reduction half-reactions must be reversed.

Second, since the number of electrons lost must equal the number gained, the half-reactions often must be multiplied by integers to achieve the balanced equation.

Before cell potentials can be calculated from standard reduction potentials, the effect of these manipulations on the $\mathscr{E}^0$ values must be recognized.

1) The sign of $\mathscr{E}^0$ is *reversed* when the direction of the half-reaction is reversed.
2) The value of $\mathscr{E}^0$ is *not changed* when the half-reaction is multiplied by an integer.

Since a standard reduction potential is an "intensive quantity" (it does not depend on how many units of reaction occur), the potential is *not* multiplied by an integer even when multiplication of the half-reaction by an integer is required to achieve the balanced cell reaction.

7.5 CALCULATIONS OF POTENTIALS FOR REDOX REACTIONS

In this section the procedure for using standard reduction potentials to calculate the potential of a galvanic cell will be discussed.

Sample Problem 7–1

Consider a galvanic cell based on the redox reaction

$$Fe^{3+}(aq) + Cu(s) \rightarrow Cu^{2+}(aq) + Fe^{2+}(aq)$$

where the pertinent half-reactions are

$$Fe^{3+} + e^- \rightarrow Fe^{2+} \qquad\qquad \mathscr{E}^0 = 0.77 \text{ V}$$

$$Cu^{2+} + 2e^- \rightarrow Cu \qquad\qquad \mathscr{E}^0 = 0.34 \text{ V}$$

Balance the cell reaction and calculate the $\mathscr{E}^0$ value of the cell.

Solution

The cell reaction involves the half-reactions

    1) $Fe^{3+} + e^- \rightarrow Fe^{2+}$

and

    2) $Cu^{2+} + 2e^- \rightarrow Cu$

To obtain the cell reaction, reaction (2) must be reversed:

    $Cu \rightarrow Cu^{2+} + 2e^-$ $-\mathscr{E}^0 = -0.34 \text{ V}$

Note the change in sign of $\mathscr{E}^0$. Also, since each Cu produces two electrons and each Fe^{3+} accepts only one electron, reaction (1) must be multiplied by two.

    $2Fe^{3+} + 2e^- \rightarrow 2Fe^{2+}$ $\mathscr{E}^0 = 0.77 \text{ V}$

Note that $\mathscr{E}^0$ is not changed in this case.

Now we can obtain the balanced cell reaction by summing the appropriately modified half-reactions.

    $Cu \rightarrow Cu^{2+} + 2e^-$ $-\mathscr{E}^0 = -0.34 \text{ V}$

    $2Fe^{3+} + 2e^- \rightarrow 2Fe^{2+}$ $\mathscr{E}^0 = 0.77 \text{ V}$

_____

    $Cu + 2Fe^{3+} \rightarrow Cu^{2+} + 2Fe^{2+}$ $\mathscr{E}^0 = -0.34 + 0.77 = \mathbf{0.43 \text{ V}}$

TEST 7–1

A. Consider a galvanic cell based on the reaction

$$Al^{3+}(aq) + Mg(s) \rightarrow Al(s) + Mg^{2+}(aq)$$

where the half-reactions are

    1) $Al^{3+} + 3e^- \rightarrow Al$ $\mathscr{E}^0 = -1.66 \text{ V}$

    2) $Mg^{2+} + 2e^- \rightarrow Mg$ $\mathscr{E}^0 \;-2.37 \text{ V}$

Give the balanced cell reaction and calculate $\mathscr{E}^0$ for the cell.

B. Consider a galvanic cell based on the reaction

$$MnO_4^-(aq) + H^+(aq) + ClO_3^-(aq) \rightarrow ClO_4^-(aq) + Mn^{2+}(aq) + H_2O(\ell)$$

where the half-reactions are:

1) $MnO_4^- + 5e^- + 8H^+ \rightarrow$ $\mathscr{E}^0 = 1.51$ V
   $Mn^{2+} + 4H_2O$

2) $ClO_4^- + 2H^+ + 2e^- \rightarrow$ $\mathscr{E}^0 = 1.19$ V
   $ClO_3^- + H_2O$

Give the balanced cell reaction and calculate $\mathscr{E}^0$ for the cell.

7.6   GALVANIC CELLS

In this section we will consider the complete description of a galvanic cell. The principles involved will be introduced in the following sample problem.

Sample Problem 7–2

Describe the galvanic cell based on the following half-reactions, and calculate the cell potential under standard conditions.

$$Fe^{2+} + 2e^- \rightarrow Fe \qquad\qquad \mathscr{E}^0 = -0.44 \text{ V}$$

$$MnO_4^- + 5e^- + 8H^+ \rightarrow Mn^{2+} + 4H_2O \qquad \mathscr{E}^0 = 1.51 \text{ V}$$

Solution

The first thing to note is that both of these reactions are reduction processes. In a working cell an oxidation must take place in one compartment and a reduction in the other (something must give up electrons and something must accept electrons). Thus one of these half-reactions must be reversed. Which one?

This question can be answered by considering the sign of the potential of a working cell: *a cell will always run spontaneously in the direction which produces a positive potential*. From this principle it is clear that the half-reaction involving iron must be reversed.

$$Fe \rightarrow Fe^{2+} + 2e^- \qquad\qquad -\mathscr{E}^0 = 0.44 \text{ V}$$

$$MnO_4^- + 5e^- + 8H^+ \rightarrow Mn^{2+} + 4H_2O \qquad \mathscr{E}^0 = 1.51 \text{ V}$$

The standard cell potential is $0.44 + 1.51 = 1.95$ V $= \mathscr{E}^0_{cell}$. The balanced cell reaction is

$$5(Fe \rightarrow Fe^{2+} + 2e^-) + 2(MnO_4^- + 5e^- + 8H^+ \rightarrow Mn^{2+} + 4H_2O)$$

$$2MnO_4^- + 5Fe + 16H^+ \rightarrow 5Fe^{2+} + 2Mn^{2+} + 8H_2O$$

Now consider the physical set-up of the cell.

Compartment I—The active components (standard states) are:

$$\text{Fe, 1.0 } M \text{ Fe}^{2+}$$

The anion present depends upon the iron salt used. It would probably be NO_3^- or SO_4^{2-}. The anions do not participate in the reaction.

The reaction that takes place in this compartment is

$$\text{Fe} \rightarrow \text{Fe}^{2+} + 2e^-$$

The electrode in this compartment would consist of iron metal.

Compartment II—The active components (standard states) are:

$$\text{1.0 } M \text{ MnO}_4^-, \text{ 1.0 } M \text{ H}^+, \text{ 1.0 } M \text{ Mn}^{2+}$$

with the appropriate counter ions (which do not participate in the reaction—they just balance the charge). The reaction in this compartment is

$$\text{MnO}_4^- + 5e^- + 8\text{H}^+ \rightarrow \text{Mn}^{2+} + 4\text{H}_2\text{O}$$

Since neither MnO_4^- nor Mn^{2+} can serve as the electrode, an inert conductor must be used. The usual choice is platinum. The cell diagram is shown in Figure 7–6.

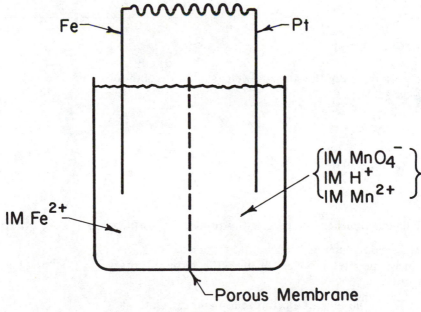

Figure 7–6

Which way do the electrons flow? In the left compartment the reaction is

$$\text{Fe} \rightarrow \text{Fe}^{2+} + 2e^-$$

This is an oxidation process.

In the right compartment the reaction is

$$MnO_4^- + 5e^- + 8H^+ \rightarrow Mn^{2+} + 4H_2O$$

This is a reduction.

Thus the electrons flow from Fe to MnO_4^- in this cell.

There are special names for the two electrodes in electrochemical cells:

anode: electrode where oxidation takes place

cathode: electrode where reduction takes place

In this cell the Fe electrode is the anode and the MnO_4^- at the Pt conductor is the cathode.

Summary

A typical description of a galvanic cell includes:
1) The cell potential. It will always be positive for a galvanic cell.
2) The balanced cell reaction.
3) The nature of each electrode and the ions present in each compartment. An inert conductor may be required if the substances that participate in the cell reaction are not conducting solids.
4) Indication of the electron flow. This is obtained simply by observing the directions of the two half-reactions which produce a positive $\mathscr{E}^0$.
5) Indication of which electrode is the anode and which is the cathode.

Sample Problem 7–3

Describe completely the galvanic cell (standard conditions) based on the following half-reactions:

$$\text{1)} \quad Ag^+ + e^- \rightarrow Ag \qquad\qquad \mathscr{E}^0 = 0.80 \text{ V}$$

$$\text{2)} \quad Fe^{3+} + e^- \rightarrow Fe^{2+} \qquad\qquad \mathscr{E}^0 = 0.77 \text{ V}$$

Solution

One half-reaction must be reversed to produce a working cell.

Step 1: Decide which half-reaction to reverse.

Since a positive $\mathscr{E}^0$ value for the cell is required, reaction (2) is the one that runs in reverse.

Step 2: Write the balanced cell reaction and calculate $\mathscr{E}^0$.

$$Ag^+ + e^- \rightarrow Ag \qquad\qquad\qquad \mathscr{E}^0 = 0.80 \text{ V}$$

$$\underline{Fe^{2+} \rightarrow Fe^{3+} + e^-} \qquad\qquad\qquad \underline{-\mathscr{E}^0 = -0.77 \text{ V}}$$

cell
reaction: $\qquad Ag^+ + Fe^{2+} \rightarrow Fe^{3+} + Ag \qquad\qquad \mathscr{E}^0_{cell} = 0.03 \text{ V}$

Step 3: Determine the direction of electron flow.

Since Ag^+ receives electrons and Fe^{2+} loses electrons in the cell reaction, the electrons will flow from the compartment containing Fe^{2+} to the compartment containing Ag^+.

Step 4: Determine the anode and cathode.

Since electrons flow from Fe^{2+} to Ag^+, oxidation occurs in the compartment containing Fe^{2+} (anode) and reduction occurs in the compartment containing Ag^+ (cathode). The electrode in the Ag, Ag^+ compartment will be Ag, while an inert conductor, such as Pt, must be used in the Fe^{2+}, Fe^{3+} compartment.

Step 5: Draw a picture that summarizes the cell operation.

The diagram for this cell is shown in Figure 7–7. Appropriate counter ions are assumed to be present.

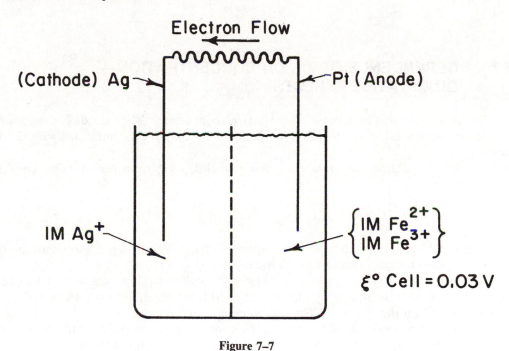

Figure 7–7

TEST 7–2

Describe the galvanic cells (standard conditions) which can be constructed from the following sets of half-reactions:

A. $Cu^{2+} + 2e^- \rightarrow Cu$ $\mathscr{E}^0 = 0.34$ V
    $Ce^{4+} + e^- \rightarrow Ce^{3+}$ $\mathscr{E}^0 = 1.70$ V

B. $Al^{3+} + 3e^- \rightarrow Al$ $\mathscr{E}^0 = -1.66$ V
    $Mn^{2+} + 2e^- \rightarrow Mn$ $\mathscr{E}^0 = -1.18$ V

In each case complete the following steps:

Step 1: Determine which half-reaction to reverse. (Remember that the overall cell potential must be positive.)

Step 2: Write the balanced cell reaction and calculate $\mathscr{E}^0$. (You may have to multiply the half-reactions by appropriate integers to equalize the numbers of electrons produced and absorbed. Remember, do *not* multiply the $\mathscr{E}^0$ values.)

Step 3: Determine the direction of electron flow, using the cell reaction.

Step 4: Determine the anode and cathode.

Step 5: Draw a picture that summarizes the cell operation.

7.7 DEPENDENCE OF $\mathscr{E}_{cell}$ ON CONCENTRATION— QUALITATIVE ASPECTS

So far the cells that have been treated have all contained only standard concentrations. In this section the effect on the cell potential of changing the concentrations will be considered.

To get a qualitative idea of how a cell potential depends on concentrations, consider the cell reaction

$$Cu(s) + 2Ce^{4+}(aq) \rightarrow Cu^{2+}(aq) + 2Ce^{3+}(aq)$$

Under standard conditions this cell has a potential of 1.36 V. What will happen to the cell potential if the concentration of Ce^{4+} is increased ($>1.0\ M$)?

It is best to answer this question qualitatively by thinking in terms of Le Chatelier's Principle. An increase in $[Ce^{4+}]$ will favor the forward reaction and thus increase the "driving force" on the electrons. The cell potential will increase.

On the other hand, an increase in the concentration of a product (Cu^{2+} or Ce^{3+} in this case) will oppose the forward reaction and decrease the cell potential.

Sample Problem 7–4

For the cell reaction

$$2Al(s) + 3Mn^{2+}(aq) \rightarrow 2Al^{3+}(aq) + 3Mn(s) \qquad \mathscr{E}^0_{cell} = 0.48\ V$$

predict whether $\mathscr{E}_{cell}$ is larger or smaller than $\mathscr{E}^0_{cell}$ for the following cases:

A. $[Al^{3+}] = 2.0\ M,$ $[Mn^{2+}] = 1.0\ M$

Solution

In this case a product concentration has been increased. This will oppose the cell reaction and will cause $\mathscr{E}_{cell}$ to be less than $\mathscr{E}^0_{cell}$:

$$\mathscr{E}_{cell} < 0.48 \text{ V}$$

B. $[Al^{3+}] = 1.0 \ M,$ $[Mn^{2+}] = 3.0 \ M$

Solution

In this case a reactant concentration has been increased and $\mathscr{E}_{cell}$ will be greater than $\mathscr{E}^0_{cell}$:

$$\mathscr{E}_{cell} > 0.48 \text{ V}$$

Sample Problem 7–5

Consider a cell constructed as shown in Figure 7–8.

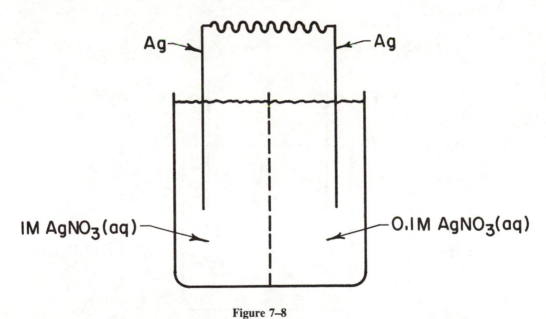

Figure 7–8

A. Does this cell exhibit a non-zero potential?

Solution

The half-reaction that is relevant to both compartments of this cell is

$$Ag^+ + e^- \to Ag \qquad \mathscr{E}^0 = 0.80 \text{ V}$$

If the cell were constructed with 1 M Ag^+ in both compartments, $\mathscr{E}^0_{cell}$ = 0.80 − 0.80 = 0 V. However, in the cell described in this problem the concentrations of Ag^+ are 1 M and 0.1 M in the two compartments. Because of the unequal Ag^+ concentrations, the half-cell potentials will not be equal and the cell will exhibit a positive voltage.

B.   In which direction do the electrons flow in this cell?

Solution

In a situation like this nature will try to equalize the Ag^+ concentrations in the two compartments. This can be done by transferring electrons from the compartment containing 0.1 M Ag^+ to the one containing 1 M Ag^+ (right to left in the above diagram). This electron transfer will produce Ag^+ in the right compartment and use up Ag^+ (to form Ag) in the left compartment.

The cell considered in this Sample Problem is called a **concentration cell**. A concentration cell has identical components in both compartments except that the concentrations are different. This difference in concentration produces a non-zero cell potential.

TEST 7–3

Consider a cell constructed as shown in Figure 7–9.

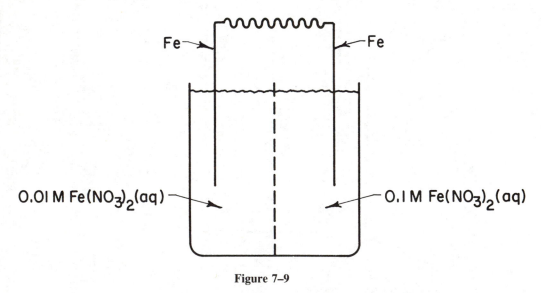

Figure 7–9

In which direction do the electrons flow in this cell?

7.8   ELECTROLYSIS

Electrolysis involves forcing a current through a solution to produce a chemical change for which $\mathscr{E}^0$ has a negative value. The focus of electrolysis problems is usually stoichiometry: How much chemical change occurs with the flow of a given amount of current for a specified time?

To do these calculations, several definitions must be recalled:

1)   Charge is measured in coulombs. One mole of electrons carries 96,486 coulombs of charge, which is called a **Faraday** and is denoted by F.

2)   Current flow is measured in amperes (amps), where one amp is one coulomb of charge per second.

Sample Problem 7–6

A current of 10.0 amps was maintained for 30.0 minutes through a solution containing excess Cu^{2+}. How much Cu (in grams) is plated out on the cathode? (Remember that reduction—in this case $Cu^{2+} + 2e^- \rightarrow Cu$—occurs at the cathode.)

Solution

The strategy for solving this type of problem is:
1)   Determine the quantity of the charge that has been passed through the solution.
2)   Convert the total charge to moles of electrons.
3)   Convert from moles of electrons to moles of product formed (Cu in this case).
4)   Convert from moles of product to grams of product.

We will follow the steps to solve this problem.

1) Coulombs of charge $=$ amps $\times$ seconds $= \dfrac{coul}{sec} \times sec$

$$= 10.0 \,\frac{coul}{sec} \times 30.0 \text{ min.} \times 60.0 \,\frac{sec}{min}$$

$$= 1.80 \times 10^4 \, coul$$

2)   One mole of electrons is equivalent to 96,486 coulombs.

$$1.80 \times 10^4 \, coul \times \frac{1 \text{ mole of electrons}}{96,486 \, coul} = 1.87 \times 10^{-1} \text{ mole of electrons}$$

3)   Each Cu^{2+} ion requires $2e^-$ to form Cu. Thus each mole of electrons produces one-half mole of Cu.

$$1.87 \times 10^{-1} \text{ mole of electrons} \times \frac{1 \text{ mole of Cu atoms}}{2 \text{ moles of electrons}} = 9.35 \times 10^{-2} \text{ mole of Cu}$$

4) 9.35×10^{-2} mole of Cu $\times \dfrac{63.546 \text{ g}}{\text{mole of Cu}} = 5.94$ g Cu plated out

Sample Problem 7–7

How long must a current of 5.00 amps be applied to a solution of Ag^+ to produce 10.5 g of Ag?

Solution

In this case we must work in reverse. We know the number of grams of Ag so we can calculate the moles of Ag, moles of electrons required, coulombs of charge required, and finally the time required.

$$10.5 \text{ g Ag} \times \frac{1 \text{ mole Ag}}{107.868 \text{ g Ag}} = 9.73 \times 10^{-2} \text{ mole}$$

Each Ag requires one electron:

$$Ag^+ + e^- \rightarrow Ag$$

Thus 9.73×10^{-2} mole of electrons is required.

$$9.73 \times 10^{-2} \text{ mole of electrons} \times \frac{96,486 \text{ coulombs}}{\text{mole of electrons}} = 9.39 \times 10^3 \text{ coulombs}$$

The current must produce 9.39×10^3 coulombs of charge. Thus

$$\left(5.00 \frac{\text{coul}}{\text{sec}}\right) (\text{time in seconds}) = 9.39 \times 10^3 \text{ coulombs}$$

$$\text{time} = \frac{9.39 \times 10^3}{5.00} \text{ seconds} = 1.88 \times 10^3 \text{ seconds}$$

$$= 31.3 \text{ minutes}$$

TEST 7–4

A. Calculate the mass of Cr plated out when a current of 57.5 amps is passed for 16.8 minutes through a solution containing excess of Cr^{3+}.

B. For what time span must a current of 15.0 amps be applied to a solution containing Cl^- to produce 26.5 g of $Cl_2(g)$?

The remaining sections of this chapter are devoted to developing and using the relationships between electrochemistry and thermodynamics.

7.9 CELL POTENTIAL, ELECTRICAL WORK, AND FREE ENERGY

The work that can be accomplished when electrons are transferred through a wire (a current) depends upon the "force" behind the electrons. This driving force is defined in terms of a **potential difference** in volts between two points in the circuit, where the **volt** is defined as a joule of work done per coulomb of charge transferred.

$$\text{potential difference} = \mathscr{E} = \frac{\text{work}}{\text{charge}}$$

$$\mathscr{E} \text{ (volts)} = \frac{\text{work (joules)}}{\text{charge (coulombs)}}$$

Thus one joule of work is produced or required when one coulomb of charge is transferred between two points in the circuit that differ by a potential of one volt.

The work done can be calculated as follows:

$$\mathscr{E} = \frac{w}{q} \quad \begin{array}{l}\nearrow \text{work} \\ \searrow \text{charge}\end{array}$$

$$w = q\mathscr{E}$$

From this equation it can be seen that the maximum work in a cell would be obtained at the maximum cell potential:

$$w_{max} = q\mathscr{E}_{max}$$

However, there is a problem. To obtain electrical work, current must flow. When current flows, some energy is inevitably wasted through frictional heating, and the maximum work is not obtained.

This brings up an important general principle. *In any real, spontaneous process some energy is always wasted—the actual work realized is always less than the maximum.* This is a consequence of nature's insistence upon increasing the entropy of the universe in any spontaneous process. For reasons which we will not explore here, in a process where the maximum work could be realized (called a reversible process), ΔS_{univ} would be zero. This is not possible and such a process cannot occur. However, it is very valuable to know w_{max} for a particular process, because it tells us the maximum possible work that might be obtained from that process. By comparing the actual work being realized from the process to the (hypothetical) maximum obtainable under reversible conditions, the efficiency of the real process can be evaluated. This allows a decision to be made concerning whether it is worthwhile to expend more effort to improve the efficiency.

The concept of free energy is closely related to maximum work. In fact, at constant T and P, ΔG is a measure of the maximum useful work that can be obtained from a process (the energy "free to do work"):

$$w_{max} = -\Delta G$$

The negative sign is necessary since ΔG is negative for any spontaneous process. For an electrochemical cell

$$w_{max} = q\mathscr{E}_{max} = -\Delta G$$

Since electrochemistry always involves chemical reactions, it is useful to consider the charge (q) in terms of the number of electrons:

q (coulombs) = moles of electrons $\times$ charge (in coulombs) per mole of electrons

$q = nF$

where

n = moles of electrons
F = 96,486 coulombs/per mole of electrons

This leads to the relationship

$$-\Delta G = q\,\mathscr{E}_{max} = nF\mathscr{E}_{max}$$

where $\mathscr{E}_{max}$ is cell potential measured under zero current (reversible) conditions.

Note from the above equation that *the maximum cell potential is directly related to the free energy difference* between the reactants and the products in the cell.

Sample Problem 7–8

A certain electrochemical cell has a maximum (reversible) potential of 2.50 V. In an experiment 1.33 moles of electrons were passed through this cell at an average potential difference of 2.10 V. Calculate:

A. The actual work done.

Solution

$$
\begin{aligned}
\text{work} &= q\mathscr{E} \\
&= 1.33 \text{ moles } e^- \times 96,486 \, \frac{\text{coul}}{\text{mole } e^-} \times 2.10 \text{ J/coul} \\
\text{work} &= 2.69 \times 10^5 \text{ J}
\end{aligned}
$$

B. The maximum possible work.

Solution

$$
\begin{aligned}
\text{work (maximum)} &= q\,\mathscr{E}_{max} \\
&= 1.33 \text{ moles } e^- \times 96,486 \, \frac{\text{coul}}{\text{mole}} \times 2.50 \text{ V} \\
&= 3.21 \times 10^5 \text{ J}
\end{aligned}
$$

C. ΔG for the cell process.

Solution

$$\Delta G = -w_{max} = -3.21 \times 10^5 \, J$$

TEST 7–5

For a certain cell process, in which 3.00 moles of electrons were passed at an average potential difference of 1.18 V, the change in free energy is known to be -5.86×10^5 J. Calculate:

A. Actual work done

B. $\mathscr{E}_{max}$

C. Maximum possible work

7.10   THE CHARACTERISTICS OF $\mathscr{E}^0$—A THERMODYNAMIC EXPLANATION

Earlier in this chapter the following characteristics of $\mathscr{E}^0$ were introduced without proof:
1) When a half-reaction is reversed, the sign of $\mathscr{E}^0$ changes.
2) When a half-reaction is multiplied by an integer, $\mathscr{E}^0$ is not multiplied by that integer.
In this section we will show how these properties of $\mathscr{E}^0$ arise from thermodynamics. Recall from the previous discussion that

$$\Delta G^0 = -nF \mathscr{E}^0$$

which upon rearrangement gives

$$\mathscr{E}^0 = \frac{-\Delta G^0}{nF}$$

When a process (reaction) is reversed, the sign of ΔG^0 is reversed. This means that the sign of $\mathscr{E}^0$ must also be reversed.
What effect does multiplication of a half-reaction by an integer have on the $\mathscr{E}^0$ for that reaction? It *does not change*. This can be seen as follows. Consider the reaction

$$A^{n+} + ne^- \rightarrow A$$

where

$$\Delta G^0 = Y$$

and

$$\mathscr{E}^0 = \frac{-\Delta G^0}{nF} = \frac{-Y}{nF}$$

If this reaction is multiplied by two:

$$2A^{n+} + 2ne^- \rightarrow 2A$$
$$\Delta G^0 = 2Y$$

and

$$\mathscr{E}^0 = -\frac{2Y}{2nF} = -\frac{Y}{nF}$$

Note that $\mathscr{E}^0$ is the same as before. The effect of the integer cancels out.

Thus, a half-cell potential is an intensive quantity—it does not depend on how many units of reaction occur.

7.11   DEPENDENCE OF $\mathscr{E}_{cell}$ ON CONCENTRATION—QUANTITATIVE ASPECTS

The dependence of the cell potential on concentration results directly from the dependence of free energy on concentration. Recall from Chapter 6 that the equation

$$\Delta G = \Delta G^0 + RT \ln Q$$

where Q is the reaction quotient, was used to calculate the effect of concentration on ΔG. Substituting $\Delta G = -nF\mathscr{E}$ into the above equation produces

$$-nF\mathscr{E} = -nF\mathscr{E}^0 + RT \ln Q$$

or

$$\mathscr{E} = \mathscr{E}^0 - \frac{RT}{nF} \ln Q$$

This equation gives the relationship between the cell potential and the concentrations of the cell components. It is commonly called the **Nernst equation**.

At 25°C and in terms of base-ten logarithms, the Nernst equation is

$$\mathscr{E} = \mathscr{E}^0 - \frac{0.0592}{n} \log Q$$

Sample Problem 7–9

Calculate $\mathscr{E}_{cell}$ at 25°C for the galvanic cell based on the reaction

$$2Al(s) + 3Mn^{2+}(aq) \rightarrow 2Al^{3+}(aq) + 3Mn(s)$$

where $\mathscr{E}^0_{cell} = 0.48$ V and the concentrations in the cell compartments are:

$$[Mn^{2+}] = 0.50 \ M$$
$$[Al^{3+}] = 1.50 \ M$$

Solution

The Nernst equation is

$$\mathscr{E} = \mathscr{E}^0 - \frac{0.0592}{n} \log Q$$

where

$$\mathscr{E}^0 = 0.48 \text{ V}$$
$$Q = \frac{[Al^{3+}]^2}{[Mn^{2+}]^3} = \frac{(1.50)^2}{(0.50)^3} = 18$$
$$n = 6 \quad \left(\begin{array}{l} 2Al \rightarrow 2Al^{3+} + 6e^- \\ 3Mn^{2+} + 6e^- \rightarrow 3Mn \end{array} \right)$$

so

$$\mathscr{E}_{cell} = 0.48 - \frac{0.0592}{6} \log (18)$$

$$= 0.48 - \frac{0.0592}{6}(1.26) = 0.48 - 0.01 = 0.47 \text{ V}$$

Summary

The Nernst equation

$$\mathscr{E} = \mathscr{E}^0 - \frac{0.0592}{n} \log Q \text{ (at 25°C)}$$

is used to calculate the potential of a cell that contains components not in the standard states. Note the following important points:

1) Q is the reaction quotient, which is obtained by application of the Law of Mass Action.

2) The potential calculated from this equation is the instantaneous, reversible potential. As the cell discharges, the concentrations change and $\mathscr{E}$ changes.

3) The cell discharges until equilibrium is reached. At this point

and
$$Q = K = \text{equilibrium constant}$$

$$\mathscr{E}_{\text{cell}} = 0$$

A "dead battery" is one in which the cell reaction has reached equilibrium.

TEST 7–6

Calculate $\mathscr{E}_{\text{cell}}$ at 25°C for the cell based on the reaction

$$\text{Cu(s)} + 2\text{Ce}^{4+}(\text{aq}) \rightarrow \text{Cu}^{2+}(\text{aq}) + 2\text{Ce}^{3+}(\text{aq})$$

where

$$\mathscr{E}^0 = 1.36 \text{ V}$$
$$[\text{Ce}^{4+}] = 3.0 \ M$$
$$[\text{Cu}^{2+}] = 1.0 \times 10^{-2} \ M$$
$$[\text{Ce}^{3+}] = 1.0 \times 10^{-4} \ M$$

Sample Problem 7–10

Describe completely the cell based on the following half-reactions:

1) $\text{VO}_2^+ + 2\text{H}^+ + e^- \rightarrow \text{VO}^{2+} + \text{H}_2\text{O}$ $\mathscr{E}^0 = 1.00 \text{ V}$

2) $\text{Zn}^{2+} + 2e^- \rightarrow \text{Zn}$ $\mathscr{E}^0 = -0.76 \text{ V}$

where

$$T = 25°C$$
$$[\text{VO}_2^+] = 2.0 \ M$$
$$[\text{H}^+] = 0.50 \ M$$
$$[\text{VO}^{2+}] = 1.0 \times 10^{-2} \ M$$
$$[\text{Zn}^{2+}] = 1.0 \times 10^{-1} \ M$$

Note: To calculate the cell potential the Nernst equation must be used, since the concentrations are not standard.

Solution

The balanced cell reaction is obtained by reversing reaction 2 and multiplying reaction 1 by two:

$$2(VO_2^+ + 2H^+ + e^- \rightarrow VO^{2+} + H_2O) \qquad \mathscr{E}^0 = 1.00 \text{ V}$$

$$Zn \rightarrow Zn^{2+} + 2e^- \qquad\qquad -\mathscr{E}^0 = 0.76 \text{ V}$$

cell reaction: $2VO_2^+ + 4H^+ + Zn \rightarrow 2VO^{2+} + 2H_2O + Zn^{2+} \quad \mathscr{E}^0_{cell} = 1.76 \text{ V}$

The Nernst equation is

$$\mathscr{E}_{cell} = \mathscr{E}^0_{cell} - \frac{0.0592}{n} \log Q$$

$$= 1.76 - \frac{0.0592}{2} \log \frac{[Zn^{2+}][VO^{2+}]^2}{[VO_2^+]^2[H^+]^4}$$

$$= 1.76 - \frac{0.0592}{2} \log \frac{(1.0 \times 10^{-1})\,(1.0 \times 10^{-2})^2}{(2.0)^2\,(0.50)^4}$$

$$= 1.76 - \frac{0.0592}{2} \log (4 \times 10^{-5}) = 1.76 + 0.13 = 1.89 \text{ V}$$

The cell diagram is given in Figure 7–10.

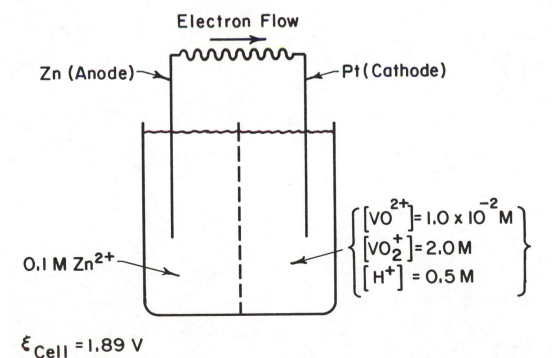

Figure 7–10

TEST 7–7

Describe completely the galvanic cell based on the following half-reactions:

$$Cr^{3+} + 3e^- \rightarrow Cr \qquad\qquad \mathscr{E}^0 = -0.74 \text{ V}$$

$$TiO^{2+} + 2H^+ + e^- \rightarrow Ti^{3+} + H_2O \qquad\qquad \mathscr{E}^0 = 0.10 \text{ V}$$

where

$$T = 25°C$$
$$[Cr^{3+}] = 1.0 \times 10^{-4} \; M$$
$$[TiO^{2+}] = 1.0 \times 10^{-1} \; M$$
$$[H^+] = 1.0 \; M$$
$$[Ti^{3+}] = 5.0 \times 10^{-2} \; M$$

7.12   CALCULATION OF EQUILIBRIUM CONSTANTS FOR REDOX REACTIONS

The relationship between $\mathscr{E}^0$ and ΔG^0 allows calculation of values of equilibrium constants for redox reactions. Recall that the Nernst equation is

$$\mathscr{E} = \mathscr{E}^0 - \frac{RT}{nF} \ln Q$$

For a cell at equilibrium, $\mathscr{E} = 0$ and $Q = K$. Under these conditions the Nernst equation reduces to

$$\ln K = \frac{nF\mathscr{E}^0}{RT} = 2.303 \log K$$

Assuming the temperature to be 25°C, plugging in the values of R and F and converting from natural to base ten logarithms gives

$$\log K = \frac{n\mathscr{E}^0}{0.0592}$$

Sample Problem 7–3

Consider the oxidation-reduction reaction involving the following reactants and products:

$$S_4O_6^{2-} + Cr^{2+} \rightarrow Cr^{3+} + S_2O_3^{2-}$$

where the appropriate half-reactions are:

1) $S_4O_6^{2-} + 2e^- \rightarrow 2S_2O_3^{2-}$ $\qquad$ $\mathcal{E}^0 = 0.17$ V

2) $Cr^{3+} + e^- \rightarrow Cr^{2+}$ $\qquad$ $\mathcal{E}^0 = -0.50$ V

Balance the redox reaction and calculate $\mathcal{E}^0$ and K (at 25°C) for the reaction.

Solution

To obtain the balanced reaction, reaction 2 must be reversed and multiplied by two:

$$2(Cr^{2+} \rightarrow Cr^{3+} + e^-) \qquad\qquad -\mathcal{E}^0 = -(-0.50) \text{ V}$$

$$S_4O_6^{2-} + 2e^- \rightarrow 2S_2O_3^{2-} \qquad\qquad \mathcal{E}^0 = 0..17 \text{ V}$$

$$2Cr^{2+} + S_4O_6^{2-} \rightarrow 2Cr^{3+} + 2S_2O_3^{2-} \qquad \mathcal{E}^0 = 0.67 \text{ V}$$

For this reaction $n = 2$. That is, two moles of electrons are transferred for every unit of reaction (2 moles of Cr^{2+} reacting with 1 mole of $S_4O_6^{2-}$ to form 2 moles of Cr^{3+} and 2 moles of $S_2O_3^{2-}$). Then

$$\log K = \frac{n\mathcal{E}^0}{0.0592} = \frac{2(0.67)}{0.0592} = 22.6$$

The value of K is found by taking the antilog of 22.6:

$$K = 10^{22.6} = 4.3 \times 10^{22}$$

Note that this is a very large equilibrium constant. This is typical for redox reactions.

TEST 7–8

A. Calculate the values of K at 25°C for the reactions considered in:
1. Sample Problem 7–1, p. 228
2. Test 7–1 Part A, p. 229
3. Test 7–1 Part B, p. 229

B. Consider the oxidation-reduction reaction involving the following reactants and products

$$H_2O + IO_3^- + SO_2 \rightarrow SO_4^{2-} + I_2 + H^+$$

where the appropriate half-reactions are:

1) $2IO_3^- + 12H^+ + 10e^- \rightarrow I_2 + 6H_2O$ $\qquad$ $\mathcal{E}^0 = 1.19$ V

2) $SO_4^{2-} + 4H^+ + 2e^- \rightarrow SO_2 + 2H_2O$ $\qquad$ $\mathcal{E}^0 = 0.17$ V

Balance the cell reaction and calculate $\mathcal{E}^0$ and K (at 25°C).

Exercises

DATA TABLE

Half-Reaction	$\mathscr{E}^0$ (V)
$Ce^{4+} + e^- \rightarrow Ce^{3+}$	1.61
$MnO_4^- + 5e^- + 8H^+ \rightarrow Mn^{2+} + 4H_2O$	1.51
$Au^{3+} + 3e^- \rightarrow Au$	1.50
$ClO_3^- + 6H^+ + 5e^- \rightarrow \dfrac{1}{2} Cl_2 + 3H_2O$	1.47
$Cl_2 + 2e^- \rightarrow 2Cl^-$	1.36
$Ag^+ + e^- \rightarrow Ag$	0.80
$Fe^{3+} + e^- \rightarrow Fe^{2+}$	0.77
$2H^+ + 2e^- \rightarrow H_2$	0
$Pb^{2+} + 2e^- \rightarrow Pb$	-0.13
$Ni^{2+} + 2e^- \rightarrow Ni$	-0.25
$Tl^+ + e^- \rightarrow Tl$	-0.34
$Cd^{2+} + 2e^- \rightarrow Cd$	-0.40
$Fe^{2+} + 2e^- \rightarrow Fe$	-0.44
$Cr^{3+} + 3e^- \rightarrow Cr$	-0.74
$Zn^{2+} + 2e^- \rightarrow Zn$	-0.76
$Mg^{2+} + 2e^- \rightarrow Mg$	-2.38

For Exercises 1 to 5, give the diagram for a galvanic cell based on each pair of half-reactions. Each diagram should include:

    (a)   the cell potential
    (b)   the composition of each electrode
    (c)   the ions in each compartment that participate in the cell reaction
    (d)   the direction of electron flow
    (e)   labels on the anode and cathode

1. $Ag^+ + e^- \rightarrow Ag$
    $Cd^{2+} + 2e^- \rightarrow Cd$

2. $Fe^{3+} + e^- \rightarrow Fe^{2+}$
    $Pb^{2+} + 2e^- \rightarrow Pb$

3. $MnO_4^- + 5e^- + 8H^+ \rightarrow Mn^{2+} + 4H_2O$
    $Cr^{3+} + 3e^- \rightarrow Cr$

4. $Ce^{4+} + e^- \rightarrow Ce^{3+}$
    $MnO_4^- + 5e^- + 8H^+ \rightarrow Mn^{2+} + 4H_2O$

5. $Au^{3+} + 3e^- \rightarrow Au$
    $Ag^+ + e^- \rightarrow Ag$

6. A current of 0.193 amp is passed through a 1.00 M NaCl solution for 10.0 minutes. Assuming that only $Cl_2(g)$ is produced at the anode, calculate the number of moles of $Cl_2(g)$ formed.

7. How many grams of Zn metal will be oxidized to Zn^{2+} in a battery if a current of 0.125 amp flows for a period of 30.0 minutes?

For Exercises 8 to 11, consider a galvanic cell that employs the reaction (at 25°C)

$$Zn(s) + Fe^{2+}(aq) \rightleftarrows Zn^{2+}(aq) + Fe(s)$$

8. Calculate $\mathscr{E}^0$ for this cell as written.

9. Is ΔG^0 positive or negative at 25°C for the cell reaction?

10. Write the reaction that occurs at the anode as the cell discharges (all substances at standard concentrations).

11. Calculate $\mathscr{E}_{cell}$ in a cell where $[Zn^{2+}] = 0.100\ M$ and $[Fe^{2+}] = 1.00 \times 10^{-5}\ M$.

For Exercises 12 to 15, consider the reaction

$$Ni^{2+}(aq) + 2Cl^-(aq) \rightarrow Cl_2(g) + Ni(s)$$

Calculate:

12. $\mathscr{E}^0$ for the reaction as written at 25°C.

13. K for the reaction as written at 25°C.

14. If a galvanic cell were constructed using this reaction, would the cell run in the direction indicated in the reaction?

15. In a working cell based on this reaction, what would be the anode?

For Exercises 16 and 17, consider the reaction

$$3Cl_2(g) + 3H_2O(\ell) \rightarrow 5Cl^-(aq) + ClO_3^-(aq) + 6H^+(aq)$$

at 25°C. Calculate

16. $\mathscr{E}^0$

17. K

For Exercises 18 to 21, consider a working galvanic cell that employs the half-reactions

$$Au^{3+} + 3e^- \rightarrow Au$$
$$Tl^+ + e^- \rightarrow Tl$$

18. Give the balanced cell reaction.

19. Calculate $\mathscr{E}^0$ for this cell at 25°C.

20. Name the anode and cathode.

21. Calculate $\mathscr{E}$ at 25°C for a cell using this reaction, where $[Au^{3+}] = 1.0 \times 10^{-2}\ M$ and $[Tl^+] = 1.0 \times 10^{-4}\ M$.

For Exercises 22 to 24, consider the reaction

$$2MnO_4^-(aq) + Cl_2(g) + 4H^+(aq) \rightarrow 2Mn^{2+}(aq) + 2H_2O(\ell) + 2ClO_3^-(aq)$$

Calculate:

22. $\mathscr{E}^0$ at 25°C

23. K at 25°C

24. ΔG^0 at 25°C

Verbalizing General Concepts

Answer the following in your own words.

25. What is an oxidation-reduction reaction?

26. How can a redox reaction be used to generate electrical energy?

27. Why is the work performed by a galvanic cell always less than the maximum possible work?

28. How does an electrolytic cell differ from a galvanic cell?

29. In describing a galvanic cell based on a given pair of reduction reactions, how does one know which half-reaction to reverse to achieve the cell reaction?

30. In the relationship $\Delta G = -w_{max}$, why is the negative sign necessary?

31. What is the potential of a galvanic cell at equilibrium? Why?

32. Using Le Chatelier's Principle, explain how concentration changes affect the cell potential.

Multiple Choice Questions

For Exercises 33–35, consider a voltaic cell in which one compartment contains a Mg electrode dipping into a solution of $Mg(NO_3)_2$ and the other compartment contains $Fe(NO_3)_2$ and $Fe(NO_3)_3$ in solution with a Pt electrode. The cell compartments are connected by a porous membrane.

33. In the reaction that occurs spontaneously under standard conditions, the oxidizing agent is:
    a) Mg   b) Mg^{2+} c) Fe^{3+} d) Fe^{2+} e) NO_3^-

34. The standard potential for this cell (for the reaction written in the spontaneous direction) is:
    a) 3.15 V
    b) 1.61 V
    c) −3.15 V
    d) 4.89 V
    e) none of these

35. The anode for this cell involves the couple:
    a) Mg, Mg^{2+}
    b) Fe^{3+}, Fe^{2+}
    c) NO_3^-, H_2O
    d) none of these

For Exercises 36 and 37, consider the voltaic cell made with $KMnO_4$, $MnSO_4$, and strong acid dissolved in water with a platinum electrode in one compartment, and $Cr(NO)_3$ in water with an electrode made of Cr in the other.

36. The equilibrium constant for the cell reaction, where

$$K = \frac{[Cr^{3+}]^5[Mn^{2+}]^3}{[MnO_4^-]^3[H^+]^{24}}$$

    is (25°C):
    a) $\sim 10^{33}$
    b) ~ 500
    c) $\sim 10^{-570}$
    d) $\sim 10^{570}$
    e) none of these

37. The potential (25°C) of this cell when $[H^+] = 1.00\ M$, $[Cr^{3+}] = 2.00\ M$, $[MnO_4^-] = 1.00 \times 10^{-3}\ M$, and $[Mn^{2+}] = 1.00\ M$ is:
    a) 2.21 V
    b) 2.29 V
    c) 2.25 V
    d) 2.23 V
    e) none of these

For Exercises 38–41, consider the electrolysis of molten Al_2O_3. A current of 5.00 amps is passed through the $Al_2O_3(\ell)$ for 11.5 hours.

38. Calculate the number of coulombs of charge transferred.
    a) 4.14×10^4 coul
    b) 6.90×10^2 coul
    c) 57.5 coul
    d) 2.07×10^5 coul
    e) none of these

39. How many moles of electrons have flowed?
    a) 4.29×10^{-1} mole
    b) 7.15×10^{-3} mole
    c) 5.96×10^{-4} mole
    d) 2.15 moles
    e) none of these

40. How many moles of Al will be plated out?
    a) 7.15×10^{-1} mole
    b) 2.14 moles
    c) 1.43×10^{-1} mole
    d) 2.38×10^{-3} mole

41. How many grams of Al will be plated out?
    a) 58.1 g
    b) 3.86 g
    c) 0.193 g
    d) 19.3 g
    e) none of these

42. A current of 4.00 amps is passed for 8.00 hours through a solution containing Cr^{3+}. How many grams of Cr are deposited on the cathode?
    a) 62.1 g
    b) 20.7 g
    c) 5.75×10^{-3} g
    d) 3.45×10^{-1} g
    e) none of these

43. How many grams of Ni could be plated from a Ni^{2+} solution by passing a current of 1.30 amps through it for 24 minutes?
    a) 0.569 g
    b) 0.545 g
    c) 1.14 g
    d) 0.00949 g
    e) 2.28 g

44. Consider a galvanic cell constructed from the half-reactions:

$$Ni^{2+} + 2e^- \rightarrow Ni$$
$$Pb^{2+} + 2e^- \rightarrow Pb$$

The potential of this cell is:
    a) 0.38 V
    b) 0.12 V
    c) -0.12 V
    d) -0.38 V
    e) 0.25 V

45. Which statement is true of the cell in Exercise 44?
    a) The Ni electrode is the anode and electrons flow from the Ni to the Pb electrode.
    b) The Ni electrode is the cathode and electrons flow from the Ni to the Pb electrode.
    c) The Ni electrode is the anode and electrons flow from the Pb to the Ni electrode.
    d) The Ni electrode is the cathode and electrons flow from the Pb to the Ni electrode.
    e) None of these.

46. A charge of 2.00×10^{-3} coulombs is transferred across a potential difference of 3.20 V. The electrical work done is:
    a) 6.40 J
    b) 6.40 kJ
    c) 1.60×10^{-3} J
    d) 6.25×10^2 J
    e) none of these

47. For the reaction

$$Zn(s) + Cu^{2+}(aq) \rightleftarrows Zn^{2+}(aq) + Cu(s) \qquad \mathscr{E}^0 = 1.10 \text{ V}$$

    the equilibrium constant at 25°C is
    a) 6.3×10^{18}
    b) 1.5×10^{37}
    c) 1.10
    d) 37.2
    e) none of these

48. The reaction for the lead storage battery is

$$Pb + PbO_2 + 2H_2SO_4 \underset{\text{recharge}}{\overset{\text{discharge}}{\rightleftharpoons}} 2PbSO_4 + 2H_2O$$

    During discharge, which of the following is true?
    a) The flow of electrons is from the PbO_2 electrode to the Pb electrode.
    b) The Pb electrode is the anode.
    c) The cell is electrolytic in nature when discharging.
    d) The balanced anodic reaction is

$$PbO_2 + H_2SO_4 \rightarrow PbSO_4 + 2H_2O + 2H^+ + 2e^-$$

    e) None of the above is true.

49. How many hours are required to plate 5.00×10^2 g of Co from a solution containing Co^{2+}, using a 25.0 amp current?
    a) 6.55×10^4 hr
    b) 4.55×10^2 hr
    c) 18.2 hr
    d) 9.1 hr
    e) none of these

50. An electrolysis cell contains $CuCl_2$ and is set up so that Cu is plated out at the cathode and Cl_2 forms at the anode. If a current of 1.5 amps is run through the cell for 5.4 minutes, how many moles of Cu are plated out during this period?
    a) 8.4×10^{-5} moles
    b) 1.0×10^{-2} moles
    c) 5.0×10^{-3} moles
    d) 2.5×10^{-3} moles
    e) none of these

51. In an electrolytic cell the anode is the electrode
    a) where oxidation occurs
    b) where reduction occurs
    c) where electrons are supplied to a reactant in solution
    d) toward which cations move
    e) none of these

COMPLETE SOLUTIONS TO TESTS

Chapter 1

Test 1–1

A. See discussion in the text.

B. 1. $K = \dfrac{[SO_3]^2}{[SO_2]^2[O_2]}$ 3. $K = \dfrac{[NO_2]^4[H_2O]^6}{[NH_3]^4[O_2]^7}$

   2. $K = \dfrac{[O_3]^2}{[O_2]^3}$ 4. $K = \dfrac{[H_2O]^3}{[H_2]^3}$

NOTE: Water is included because it is in the gas phase.

C. 1. $K = \dfrac{[D]^2[C]^3}{[B]^2[A]}$

   2. (a) $K = \dfrac{(0.50 \text{ mole}/\ell)^2 (1.0 \text{ mole}/\ell)^3}{(0.20 \text{ mole}/\ell)^2(0.35 \text{ mole}/\ell)} = 18 \ (\text{mole}/\ell)^2$

   $\Delta n = 5 - 3 = 2$

   $K_p = K \cdot (RT)^{\Delta n}$

   $T = 298 \text{ K}, \ R = 0.0821 \ \ell \cdot \text{atm/K} \cdot \text{mole}$

   $K_p = \left[18\left(\dfrac{\text{mole}}{\ell}\right)^2 \right] \left[\left(0.0821 \ \dfrac{\ell \cdot \text{atm}}{\text{K} \cdot \text{mole}}\right)(298 \text{ K}) \right]^2$

   $= 1.1 \times 10^4 \text{ atm}^2$

Test 1–2

Some NH_3 decomposes to form 0.399 mole of N_2 and an unknown amount of H_2. Using the stoichiometry dictated by the balanced equation, the amounts of NH_3 and H_2 present at equilibrium can be calculated.

$$0.399 \text{ mole } N_2 \times \dfrac{2 \text{ moles } NH_3}{1 \text{ mole } N_2} = 0.798 \text{ mole of } NH_3 \text{ consumed to produce } 0.399 \text{ mole of } N_2$$

NH_3 remaining $= 1.000 - 0.798 = 0.202$ mole

At equilibrium $[NH_3] = [NH_3]_0$ plus the change to reach equilibrium

$$= \dfrac{1.000 \text{ mole}}{1.000 \ \ell} - \dfrac{0.798 \text{ mole}}{1.000 \ \ell} = 0.202 \text{ mole}/\ell$$

The amount of H_2 produced is given by

$$0.399 \text{ mole } N_2 \times \frac{3 \text{ moles } H_2}{1 \text{ mole } N_2} = 1.197 \text{ moles } H_2$$

Since no H_2 was originally present in the flask:

$$[H_2] = [H_2]_0 \text{ plus the change to reach equilibrium}$$

$$= 0 + \frac{1.197 \text{ mole}}{1.000 \ \ell} = 1.197 \text{ moles}/\ell$$

Test 1–3

A. $K = \dfrac{P^2_{NO_2}}{P_{N_2O_4}}$

B. $P^{\text{initial}}_{N_2O_4} = 2.0 \text{ atm};$ $P^{\text{equilibrium}}_{N_2O_4} = 1.8 \text{ atm};$
    $P^{\text{initial}}_{N_2O_4} - P^{\text{equilibrium}}_{N_2O_4} = 0.2 \text{ atm}$

Thus, 0.2 atm of $N_2O_4(g)$ was consumed as the system proceeded to equilibrium.

C. Since $N_2O_4(g) \rightarrow 2NO_2(g)$
    0.2 atm $N_2O_4(g)$ produces 0.4 atm $NO_2(g)$

D. $K = \dfrac{P_{NO_2}{}^2}{P_{N_2O_4}} = \dfrac{(0.4)^2}{(1.8)} = 9 \times 10^{-2} \text{ atm}$

Test 1–4

For each experiment (I, II, and III), the value of K is 6×10^{-2}. That is,

$$\frac{[NH_3]^2}{[N_2][H_2]^3} = 6 \times 10^{-2}$$

for each case.

Test 1–5

A. 1. The initial concentrations are

$$[SO_2]_0 = 2.00 \text{ moles}/\ell$$
$$[O_2]_0 = 1.50 \text{ moles}/\ell$$
$$[SO_3]_0 = 3.00 \text{ moles}/\ell$$

At equilibrium, $[SO_3] = 3.50 \text{ moles}/\ell$. The increase in SO_3 concentration is 3.50 mole/ℓ − 3.00 mole/ℓ or 0.50 mole/ℓ of SO_3. Now calculate the corresponding changes in $[O_2]$ and $[SO_2]$.

$$0.50 \text{ mole } SO_3 \times \frac{2 \text{ moles } SO_2}{2 \text{ moles } SO_3} = 0.50 \text{ moles of } SO_2 \text{ formed to reach}$$

equilibrium.

The change in $[SO_2]$ is negative $\dfrac{0.50 \text{ mole}}{1.00 \ \ell}$ since some SO_2 must be consumed.

0.50 moles $SO_3 \times \dfrac{1 \text{ mole } O_2}{2 \text{ mole } SO_3} = 0.25$ mole of O_2 formed to reach equilibrium.

The change in $[O_2]$ is negative $\dfrac{0.25 \text{ mole}}{1.00 \ \ell}$ since some O_2 must be consumed. Now compute the equilibrium concentrations:

$$[SO_2] = [SO_2]_0 \text{ plus change}$$

$$= \frac{2.00 \text{ mole}}{1.00 \ \ell} - \frac{0.50 \text{ mole}}{1.00 \ \ell} = 1.50 \text{ mole}/\ell$$

$$[O_2]_0 = [O_2]_0 \text{ plus change}$$

$$= \frac{1.50 \text{ mole}}{1.00 \ \ell} - \frac{0.25 \text{ mole}}{1.00 \ \ell} = 1.25 \text{ mole}/\ell$$

2. $K = \dfrac{[SO_3]^2}{[SO_2]^2[O_2]} = \dfrac{(3.50 \text{ moles}/\ell)^2}{(1.50 \text{ moles}/\ell)^2 \ (1.25 \text{ moles}/\ell)} = 4.36 \ \ell/\text{mole}$

3. $K_p = K(RT)^{\Delta n}$
$\Delta n = 2 - (2+1) = -1$
$K = 4.36 \ \ell/\text{mole}$
$T = 600°C = 600 + 273 = 873 \text{ K}$
$R = 0.08206 \ \ell \cdot \text{atm}/\text{K} \cdot \text{mole}$

$$K_p = (4.36) \ (RT)^{-1} = \frac{4.36}{RT} = \frac{4.36 \ \ell/\text{mole}}{\left(0.08206 \ \dfrac{\ell \cdot \text{atm}}{\text{K} \cdot \text{mole}}\right) (873 \text{ K})}$$

$$= 6.08 \times 10^{-2} \text{ atm}^{-1}$$

B. 1. The initial concentrations are

$$[SO_2]_0 = 0.500 \ \text{mole}/\ell$$
$$[SO_3]_0 = 0.350 \text{ mole}/\ell$$
$$[O_2]_0 = 0$$

The concentration of O_2 at equilibrium is

$$[O_2] = 0.045 \text{ mole}/\ell$$

Thus, to reach equilibrium, 0.045 mole/ℓ of O_2 has been formed. This means that SO_3 has been consumed to form SO_2 and O_2. Compute the changes needed to reach equilibrium:

Change in $[O_2]$: 0.045 mole/ℓ
Change in $[SO_3]$:

0.045 mole/ℓ $O_2 \times \dfrac{2 \text{ moles } SO_3}{1 \text{ mole } O_2} =$

0.090 mole/ℓ of SO_3 *consumed* to reach equilibrium

Change in $[SO_2]$:

$$0.045 \text{ mole/}\ell \text{ } O_2 \times \frac{2 \text{ moles } SO_2}{1 \text{ mole } O_2} =$$

$$0.090 \text{ mole/}\ell \text{ of } SO_2 \text{ } \textit{formed} \text{ to reach equilibrium}$$

Now calculate the equilibrium concentrations:

$[O_2] = [O_2]_0$ plus the change to reach equilibrium
    $= 0 + 0.045 \text{ mole/}\ell = 0.045 \text{ mole/}\ell$
$[SO_3] = [SO_3]_0$ plus the change to reach equilibrium
    $= 0.350 \text{ mole/}\ell - 0.090 \text{ mole/}\ell = 0.260 \text{ mole/}\ell$
$[SO_2] = [SO_2]_0$ plus the change to reach equilibrium
    $= 0.500 \text{ mole/}\ell + 0.090 \text{ mole/}\ell = 0.590 \text{ mole/}\ell$

B. 2. $K = \dfrac{[SO_3]^2}{[SO_2]^2[O_2]} = \dfrac{(0.260 \text{ mole/}\ell)^2}{(0.590 \text{ mole/}\ell)^2 (0.045 \text{ mole/}\ell)} = 4.32 \text{ } \ell/\text{mole}$

Note that K calculated here has the same value (within the error caused by round-off) as calculated in Part A. This again demonstrates the constancy of K at a given temperature. The experiments in Parts A and B produce different equilibrium positions because the initial concentrations were different, but give the same ratio defined by the equilibrium expression.

Test 1–6

The initial concentrations are

$$[NOCl]_0 = \frac{1.0 \times 10^{-1} \text{ mole}}{2.0 \text{ } \ell} = 5.0 \times 10^{-2} \text{ mole/}\ell$$

$$[NO]_0 = \frac{1.0 \times 10^{-3} \text{ mole}}{2.0 \text{ } \ell} = 5.0 \times 10^{-4} \text{ mole/}\ell$$

$$[Cl_2]_0 = \frac{1.0 \times 10^{-4} \text{ mole}}{2.0 \text{ } \ell} = 5.0 \times 10^{-5} \text{ mole/}\ell$$

$$Q = \frac{[NO]_0^2[Cl_2]_0}{[NOCl]_0^2} = \frac{(5.0 \times 10^{-4})^2(5.0 \times 10^{-5})}{(5.0 \times 10^{-2})^2}$$

$$= 5.0 \times 10^{-9} \text{ mole/}\ell$$

K is $1.55 \times 10^{-5} \text{ mole/}\ell$

Thus Q is less than K, and the system will proceed to the right to reach equilibrium.

Test 1–7

The equilibrium expression is

$$K = 5.0 = \frac{[CO_2][H_2]}{[CO][H_2O]}$$

The initial concentrations are

$$[CO]_0 = \frac{3.00 \text{ mole}}{1.00 \ \ell} = 3.00 \text{ mole}/\ell$$

$$[H_2O]_0 = \frac{0.50 \text{ mole}}{1.00 \ \ell} = 3.00 \text{ mole}/\ell$$

$$[CO_2]_0 = 0$$

$$[H_2]_0 = 0$$

Let x be the number of moles/ℓ of CO_2 formed as the system reaches equilibrium. This means that

x moles/ℓ of H_2 are formed.

x moles/ℓ of H_2O are consumed.

x moles/ℓ of CO are consumed.

The equilibrium concentrations are

$$[CO_2] = [CO_2]_0 + x = 0 + x \text{ moles}/\ell$$
$$[H_2] = [H_2]_0 + x = 0 + x \text{ moles}/\ell$$
$$[CO] = [CO]_0 - x = 3.00 \text{ moles}/\ell - x \text{ moles}/\ell$$
$$[H_2O] = [H_2O]_0 - x = 3.00 \text{ moles}/\ell - x \text{ moles}/\ell$$

Now substitute these equilibrium concentrations into the equilibrium constant expression:

$$K = 5.10 = \frac{[CO_2][H_2]}{[CO][H_2O]} = \frac{(x)\,(x)}{(3.00 - x)\,(3.00 - x)} = \frac{x^2}{(3.00 - x)^2}$$

Taking the square root of both sides:

$$\frac{x}{3.00 - x} = \sqrt{5.10} = 2.26$$

$$x = 2.26(3.00 - x) = 6.78 - 2.26x$$

$$3.26x = 6.78$$

$$x = \frac{6.78}{3.26} = 2.08 \text{ moles}/\ell$$

Now compute the equilibrium concentrations:

$$[CO_2] = x = 2.08 \text{ moles}/\ell$$
$$[H_2] = x = 2.08 \text{ moles}/\ell$$
$$[CO] = 3.00 - x = 0.92 \text{ mole}/\ell$$
$$[H_2O] = 3.00 - x = 0.92 \text{ mole}/\ell$$

Test 1–8

The equilibrium expression is

$$K = 60.0 = \frac{[HI]^2}{[H_2][I_2]}$$

The initial concentrations are

$$[H_2]_0 = \frac{1.50 \text{ moles}}{1.00 \text{ } \ell} = 1.50 \text{ moles/}\ell$$

$$[I_2]_0 = \frac{2.50 \text{ moles}}{1.00 \text{ } \ell} = 2.50 \text{ moles/}\ell$$

$$[HI]_0 = 0$$

Assume that x moles/ℓ of H_2 are consumed to reach equilibrium. Using the balanced equation:

$$x \text{ moles/}\ell \text{ } H_2 + x \text{ moles/}\ell \text{ } I_2 \rightarrow 2x \text{ moles/}\ell \text{ } HI$$

The equilibrium concentrations are

$$[H_2] = [H_2]_0 + \text{change} = 1.50 \text{ moles/}\ell - x \text{ moles/}\ell$$
$$[I_2] = [I_2]_0 + \text{change} = 2.50 \text{ moles/}\ell - x \text{ moles/}\ell$$
$$[HI] = [HI]_0 + \text{change} = 0 + 2x \text{ moles/}\ell$$

Now substitute into the equilibrium constant expression:

$$K = 60.0 = \frac{(2x)^2}{(1.50 - x)(2.50 - x)} = \frac{4x^2}{3.75 - 4.00x + x^2}$$

Multiply this out and collect terms

$$225 - 240x + 60.0x^2 = 4x^2$$
$$56.0x^2 - 240x + 225 = 0$$

This is a quadratic equation where $a = 56.0$, $b = -240$, $c = 225$. Substituting into the quadratic formula,

$$x = \frac{-b \pm \sqrt{b^2 - 4ac}}{2a} = \frac{-(-240) \pm \sqrt{(-240)^2 - 4(56.0)(225)}}{2(56.0)}$$

The two roots are $x = 2.90$ and $x = 1.38$. Since $[H_2] = 1.50 - x$, $x = 2.90$ cannot be correct since the $[H_2]$ cannot be negative. Thus $x = 1.38$ moles/ℓ is the physically correct root. Now calculate the equilibrium concentrations:

$$[H_2] = 1.50 - x = 1.50 \text{ moles/}\ell - 1.38 \text{ moles/}\ell = 0.12 \text{ mole/}\ell$$
$$[I_2] = 2.50 - x = 2.50 \text{ moles/}\ell - 1.38 \text{ moles/}\ell = 1.12 \text{ moles/}\ell$$
$$[HI] = 2x = 2(1.38 \text{ moles/}\ell) = 2.76 \text{ moles/}\ell$$

Test 1–9

A. $[PCl_5]_0 = \dfrac{0.200 \text{ mole}}{2.00 \; \ell} = 0.100 \text{ mole}/\ell$

$[PCl_3]_0 = \dfrac{0.500 \text{ mole}}{2.00 \; \ell} = 0.250 \text{ mole}/\ell$

$[Cl_2]_0 = \dfrac{0.300 \text{ mole}}{2.00 \; \ell} = 0.150 \text{ mole}/\ell$

B. $Q = \dfrac{[PCl_3][Cl_2]}{[PCl_5]} = \dfrac{(0.250)\,(0.150)}{(0.100)} = 0.375$

C. Q is greater than K (which equals 5.0×10^{-2}). Thus, the system will adjust to the left to come to equilibrium.

D. Let x = moles/ℓ of $PCl_5(g)$ formed to come to equilibrium.

E. $[PCl_5] = 0.100 + x$
$[PCl_3] = 0.250 - x$
$[Cl_2] = 0.150 - x$

F. $K = \dfrac{[PCl_3][Cl_2]}{[PCl_5]} = \dfrac{(0.250 - x)\,(0.150 - x)}{(0.100 + x)} = 5.0 \times 10^{-2}$

This produces the quadratic equation

$$x^2 - 0.450x + 0.0325 = 0$$

Using the quadratic formula
$$x = 0.090 \text{ mole}/\ell$$

G. $[PCl_5] = 0.100 + 0.090 = 0.190 \text{ mole}/\ell$
$[PCl_3] = 0.250 - 0.090 = 0.160 \text{ mole}/\ell$
$[Cl_2] = 0.150 - 0.090 = 0.060 \text{ mole}/\ell$

Test 1–10

A. Shifts to the right.
B. Shifts to the right.
C. Shifts to the left (the reactants have smaller volume than the products).
D. No effect.
E. Shifts to the left. The reaction is exothermic.

$$2NO_2(g) \rightleftarrows N_2(g) + 2O_2(g) + \text{heat}$$

Added heat will drive the equilibrium to the left. (In this case, K will decrease with increasing temperature.)

Chapter 2

Test 2–1

A. See discussion in the chapter.
B. 1. $HCN \rightleftarrows H^+ + CN^-$
2. $C_6H_5NH_3^+ \rightleftarrows C_6H_5NH_2 + H^+$
3. $Al(OH_2)_6^{3+} \rightleftarrows Al(OH)(OH_2)_5^{2+} + H^+$

C. This reaction is the reverse of the K_a reaction for HCN:

$$K = \frac{[HCN]}{[H^+][CN^-]} = \frac{1}{K_a} = \frac{1}{6.2 \times 10^{-10}} = 1.6 \times 10^9$$

D. 1. OCl^- is the strongest base. This is clear because K_a for $HOCl$ is the smallest of all of those listed.

2. Base strength: (use the K_a values for the acids)

$$OCl^- > NO_2^- > F^- > IO_3^-$$

strongest base   weakest base
(smallest K_a (largest K_a
for HA)   for HA)

3. Acid strength:

$$HOCl < HNO_2 < HF < HIO_3$$

weakest   strongest
(smallest K_a)   (largest K_a)

Test 2–2

A. $[OH^-] = 2.0 \times 10^{-4} M$
$[H^+][OH^-] = 1.0 \times 10^{-14}$
$[H^+](2.0 \times 10^{-4}) = 1.0 \times 10^{-14}$

$$[H^+] = \frac{1.0 \times 10^{-14}}{2.0 \times 10^{-4}} = 5.0 \times 10^{-11} M$$

$pH = -\log [H^+] = -\log (5.0 \times 10^{-11}) = 10.30$

B. $[H^+] = 5.0 \times 10^{-3} M$
$[H^+][OH^-] = 1.0 \times 10^{-14} = (5.0 \times 10^{-3})[OH^-]$

$$[OH^-] = \frac{1.0 \times 10^{-14}}{5.0 \times 10^{-3}} = 2.0 \times 10^{-12} M$$

$pOH = -\log[OH^-] = -\log(2.0 \times 10^{-12}) = 11.70$

Test 2–3

A. 1. HNO_3, H_2O. The solution really contains H^+, NO_3^-, H_2O as major
   ↑   species.
   (strong acid)

2. $0.1 M$ H^+ from HNO_3 is the major source. H_2O is the minor source.
3. Assume that the contribution of water to $[H^+]$ can be neglected.
4. $[H^+] = 0.10 M = 1.0 \times 10^{-1} M$
   $pH = -\log[H^+] = -\log(1.0 \times 10^{-1}) = 1.00$

B. 1. HCl is a strong acid: H^+, Cl^-, H_2O
2. H^+ from acid and dissociation of H_2O are the sources of H^+.
3. In this case,

$$[H^+]_{HCl} = 1.0 \times 10^{-10} M$$

This is very small compared to the amount from dissociation of water $(1.0 \times 10^{-7}\ M)$. H_2O is the dominant source of H^+.

4. $[H^+] = 1.0 \times 10^{-7}$

   $pH = 7.00$

Here, the strong acid is so dilute that the solution is still neutral within the uncertainties of measurement.

Test 2–4

A. 1. $HOCl$, H_2O

   2. $HOCl$ is a stonger acid than H_2O (K_a for $HOCl$ is larger than K_w) and will dominate.

   3. $HOCl \rightleftharpoons H^+ + OCl^-$

$$K_a = \frac{[H^+][OCl^-]}{[HOCl]} = 3.5 \times 10^{-8}$$

   4. No dissociation has occurred.

   $[HOCl]_0 = 0.100\ M$

   $[OCl^-]_0 = 0$

   $[H^+]_0 \approx 0$ neglect contribution from H_2O

   5. $x = $ moles/ℓ of $HOCl$ that will dissociate as the system comes to equilibrium.

   6. $[HOCl] = 0.100 - x$

   $[OCl^-] = x$

   $[H^+] = x$

7,8. $3.5 \times 10^{-8} = \dfrac{[H^+][OCl^-]}{[HOCl]} = \dfrac{(x)(x)}{(0.100 - x)} \approx \dfrac{x^2}{0.100}$

   $x^2 \approx (3.5 \times 10^{-8})(0.100) = 3.5 \times 10^{-9}$

   $x \approx 5.9 \times 10^{-5}$

   9. $\dfrac{5.9 \times 10^{-5}}{0.100} \times 100 = 5.9 \times 10^{-2}\%$

   $0.100 \gg 5.9 \times 10^{-5}$

   $0.100 - 5.9 \times 10^{-5} = 0.100$ (assumption is valid)

   10. $[H^+] = x = 5.9 \times 10^{-5}$

   $pH = -\log(5.9 \times 10^{-5}) = 4.23$

   11. $[OCl^-] = [H^+] = 5.9 \times 10^{-5}$

   12. Percent dissociation $= \dfrac{[OCl^-]}{[HOCl]_0} \times 100 = \dfrac{5.9 \times 10^{-5}}{(0.100)} \times 100$

   $= 5.9 \times 10^{-2}\%$

   13. $[H^+][OH^-] = K_w = 1.0 \times 10^{-14}$

   $(5.9 \times 10^{-5})[OH^-] = 1.0 \times 10^{-14}$

   $[OH^-] = 1.7 \times 10^{-10}\ M$

B. In solution, we have H_3BO_3 (boric acid) and H_2O. Boric acid is a very weak acid ($K_a = 5.8 \times 10^{-10}$), but is stronger than H_2O ($K_w = 10^{-14}$). Thus, the boric acid dissociation will determine the $[H^+]$:

$$H_3BO_3 \rightleftharpoons H^+ + H_2BO_3^- \qquad K_a = \frac{[H^+][H_2BO_3^-]}{[H_3BO_3]} = 5.8 \times 10^{-10}$$

Initial Concentrations
(before any dissociation)
$[H_3BO_3]_0 = 0.50\ M$
$[H_2BO_3^-]_0 = 0$
$[H^+]_0 \approx 0$

Let x moles/ℓ
————of H_3BO_3————→
dissociate

Equilibrium Concentrations
$[H_3BO_3] = 0.50 - x$
$[H_2BO_3^-] = x$
$[H^+] = x$

$$5.8 \times 10^{-10} = K_a = \frac{[H^+][H_2BO_3^-]}{[H_3BO_3]} = \frac{(x)(x)}{0.50 - x} \approx \frac{x^2}{0.5}$$

$$x^2 \approx 2.9 \times 10^{-10}$$
$$x \approx 1.7 \times 10^{-5}$$

Note that $0.50 \gg 1.7 \times 10^{-5}$, so $[H^+] = x = 1.7 \times 10^{-5}\ M$.
$pH = -\log(1.7 \times 10^{-5}) = 4.77$

Test 2–5

The solution contains: HA, Na^+, A^-, H_2O. The equilibrium of interest is

$$HA \rightleftharpoons H^+ + A^-$$
$$[H^+] = 10^{-pH} = 1.0 \times 10^{-4}$$

$$K_a = \frac{[H^+][A^-]}{[HA]} = \frac{(1.0 \times 10^{-4})(0.025)}{(0.050)} = 5.0 \times 10^{-5}$$

Test 2–6

A. The solution contains the major species: K^+, OH^- and H_2O.

B. The OH^- from the dissolved KOH.

C. Assume that H_2O produces a neglible amount of OH^-, so $[OH^-] = 0.10\ M$.

D. $[H^+][OH^-] = K_w = 1.00 \times 10^{-14}$
$[H^+](0.10) = 1.00 \times 10^{-14}$
$$[H^+] = \frac{(1.00 \times 10^{-14})}{(0.10)} = 1.0 \times 10^{-13}\ M$$

E. $pH = -\log[H^+] = -\log(1.0 \times 10^{-13}) = 13.00$

Test 2–7

A. A base reacting with H_2O to produce OH^- and the conjugate acid.

B. See the discussion in the chapter.

C. $K_b \neq \dfrac{1}{K_a}$

$$B + H_2O \rightleftharpoons BH^+ + OH^- \qquad K_b = \frac{[BH^+][OH^-]}{[B]}$$

$$BH^+ \rightleftharpoons B + H^+ \qquad K_a = \frac{[B][H^+]}{[BH^+]}$$

$$B + H^+ \rightleftarrows BH^+ \qquad K = \frac{1}{K_a} = \frac{[BH^+]}{[B][H^+]}$$

K_b and $\dfrac{1}{K_a}$ refer to entirely different reactions.

D. 1. CH_3NH_2, H_2O
   2. $CH_3NH_2 + H_2O \rightleftarrows CH_3NH_3^+ + OH^-$
   3. K_b for CH_3NH_2 (4.38×10^{-4}) is much greater than K_w. CH_3NH_2 will dominate.

   4. $K_b = \dfrac{[CH_3NH_3^+][OH^-]}{[CH_3NH_2]}$

   5. $[CH_3NH_2]_0 = 1.0\ M$
      $[CH_3NH_3^+]_0 = 0$
      $[OH^-] \approx 0$ (neglect contribution of H_2O)
   6. x = moles/ℓ of CH_3NH_2 that react with H_2O to come to equilibrium.
   7. $[CH_3NH_2] = 1.0 - x$
      $[CH_3NH_3^+] = x$
      $[OH^-] = x$

   8. $4.38 \times 10^{-4} = K_b = \dfrac{[CH_3NH_3^+][OH^-]}{[CH_3NH_2]} = \dfrac{(x)(x)}{(1.0 - x)} \approx \dfrac{x^2}{1.0}$

   $$x^2 \approx 4.38 \times 10^{-4}$$
   $$x \approx 2.1 \times 10^{-2}$$

   $$\frac{x}{[CH_3NH_2]_0} \times 100 = \frac{2.1 \times 10^{-2}}{1.0} \times 100 = 2.1\%$$

   The assumption that $1.0 - x \approx 1.0$ is acceptable.
   9. $[OH^-] = x = 2.1 \times 10^{-2}\ M$
      $[H^+][OH^-] = 1.0 \times 10^{-14}$
      $[H^+](2.1 \times 10^{-2}) = 1.0 \times 10^{-14}$

      $$[H^+] = \frac{1.0 \times 10^{-14}}{2.1 \times 10^{-2}} = 4.8 \times 10^{-13}\ M$$

   pH $= 12.32$

E. In solution, the major species are: C_5H_5N and H_2O. C_5H_5N is a base ($K_b = 1.4 \times 10^{-9}$) which will dominate H_2O in the production of OH^-:

   $$C_5H_5N + H_2O \rightleftarrows C_5H_5NH^+ + OH^-$$
   $$K_b = \frac{[C_5H_5NH^+][OH^-]}{[C_5H_5N]} = 1.4 \times 10^{-9}$$

Initial Concentrations		*Equilibrium Concentrations*
$[C_5H_5N]_0 = 0.10\ M$	Let x moles/ℓ C_5H_5N react with H_2O to reach equilibrium	$[C_5H_5N] = 0.10 - x$
$[C_5H_5NH^+]_0 = 0$		$[C_5H_5NH^+] = x$
$[OH^-]_0 \approx 0$		$[OH^-] = x$

$$1.4 \times 10^{-9} = K_b = \frac{[C_5H_5NH^+][OH^-]}{[C_5H_5N]} = \frac{(x)(x)}{(0.10 - x)} \approx \frac{x^2}{0.10}$$

$$x^2 \approx (1.4 \times 10^{-9})(0.10) = 1.4 \times 10^{-10}$$

$$x \approx 1.2 \times 10^{-5}$$

Assumption that $0.1 - x \approx 0.1$ is valid.

$[OH^-] = x = 1.2 \times 10^{-5}$

$[H^+][OH^-] = K_w = 1.0 \times 10^{-14}$

$$[H^+] = \frac{1.0 \times 10^{-14}}{[OH^-]} = \frac{1.0 \times 10^{-14}}{1.2 \times 10^{-5}} = 8.4 \times 10^{-10}$$

$pH = 9.08$

Test 2–8

A. 1. The solution contains: HOAc, OAc$^-$, Na$^+$, H$_2$O. The acetic acid dissociation equilibrium will control the [H$^+$]:

$$HOAc \rightleftarrows H^+ + OAc^-$$

$$K_a = \frac{[H^+][OAc^-]}{[HOAc]} = 1.8 \times 10^{-5}$$

Initial Concentrations

$[HOAc]_0 = 0.20\ M$

$[OAc^-]_0 = 0.10\ M$

$[H^+]_0 \approx 0$

Let x moles/ℓ
———HOAc———→
dissociate

Equilibrium Concentrations

$[HOAc] = 0.20 - x$

$[OAc^-] = 0.10 + x$

$[H^+] = x$

$$1.8 \times 10^{-5} = K_a = \frac{[H^+][OAc^-]}{[HOAc]} = \frac{(x)(0.10 + x)}{0.20 - x} \approx \frac{(x)(0.10)}{0.20}$$

$$x \approx 3.6 \times 10^{-5}$$

Assumptions are valid.

$[H^+] = 3.6 \times 10^{-5}$; pH $= 4.44$

2. Before any reaction, the solution contains the major species:
    H$^+$, Cl$^-$, Na$^+$, OAc$^-$, HOAc, H$_2$O. The reaction which will occur is:

	H$^+$	+	OAc$^-$	→	HOAc
Before the reaction	0.02 mole		0.10 mole		0.20 mole
After the reaction	0		0.10 − 0.02 = 0.080 mole		0.20 + 0.02 = 0.22 mole

After the reaction, the solution contains: HOAc, OAc$^-$, Na$^+$, Cl$^-$, H$_2$O. The equilibrium of interest is:

$$HOAc \rightleftarrows H^+ + OAc^-$$

$$K_a = \frac{[H^+][OAc^-]}{[HOAc]} = 1.8 \times 10^{-5}$$

Initial Concentrations

$[HOAc]_0 = \dfrac{0.22 \text{ mole}}{1.0 \, \ell} =$

$0.22 \, M$

$[OAc^-]_0 = \dfrac{0.080 \text{ mole}}{1.0 \, \ell} =$

$0.080 \, M$

$[H^+]_0 \approx 0$

Let x moles/ℓ —HOAc— dissociate $\longrightarrow$

Equilibrium Concentrations

$[HOAc] = 0.22 - x$

$[OAc^-] = 0.08 + x$

$[H^+] = x$

$$1.8 \times 10^{-5} = K_a = \frac{[H^+][OAc^-]}{[HOAc]} = \frac{(x)(0.080 + x)}{(0.22 - x)} \approx \frac{(x)(0.080)}{(0.22)}$$

$$x \approx \frac{(0.22)(1.8 \times 10^{-5})}{(0.080)} = 5.0 \times 10^{-5}$$

Assumptions are valid: $[H^+] = 4.9 \times 10^{-5}$; pH $= 4.30$

Thus, adding 0.02 mole of HCl(g) to this solution changes the pH from 4.44 to 4.30. This is a relatively small change.

3. Before any reaction, the solution contains the major species: Na^+, OH^-, OAc^-, HOAc, H_2O. The reaction which will occur is:

	OH^-	$+$	HOAc	$\rightarrow$	OAc^-	$+$	H_2O
Before the reaction	0.02 mole		0.20 mole		0.10 mole		
After the rection	0		0.20 − 0.02 = 0.18 mole		0.10 + 0.02 = 0.12 mole		

After the reaction, the solution contains: Na^+, OAc^-, HOAc, H_2O. The equilibrium of interest is:

$$HOAc \rightleftarrows H^+ + OAc^-$$

$$K_a = \frac{[H^+][OAc^-]}{[HOAc]} = 1.8 \times 10^{-5}$$

Initial Concentrations

$[HOAc]_0 = 0.18 \, M$
$[OAc^-]_0 = 0.12 \, M$
$[H^+]_0 \approx 0$

Let x moles/ℓ —HOAc— dissociate $\longrightarrow$

Equilibrium Concentrations

$[HOAc] = 0.18 - x$
$[OAc^-] = 0.12 + x$
$[H^+] = x$

$$1.8 \times 10^{-5} = K_a = \frac{[H^+][OAc^-]}{[HOAc]} = \frac{(x)(0.12 + x)}{0.18 - x} \approx \frac{(x)(0.12)}{0.18}$$

$$x \approx \frac{(1.8 \times 10^{-5})(0.18)}{(0.12)} = 2.7 \times 10^{-5}$$

The assumptions are valid: $[H^+] = 2.7 \times 10^{-5}$; pH $= 4.57$

Thus, adding 0.02 mole of NaOH to the solution changes the pH from 4.44 to 4.57.

Test 2–9

1.   I. $K_a = 1.0 \times 10^{-5} = \dfrac{[H^+][A^-]}{[HA]}$ where $[A^-] = [HA] = 1.0\ M$

$[H^+] = 1.0 \times 10^{-5}$; pH = 5.00

II. $K_a = 1.0 \times 10^{-5} = \dfrac{[H^+][A^-]}{[HA]}$ where $[A^-] = [HA] = 0.10\ M$

$[H^+] = 1.0 \times 10^{-5}$; pH = 5.00

Both solutions have the same pH, since the $[A^-]/[HA]$ is the same in both.

2.   I has the greater capacity.

3.   In each case, the reaction is:

$$HA + OH^- \rightarrow H_2O + A^-$$

and in each case 0.05 mole of HA will be changed to 0.05 mole of A^-. Thus, the [HA] will decrease by 0.05 mole/ℓ.

I.   New pH: $K_a = 1.0 \times 10^{-5} = \dfrac{[H^+][A^-]}{[HA]}$ where $[A^-] = 1.05\ M$, $[HA] = 0.95\ M$

$[H^-] = 9.0 \times 10^{-6}$; pH = 5.04

II.   New pH: $K_a = 1.0 \times 10^{-5} = \dfrac{[H^+][A^-]}{[HA]}$ where $[A^-] = 0.15\ M$, $[HA] = 0.05\ M$

$[H^+] = 3.3 \times 10^{-6}$; pH = 5.48

The original pH for both solutions was 5.00. Note that I resists a change in pH much better than II.

Test 2–10

A.   1.   Since $[HA] \approx [A^-]$:

$$[H^+] = K_a \frac{[HA]}{[A^-]} \approx K_a = 1.0 \times 10^{-6}$$
$$pH = 6.0$$

2.   Before the reaction, the solution contains the major species: HA, A^-, Na^+, OH^-, H_2O. OH^- will react with HA as follows:

	OH^-	+	HA	$\rightarrow$	A^-	+	H_2O
Before the reaction	0.10 mole		0.50 mole		0.50 mole		
After the reaction	0		0.50 − 0.10 = 0.40 mole		0.50 + 0.10 = 0.60 mole		

After the reaction, the solution contains the major species: HA, A^-, Na^+, H_2O, and the equilibrium of interest is:

$$HA \rightleftarrows H^+ + A^-$$

$$K_a = \frac{[H^+][A^-]}{[HA]} = 1.0 \times 10^{-6}$$

Initial Concentrations
(before dissociation of HA)

$[HA]_0 = \dfrac{0.40 \text{ mole}}{1.0 \text{ } \ell} = 0.40 \text{ } M$

Equilibrium Concentrations

$[HA] = 0.40 \text{ } M - x$

Let x moles/ℓ
$\xrightarrow{\text{HA}}$
dissociate

$[A^-]_0 = \dfrac{0.60 \text{ mole}}{1.0 \text{ } \ell} = 0.60 \text{ } M$

$[A^-] = 0.60 \text{ } M + x$

$[H^+]_0 \approx 0$

$[H^+] = x$

$$1.0 \times 10^{-6} = K_a = \frac{[H^+][A^-]}{[HA]} = \frac{(x)(0.60 + x)}{(0.40 - x)} \approx \frac{(x)(0.60)}{(0.40)}$$

$$x = [H^+] = 6.7 \times 10^{-7} \text{ } M \qquad \text{(assumption is valid)}$$

$$pH = -\log[H^+] = -\log(6.7 \times 10^{-7}) = 6.17$$

3. The reaction is:

	H^+	$+$	A^-	$\rightarrow$	HA
Before the reaction	0.10 mole		0.50 mole		0.50 mole
After the reaction	0		$0.50 - 0.10 = 0.40$ mole		$0.50 + 0.10 = 0.60$ mole

Initial Concentrations
(before dissociation of HA)

$[HA]_0 = \dfrac{0.60 \text{ mole}}{1.0 \text{ } \ell} = 0.60 \text{ } M$

Equilibrium Concentrations

$[HA] = 0.60 \text{ } M - x$

Let x moles/ℓ
$\xrightarrow{\text{HA}}$
dissociate

$[A^-]_0 = \dfrac{0.40 \text{ mole}}{1.0 \text{ } \ell} = 0.40 \text{ } M$

$[A^-] = 0.40 \text{ } M + x$

$[H^+]_0 \approx 0$

$[H^+] = x$

$$1.0 \times 10^{-6} = K_a = \frac{[H^+][A^-]}{[HA]} = \frac{(x)(0.40 + x)}{(0.60 - x)} \approx \frac{(x)(0.40)}{(0.60)}$$

$$x = [H^+] = 1.5 \times 10^{-6} \text{ } M$$

$$pH = -\log[H^+] = -\log(1.5 \times 10^{-6}) = 5.82$$

B. 1. In each solution $[H^+] = K_a = 7.2 \times 10^{-4}$. Since in each case $[HF] = [F^-]$, pH = 3.14 for each.

   2. Solution II has the largest capacity.

   3. In each case, the reaction when H^+ is added is:

$$H^+ + F^- \rightarrow HF$$

   and in each case the $[F^-]$ will decrease by 0.050 mole/ℓ and the $[HF]$ will increase by 0.050 mole/ℓ.

I.   New pH:

$$7.2 \times 10^{-4} = K_a = \frac{[H^+][F^-]}{[HF]} = \frac{[H^+](0.45)}{(0.55)}$$

$$[H^+] = \frac{(0.55)(7.2 \times 10^{-4})}{(0.45)} = 8.8 \times 10^{-4}; \text{pH} = 3.06$$

II.   New pH:

$$7.2 \times 10^{-4} = K_a = \frac{[H^+](4.95)}{(5.05)}$$

$$[H^+] = 7.3 \times 10^{-4}; \text{pH} = 3.13$$

II resists a change in pH better than I, because it contains larger amounts of buffering materials.

C. $HNO_2 \rightleftarrows H^+ + NO_2^-$

$$K_a = 4.0 \times 10^{-4} = \frac{[H^+][NO_2^-]}{[HNO_2]}$$

pH = 3.00
$[H^+] = 10^{-\text{pH}} = 1.0 \times 10^{-3} \ M$
$[HNO_2] = 0.050 \ M$

$$4.0 \times 10^{-4} = \frac{(1.0 \times 10^{-3})[NO_2^-]}{(0.050)}$$

$$[NO_2^-] = \frac{(0.050)(4.0 \times 10^{-4})}{1.0 \times 10^{-3}} = 2.0 \times 10^{-2} \ M$$

0.020 mole of $NaNO_2(s)$ must be added to each liter of the 0.050 M solution to produce a buffer with pH = 3.00.

D. Before the reaction, the major species are: H^+, Cl^-, Na^+, OAc^-, H_2O. The reaction which will take place is

	H^+	+	OAc^-	$\rightarrow$	HOAc
Before the reaction	50.0 m$\ell \times 0.050 \ M$ = 2.5 mmole		100.0 m$\ell \times 0.10 \ M$ = 10.0 mmole		0
After the reaction	0		10.0−2.5=7.5 mmole		2.5 mmole

In solution after the reaction: HOAc, OAc^-, Na^+, H_2O. The equilibrium to use is:

$$HOAc \rightleftarrows H^+ + OAc^-$$

Initial Concentrations

$$[HOAc]_0 = \frac{2.5 \text{ mmole}}{(100.0 + 50.0)m\ell}$$
$$= 1.7 \times 10^{-2} \, M$$

$$[OAc^-]_0 = \frac{7.5 \text{ mmole}}{(100.0 + 50.0)m\ell}$$
$$= 5.0 \times 10^{-2} \, M$$

$$[H^+]_0 \approx 0$$

Let x mole/ℓ
———HOAc———→
dissociate

Equilibrium Concentrations

$$[HOAc] = 1.7 \times 10^{-2} - x$$

$$[OAc^-] = 5.0 \times 10^{-2} + x$$

$$[H^+] = x$$

Plugging into the K_a expression gives:

$$x = 6.1 \times 10^{-6}; \text{pH} = 5.21$$

E.   Before the reaction, the major species are: NH_4^+, Cl^-, Na^+, OH^-, H_2O. The reaction will be:

	OH^-	+	NH_4^+	→	NH_3
Before the reaction	0.10 mole		0.500 mole		0
After the reaction	0		0.40 mole		0.10 mole

After the reaction, the solution contains the major species: NH_4^+, Cl^-, NH_3, Na^+, H_2O. The equilibrium to use is:

$$NH_3 + H_2O \rightleftarrows NH_4^+ + OH^-$$

$$K_b = 1.8 \times 10^{-5} = \frac{[NH_4^+][OH^-]}{[NH_3]}$$

Initial Concentrations
(before dissociation of NH_4^+)

$$[NH_4^+]_0 = 0.4 \, M$$
$$[NH_3]_0 = 0.10 \, M$$
$$[OH^-]_0 \approx 0$$

Let x moles/ℓ
———NH_3———→
react with H_2O

Equilibrium Concentrations

$$[NH_4^+] = 0.40 + x$$
$$[NH_3] = 0.10 - x$$
$$[OH^-] = x$$

$$1.8 \times 10^{-5} = K_b = \frac{[NH_4^+][OH^-]}{[NH_3]}$$
$$= \frac{(0.40 + x)(x)}{(0.10 - x)} \approx \frac{(0.40)(x)}{0.10}$$
$$x \approx 4.5 \times 10^{-6}$$

The approximations are valid.

$$[OH^-] = x = 4.5 \times 10^{-6}$$
$$[H^+] = \frac{K_w}{[OH^-]} = \frac{1.0 \times 10^{-14}}{4.5 \times 10^{-6}} = 2.2 \times 10^{-9}$$
$$\text{pH} = 8.65$$

Test 2–11

A. 1. In solution: $C_6H_5NH_3^+$, Cl^-, H_2O

2. $K_a \cdot K_b = K_w$

$$K_a = \frac{K_w}{K_b} = \frac{1.0 \times 10^{-14}}{3.8 \times 10^{-10}} = 2.6 \times 10^{-5}$$

3. $C_6H_5NH_3^+ \rightleftarrows C_6H_5NH_2 + H^+$

4. $K_a = \dfrac{[C_6H_5NH_2][H^+]}{[C_6H_5NH_3^+]} = 2.6 \times 10^{-5}$

5. $[C_6H_5NH_3^+]_0 = 0.10\ M$
$[C_6H_5NH_2]_0 = 0$
$[H^+]_0 \approx 0$

6. x = moles/ℓ of $C_6H_5NH_3^+$ that dissociate to reach equilibrium.

7. $[C_6H_5NH_3^+] = 0.10 - x$
$[C_6H_5NH_2] = x$
$[H^+] = x$

8. $2.6 \times 10^{-5} = K_a = \dfrac{[C_6H_5NH_2][H^+]}{[C_6H_5NH_3^+]} = \dfrac{(x)(x)}{(0.10 - x)} \approx \dfrac{x^2}{0.10}$

$$x^2 \approx (2.6 \times 10^{-5})(0.1) = 2.6 \times 10^{-6}$$
$$x = 1.6 \times 10^{-3}\ M = [H^+]$$

Assumption is valid.

9. $pH = 2.79$

B. In solution: $Cr(OH_2)_6^{3+}$, Cl^-, H_2O. $Cr(OH_2)_6^{3+}$ is the strongest acid in solution:

$$Cr(OH_2)_6^{3+} \rightleftarrows Cr(OH)(OH_2)_5^{2+} + H^+$$

$$K_a = \frac{[Cr(OH)(OH_2)_5^{2+}][H^+]}{[Cr(OH_2)_6^{3+}]} = 1.5 \times 10^{-4}$$

Initial Concentrations
$[Cr(OH_2)_6^{3+}]_0 = 0.20\ M$
$[Cr(OH)(OH_2)_5^{2+}]_0 = 0$
$[H^+]_0 \approx 0$

Let x moles/ℓ
$Cr(OH_2)_6^{3+}$
dissociate $\longrightarrow$

Equilibrium Concentrations
$[Cr(OH_2)_6^{3+}]_0 = 0.20 - x$
$[Cr(OH)(OH_2)_5^{2+}] = x$
$[H^+] = x$

$$1.5 \times 10^{-4} = K_a = \frac{(x)(x)}{0.20 - x} \approx \frac{x^2}{0.20}$$
$$x^2 = (0.20)(1.5 \times 10^{-4}) = 3.0 \times 10^{-5}$$
$$x \approx 5.5 \times 10^{-3} = [H^+]$$
$$pH = 2.26$$

Test 2–12

A. 1. Na^+, Cl^-, H_2O; Neutral; Neither Na^+ nor Cl^- is a significant acid or base.

2. NH_4^+, NO_3^-, H_2O. NO_3^- is a *very* weak base (HNO_3 is a strong acid). NH_4^+ is a weak acid:

$$NH_4^+ \rightleftarrows NH_3 + H^+$$

The solution will be acidic.

3. $Al_{(aq)}^{3+}$, NO_3^-, H_2O. $Al_{(aq)}^{3+}$ is $Al(OH_2)_6^{3+}$, which is a weak acid:

$$Al(OH_2)_6^{3+} \rightleftarrows Al(OH)(OH_2)_5^{2+} + H^+$$

The solution will be acidic.

4. Na^+, CN^-, H_2O. CN^- is a base (HCN is a very weak acid, $K_a = 6.2 \times 10^{-10}$):

$$CN^- + H_2O \rightleftarrows HCN + OH^-$$

The solution will be basic.

5. $(CH_3)_3 NH^+$, Cl^-, H_2O. $(CH_3)_3NH^+$ is a weak acid
$$\left(K_a = \frac{K_w}{K_b} = \frac{1.0 \times 10^{-14}}{5.3 \times 10^{-5}} = 1.9 \times 10^{-10} \right):$$
$$(CH_3)_3NH^+ \rightleftarrows (CH_3)_3N + H^+$$

The solution will be acidic.

B. The statement that OAc^- is a "good base" is based on the reaction:

$$HOAc \rightleftarrows H^+ + OAc^-$$

where the equilibrium lies to the left ($K_a = 1.8 \times 10^{-5}$). This reaction is really:

$$HOAc + H_2O \rightleftarrows H_3O^+ + OAc^-$$

where OAc^- and H_2O are competing for H^+, and OAc^- wins. In the reaction

$$OAc^- + H_2O \rightleftarrows HOAc + OH^-$$

OAc^- is competing with OH^-, which is a *very* strong base. OAc^- is a strong base compared to H_2O, but a weak base compared to OH^-. Thus, the order of base strength is:

$$OH^- > OAc^- > H_2O$$

Chapter 3

Test 3–1

A. $[OH^-] = 0.50\ M$
$[H^+] = 2.0 \times 10^{-14}$ (using K_w)
$pH = 13.70$

B. In solution before the reaction H^+, Cl^-, Na^+, OH^-, H_2O. The reaction is:

$$H^+ \qquad + \qquad OH^- \qquad \rightarrow \qquad H_2O$$

Before the reaction	$25.0 \text{ m}\ell \times 1.0 \text{ } M$ $= 25 \text{ mmole}$	$100.0 \text{ m}\ell \times 0.50 \text{ } M$ $= 50 \text{ mmole}$	—
After the reaction	0	$50 - 25 = 25$	—

In solution after the reaction: Na^+, Cl^-, OH^-, H_2O.

$$[OH^-] = \frac{\text{moles } OH^-}{\text{m}\ell \text{ of solution}} = \frac{25}{100.0 + 25.0} = 2.0 \times 10^{-1}$$

$$[H^+] = \frac{K_w}{[OH^-]} = \frac{1.00 \times 10^{-14}}{2.0 \times 10^{-1}} = 5.0 \times 10^{-14}$$

$$pH = 13.30$$

C. This is the equivalence point. $50.0 \text{ m}\ell \times 1.0 \text{ } M \text{ HCl} = 50$ mmoles of HCl have been added, which exactly react with the 50 mmoles of NaOH originally present. After this reaction, the solution contains: Na^+, Cl^-, H_2O. Since neither Na^+ nor Cl^- will affect the pH, then pH $= 7.00$.

D. Excess HCl has now been added. $75.0 \text{ m}\ell \times 1.0 \text{ } M \text{ HCl} = 75$ mmoles HCl added:

75 mmole	−	50 mmole	=	25 mmole HCl
↑		↑		↑
total added		consumed by NaOH		excess

The solution contains: H^+, Cl^-, Na^+, H_2O.

$$[H^+] = \frac{\text{mmoles HCl in excess}}{\text{m}\ell \text{ of solution}} = \frac{25}{175.0} = 1.4 \times 10^{-1} \text{ } M$$
$$pH = 0.85$$

Test 3–2

1. $HOAc$, Na^+, OH^-, H_2O
2. $OH^- + HOAc \rightarrow H_2O + OAc^-$
3.

$$OH^- \qquad + \qquad HOAc \qquad \rightarrow \qquad OAc^- \qquad + H_2O$$

Before reaction	$25.0 \text{ m}\ell \times 0.10 \text{ } M$ $= 2.5 \text{ mmoles}$	$5.0 \text{ m}\ell \times 0.10 \text{ } M$ $= 5.0 \text{ mmoles}$	0	—
After reaction	$2.5 - 2.5 = 0$	$5.0 - 2.5$ $= 2.5 \text{ mmoles}$	2.5 mmoles	—

After the reaction goes to completion, the solution contains 2.5 mmoles HOAc and 2.5 mmoles OAc^-.

4. After the reaction, the major species in solution are: $HOAc$, OAc^-, Na^+, H_2O. The equilibrium that will control the pH is:

$$HOAc \rightleftharpoons H^+ + OAc^-$$

$$K_a = \frac{[H^+][OAc^-]}{[HOAc]} = 1.8 \times 10^{-5}$$

Initial Concentrations   *Equilibrium Concentrations*
(before any dissociation of HOAc)

$$[HOAc]_0 = \frac{2.5 \text{ mmoles}}{(50.0 + 25.0)m\ell}$$ $$[HOAc] = \frac{2.5}{75} - x$$

$$[OAc^-]_0 = \frac{2.5 \text{ mmoles}}{(50.0 + 25.0)m\ell}$$ $$[OAc^-] = \frac{2.5}{75} + x$$

$$[H^+]_0 \approx 0$$ $$[H^+] = x$$

$$1.8 \times 10^{-5} = K_a = \frac{[H^+][OAc^-]}{[HOAc]} = \frac{(x)\left(\dfrac{2.5}{75} + x\right)}{\left(\dfrac{2.5}{75} - x\right)} \approx \frac{x\left(\dfrac{2.5}{75}\right)}{\left(\dfrac{2.5}{75}\right)}$$

$$x = 1.8 \times 10^{-5} = [H^+]$$
$$pH = -\log[H^+] = -\log(1.8 \times 10^{-5}) = 4.74$$

Test 3–3

A. 1. 25.0 mℓ × 0.30 M HNO$_2$ = 7.5 mmole HNO$_2$. The titration reaction is:

$$OH^- + HNO_2 \rightarrow H_2O + NO_2^-$$

Thus, 7.5 mmole of OH$^-$ will be required:

$$(x \text{ m}\ell)(0.50 \, M \text{ NaOH}) = 7.5 \text{ mmoles OH}^-$$

$$x = \frac{7.5}{0.50} = 15 \text{ m}\ell$$

2. (a)   Before any reaction, the solution contains: HNO$_2$, Na$^+$, OH$^-$, H$_2$O. The reaction will be:

	HNO$_2$	+	OH$^-$	→	NO$_2^-$	+	H$_2$O
Before the reaction	25.0 mℓ×0.30 M = 7.5 mmole		5.0 mℓ×0.50 M = 2.5 mmole		0		—
After the reaction	7.5 − 2.5 = 5.0 mmole		0		2.5 mmole		—

After the reaction, the solution contains: HNO$_2$, NO$_2^-$, Na$^-$, H$_2$O. The equilibrium that will control the [H$^+$] is:

$$HNO_2 \rightleftarrows H^+ + NO_2^-$$

$$K_a = \frac{[H^+][NO_2^-]}{[HNO_2]} = 4.0 \times 10^{-4}$$

Initial Concentrations   *Equilibrium Concentrations*

$$[HNO_2]_0 = \frac{5.0 \text{ mmole}}{(25.0 + 5.0)m\ell}$$ $$[HNO_2] = 1.7 \times 10^{-1} - x$$
$$= 1.7 \times 10^{-1} \, M$$

$$[NO_2^-]_0 = \frac{2.5 \text{ mmole}}{(25.0 + 5.0)m\ell}$$ $$[NO_2^-] = 8.3 \times 10^{-2} + x$$
$$= 8.3 \times 10^{-2} \, M$$

$$[H^+]_0 \approx 0 \qquad\qquad\qquad\qquad [H^+] = x$$

$$4.0 \times 10^{-4} = K_a = \frac{[H^+][NO_2^-]}{[HNO_2]} = \frac{(x)(8.3 \times 10^{-2} + x)}{(1.7 \times 10^{-1} - x)} \approx \frac{(x)(8.3 \times 10^{-2})}{(1.7 \times 10^{-1})}$$

$$x \approx \frac{4.0 \times 10^{-4}(1.7 \times 10^{-1})}{8.3 \times 10^{-2}} = 8.2 \times 10^{-4}$$

Assumptions are valid.
$[H^+] = 8.2 \times 10^{-4}$; pH $= 3.09$

2. (b) At this point, 7.5 mℓ $\times$ 0.50 M NaOH $= 3.75$ mmoles of NaOH have been added. This will react with half of the 7.5 mmole of HNO_2 originally present. Thus, this point is halfway to the equivalence point, so

$$[HNO_2] \approx [NO_2^-]$$

and

$$K_a = \frac{[H^+][NO_2^-]}{[HNO_2]} = [H^+]$$
$$[H^+] = 4.0 \times 10^{-4}; \text{pH} = 3.40$$

2. (c) This is the equivalence point: the 7.5 mmoles HNO_2 have been changed to 7.5 mmoles of NO_2^-. After the titration reaction, the solution contains: NO_2^-, Na^+, H_2O. Note that NO_2^- is a base (HNO_2 is a weak acid):

$$NO_2^- + H_2O \rightleftarrows HNO_2 + OH^-$$

$$K_b = \frac{[HNO_2][OH^-]}{[NO_2^-]} = \frac{K_w}{K_a} = \frac{1.00 \times 10^{-14}}{4.0 \times 10^{-4}} = 2.5 \times 10^{-11}$$

Initial Concentrations $\qquad\qquad\qquad\qquad$ *Equilibrium Concentrations*

$$[NO_2^-]_0 = \frac{7.5 \text{ mmole}}{(25.0 + 15.0)m\ell} \qquad\qquad [NO_2^-] = 0.19 - x$$

$$= 1.9 \times 10^{-1} M \qquad \begin{array}{c}\text{Let } x \text{ moles/}\ell \\ \underline{\quad NO_2^- \longrightarrow} \\ \text{react}\end{array}$$

$$[HNO_2]_0 = 0 \qquad\qquad\qquad\qquad [HNO_2] = x$$
$$[OH^-]_0 \approx 0 \qquad\qquad\qquad\qquad [OH^-] = x$$

$$2.5 \times 10^{-11} = K_b = \frac{(x)(x)}{0.19 - x} \approx \frac{x^2}{0.19}$$
$$x^2 \approx 4.7 \times 10^{-12}$$
$$x \approx 2.2 \times 10^{-6}$$

The assumption is valid.
$[OH] = x = 2.2 \times 10^{-6}$

$$[H^+] = \frac{K_w}{[OH^-]} = \frac{1.0 \times 10^{-14}}{2.2 \times 10^{-6}} = 4.6 \times 10^{-9}$$

pH $= 8.34$

2. (d) This is 5.0 mℓ beyond the equivalence point. The solution contains: OH^-, Na^+, NO_2^-, H_2O. The excess OH^- will determine the pH.

$$[OH^-] = \frac{10.0 \text{ mmole added} - 7.5 \text{ mmole consumed}}{(25.0 + 20.0)\text{m}\ell}$$

$$= \frac{2.5}{45} = 5.6 \times 10^{-2}$$

$$[H^+] = \frac{K_w}{[OH^-]} = \frac{1.0 \times 10^{-14}}{5.6 \times 10^{-2}} = 1.8 \times 10^{-13} \ M$$

$$pH = 12.74$$

B. 1. $40.0 \text{ m}\ell \times 0.0500 \ M \text{ NaOH} = 2.00 \text{ mmoles NaOH}$. The titration reaction is:

$$OH^- + HA \rightarrow A^- + H_2O$$

Since NaOH reacts with HA in a 1:1 ratio, the original solution must have contained 2.00 mmoles of HA.
$0.200 \text{ g HA} = 2.00 \text{ mmoles HA} = 2.00 \times 10^{-3} \text{ mole HA}$

$$\frac{0.20 \text{ g HA}}{2.00 \times 10^{-3} \text{ mole HA}} = 1.00 \times 10^2 \text{ g/mole}$$

The molecular weight of HA is 100 g/mole.

2. The titration reaction is:

	HA	+	OH^-	$\rightarrow$ H_2O	+	A^-
Before the reaction	2.00 mmole (see Part 1)		20.0 mℓ × 0.0500 M = 1.00 mmole			0
After the reaction	2.00 − 1.00 = 1.00 mmole		1.00 − 1.00 = 0			1.00 mmole

After the reaction, the solution contains: HA, A^-, Na^+, H_2O. The pH will be determined by the reaction:

$$HA \rightleftharpoons H^+ + A^-$$

$$K_a = \frac{[H^+][A^-]}{[HA]}$$

Initial Concentrations

$$[HA]_0 = \frac{1.00 \text{ mmole}}{(100.0 + 20.0)\text{m}\ell}$$
$$= 8.33 \times 10^{-3} \ M$$

$$[A^-]_0 = \frac{1.00 \text{ mmole}}{(100.0 + 20.0)\text{m}\ell}$$
$$= 8.33 \times 10^{-3} \ M$$

$$[H^+]_0 \approx 0$$

Let x moles/ℓ
$\xrightarrow{\text{HA}}$
dissociate

Equilibrium Concentrations

$$[HA] = 8.33 \times 10^{-3} - x$$

$$[A^-] = 8.33 \times 10^{-3} + x$$

$$[H^+] = x$$

In this case, the pH = 6.0. Thus, $[H^+] = 10^{-pH} = 1.0 \times 10^{-6} = x$.

$$K_a = \frac{[H^+][A^-]}{[HA]} = \frac{(1.0 \times 10^{-6})(8.33 \times 10^{-3} + 1.0 \times 10^{-6})}{(8.33 \times 10^{-3} - 1.0 \times 10^{-6})}$$

$$\approx \frac{(1.0 \times 10^{-6})(8.33 \times 10^{-3})}{(8.33 \times 10^{-3})}$$

$$K_a = 1.0 \times 10^{-6}$$

Note that there is an easier way to think about this problem. Since the original solution contained 2.00 mmole of HA, and 20.0 mℓ of added 0.0500 M NaOH contains 1.00 mmole of OH$^-$, this is the halfway point in the titration where $[HA] \approx [A^-]$. (This is demonstrated above.) Thus,

$$[H^+] = K_a = 1.0 \times 10^{-6}$$

3. At the equivalence point (40.0 mℓ of added 0.0500 M NaOH), the solution contains: A$^-$, Na$^+$, H$_2$O. A$^-$ is a base (HA is a weak acid), and will react with H$_2$O:

$$A^- + H_2O \rightleftharpoons HA + OH^-$$

$$K_b = \frac{[HA][OH^-]}{[A^-]} = \frac{K_w}{K_a} = \frac{1.0 \times 10^{-14}}{1.0 \times 10^{-6}} = 1.0 \times 10^{-8}$$

Initial Concentrations

$$[A^-]_0 = \frac{2.0 \text{ mmole}}{(100.0 + 40.0)\text{m}\ell}$$
$$= 1.4 \times 10^{-2} \ M$$
$$[HA]_0 = 0$$
$$[OH^-]_0 \approx 0$$

Let x moles/ℓ ———of A$^-$——→ react

Equilibrium Concentrations

$$[A^-] = 1.4 \times 10^{-2} - x$$

$$[HA] = x$$
$$[OH^-] = x$$

$$1.0 \times 10^{-8} = K_b = \frac{[OH^-][HA]}{[A^-]} = \frac{(x)(x)}{(1.4 \times 10^{-2} - x)} \approx \frac{x^2}{1.4 \times 10^{-2}}$$
$$x^2 \approx 1.4 \times 10^{-10}$$
$$x \approx 1.2 \times 10^{-5}$$

Assumption is valid.
$$[OH^-] = 1.2 \times 10^{-5}$$

$$[H^+] = \frac{K_w}{[OH^-]} = \frac{1.0 \times 10^{-14}}{1.2 \times 10^{-5}} = 8.3 \times 10^{-10}; \ pH = 9.08$$

Test 3–4

A. The major species in solution are NH$_3$ and H$_2$O. The dominant equilibrium is:

$$NH_3 + H_2O \rightleftharpoons NH_4^+ + OH^-$$

$$K_b = \frac{[NH_4^+][OH^-]}{[NH_3]} = 1.8 \times 10^{-5}$$

Initial Concentrations
(before any NH_3 reacts with H_2O)

$[NH_3]_0 = 0.05\ M$

$[NH_4^+]_0 = 0$

$[OH^-]_0 \approx 0$

Let x mole/ℓ
$\xrightarrow{NH_3}$
react

Equilibrium Concentrations

$[NH_3] = 0.050 - x$

$[NH_4^+] = x$

$[OH^-] = x$

$$1.8 \times 10^{-5} = K_b = \frac{[NH_4^+][OH^-]}{[NH_3]} = \frac{(x)(x)}{(0.050 - x)} \approx \frac{x^2}{0.050}$$

$$x^2 \approx (5.0 \times 10^{-2})(1.8 \times 10^{-5}) = 9.0 \times 10^{-7}$$

$$x \approx 9.5 \times 10^{-4}$$

$$[OH^-] = x = 9.5 \times 10^{-4}\ M$$

$$[H^+][OH^-] = 1.00 \times 10^{-14} = [H^+](9.5 \times 10^{-4})$$

$$[H^+] = \frac{1.00 \times 10^{-14}}{9.5 \times 10^{-4}} = 1.1 \times 10^{-11}\ M$$

$$pH = 10.98$$

B. 1.   The Stoichiometry Problem:

	NH_3	$+$	H^+	$\rightarrow$	NH_4^+
Before the reaction	$100.0\ m\ell \times 0.050\ M$ $= 5.0$ mmole		$10.0\ m\ell \times 0.10\ M$ $= 1.0$ mmole		0
After the reaction	$5.0 - 1.0$ $= 4.0$ mmoles		0		1.0 mmole

2.   The Equilibrium Problem: After the reaction, the solution contains: NH_3, NH_4^+, Cl^-, H_2O. We must use an equilibrium that involves both NH_3 and NH_4^+. There are two choices:

$$NH_4^+ \rightleftharpoons NH_3 + H^+ \qquad K_a$$

$$NH_3 + H_2O \rightleftharpoons NH_4^+ + OH^- \qquad K_b$$

Either will give the correct answer. Let's use the dissociation equilibrium of NH_4^+, since it contains H^+, which will allow us to calculate the $[H^+]$ directly:

$$K_a = \frac{K_w}{K_b} = \frac{1.00 \times 10^{-14}}{1.8 \times 10^{-5}} = \frac{[NH_3][H^+]}{[NH_4^+]} = 5.6 \times 10^{-10}$$

Initial Concentrations
(before NH_4^+ dissociates)

$[NH_4^+]_0 = \dfrac{1.0\ \text{mmole}}{(100.0 + 10.0)m\ell}$

$[NH_3]_0 = \dfrac{4.0\ \text{mmole}}{(100.0 + 10.0)m\ell}$

$[H^+]_0 \approx 0$

Let x mole/ℓ
$\xrightarrow{NH_4^+}$
dissociate

Equilibrium Concentrations

$[NH_4^+] = \dfrac{1}{110} - x$

$[NH_3] = \dfrac{4}{110} + x$

$[H^+] = x$

$$5.6 \times 10^{-10} = K_a = \frac{[H^+][NH_3]}{[NH_4^+]} = \frac{(x)\left(\dfrac{4}{110} + x\right)}{\left(\dfrac{1}{110} - x\right)} \approx \frac{(x)\left(\dfrac{4}{110}\right)}{\left(\dfrac{1}{110}\right)} = \frac{(x)(4)}{1}$$

$$x \approx \left(\frac{5.6 \times 10^{-10}}{4}\right) = 1.4 \times 10^{-10}\ M = [H^+]$$

$$pH = 9.85$$

C. 25.0 mℓ of 0.10 M HCl has been added. 25.0 mℓ $\times$ 0.10 M = 2.5 mmoles H^+ have been added. Originally, there were 100.0 mℓ $\times$ 0.050 M = 5.0 mmoles NH_3. Thus, 25.0 mℓ of added 0.10 M HCl represents the halfway point in this titration (half of the NH_3 has been converted to NH_4^+). At this point, $[NH_3] \approx [NH_4^+]$.

$$K_a = \frac{[H^+][NH_3]}{[NH_4^+]} = 5.6 \times 10^{-10}$$

$$[H^+] = 5.6 \times 10^{-10}\ M$$
$$pH = 9.25$$

D. 50.0 mℓ of added 0.10 M HCl corresponds to the equivalence point of this titration: 5.0 mmole H^+ reacts with 5.0 mmole NH_3 to produce 5.0 mmole NH_4^+. After the titration reaction, the solution contains the major species: NH_4^+, Cl^-, H_2O. The equilibrium which will dominate is:

$$NH_4^+ \rightleftarrows NH_3 + H^+$$

$$K_a = 5.6 \times 10^{-10} = \frac{[NH_3][H^+]}{[NH_4^+]}$$

Initial Concentrations   *Equilibrium Concentrations*
(before any NH_4^+ dissociates)

$[NH_4^+]_0 = \dfrac{5.0\ \text{mmole}}{(100.0 + 50.0)\text{mℓ}}$ Let x moles/ℓ $[NH_4^+] = \dfrac{5}{150} - x$
                                                        $\xrightarrow{\quad NH_4^+ \quad}$
$[NH_3]_0 = 0$ dissociate $[NH_3] = x$
$[H^+]_0 \approx 0$ $[H^+] = x$

$$5.6 \times 10^{-10} = \frac{[NH_3][H^+]}{[NH_4^+]} = \frac{(x)(x)}{\left(\dfrac{5}{150} - x\right)} \approx \frac{x^2}{\dfrac{5}{150}} = \frac{x^2}{3.3 \times 10^{-2}}$$

$$x^2 \approx 1.87 \times 10^{-11}$$
$$x \approx 4.3 \times 10^{-6} = [H^+]$$
$$pH = -\log(4.3 \times 10^{-6}) = 5.36$$

E. 60.0 mℓ of added 0.10 M HCl represents 10.0 mℓ beyond the equivalence point. Thus, the solution contains excess H^+.
60.0 mℓ $\times$ 0.10 M = 6.0 mmoles H^+ added
100.0 mℓ $\times$ 0.050 M = 5.0 mmoles NH_3 originally present
6.0 − 5.0 = 1.0 mmoles H^+ in excess

$$[H^+] = \frac{1.0 \text{ mmole}}{160 \text{ m}\ell} = 6.3 \times 10^{-3} \, M$$

$$pH = 2.20$$

Test 3–5

1. Yellow (The solution is very acidic, so the indicator is present as HIn.)
2. The normal assumption is that the color change will be visible when

$$\frac{[In^-]}{[HIn]} \approx \frac{1}{10}$$

$$K_a = 1.0 \times 10^{-8} = \frac{[H^+][In^-]}{[HIn]} = [H^+]\frac{1}{10}$$

$$[H^+] = (10)(1.0 \times 10^{-8}) = 1.0 \times 10^{-7} \, M$$

This is the $[H^+]$ when the color change should first be visible. $pH = 7.0$ at color change.

3. 300.0 mℓ of NaOH represents an excess. The solution will be blue. In a basic solution, the indicator will be predominantly in the In$^-$ form.

Test 3–6

The normal assumption is that the color change will be visible when $[In^-]/[HIn] = 1/10$. For a color change at pH 5 ($[H^+] = 1.0 \times 10^{-5}$):

$$K_a = [H^+]\frac{[In^-]}{[HIn]} = (1.0 \times 10^{-5})\left(\frac{1}{10}\right) = 1.0 \times 10^{-6}$$

For a color change at pH 9 ($[H^+] = 1.0 \times 10^{-9}$):

$$K_a = [H^+]\frac{[In^-]}{[HIn]} = (1.0 \times 10^{-9})\left(\frac{1}{10}\right) = 1.0 \times 10^{-10}$$

Thus, any indicator with a K_a value in the range from 10^{-6} to 10^{-10} will serve nicely to mark the endpoint of a typical titration of a strong acid with a strong base.

Test 3–7

The titration reaction is:

$$HCN + OH^- \rightarrow CN^- + H_2O$$

The solution originally contains $(100.0 \text{ m}\ell)(0.100 \, M) = 10.0$ mmoles of HCN. This will be changed to 10.0 mmoles of CN$^-$ at the equivalence point. (100.0 mℓ of 0.100 M NaOH is required to reach the equilvalence point.) At the equivalence point, the solution contains the major species: Na$^+$, CN$^-$, H$_2$O. The equilibrium that will dominate is:

$$CN^- + H_2O \rightleftarrows HCN + OH^-$$

$$K_b = \frac{[HCN][OH^-]}{[CN^-]} = \frac{K_w}{K_a} = \frac{1.0 \times 10^{-14}}{6.2 \times 10^{-10}} = 1.6 \times 10^{-5}$$

Initial Concentrations   *Equilibrium Concentrations*

$$[CN^-]_0 = \frac{10.0 \text{ mmole}}{(100.0 + 100.0)\text{m}\ell}$$

Let x moles/ℓ
——CN^- react——→
with H_2O

$$[CN^-] = 5.00 \times 10^{-2} - x$$

$$= 5.00 \times 10^{-2} M$$

$$[HCN]_0 = 0$$
$$[OH^-]_0 \approx 0$$

$$[HCN] = x$$
$$[OH^-] = x$$

$$1.6 \times 10^{-5} = K_b = \frac{[HCN][OH^-]}{[CN^-]} = \frac{(x)(x)}{(5.00 \times 10^{-2} - x)} \approx \frac{x^2}{5.00 \times 10^{-2}}$$

$$x^2 \approx 8.1 \times 10^{-7}$$
$$x \approx 9.0 \times 10^{-4}$$

Simplification is valid, so:
$$[OH^-] = x = 9.0 \times 10^{-4}$$
$$[H^+][OH^-] = 1.00 \times 10^{-14} = [H^+](9.0 \times 10^{-4})$$

$$[H^+] = \frac{1.00 \times 10^{-14}}{9.0 \times 10^{-4}} = 1.11 \times 10^{-11} M$$

pH = 10.95

The pH at the equivalence point is 10.95. The indicator equilibrium is:

$$HIn \rightleftarrows H^+ + In^-$$

$$K_a = [H^+]\left\{\frac{[In^-]}{[HIn]}\right\} = (1.1 \times 10^{-11})\left(\frac{1}{10}\right) = 1.1 \times 10^{-12}$$

The indicator should have a K_a value near 10^{-12}.

Test 3–8

The indicator is of the form HIn:

$$HIn \rightleftarrows H^+ + In^-$$

Ammonia is a base, so the ammonia solution will be basic, which will cause the indicator to be predominately in the In^- form. The color change will be apparent when enough acid has been added so that $[In^-]/[HIn] \approx 10/1$. The pH at the equivalence point is 5, so $[H^+] = 10^{-5}$.

$$K_a = \frac{[H^+][In^-]}{[HIn]} = [H^+]\left\{\frac{[In^-]}{[HIn]}\right\} = (10^{-5})\left(\frac{10}{1}\right) = 10^{-4}$$

K_a for an appropriate indicator should be approximately 10^{-4}.

Chapter 4

Test 4–1

A. $AgI(s) \rightleftarrows Ag^+ + I^-$

B. $K_{sp} = [Ag^+][I^-]$

C. $[Ag^+]_0 = 0$
$[I^-]_0 = 0$

D. x = moles/ℓ of AgI(s) which dissolve to come to equilibrium.

E. $[Ag^+] = x$
$[I^-] = x$

F. In this case, x = solubility = 1.2×10^{-8} moles/ℓ.

G. $K_{sp} = [Ag^+][I^-] = (x)(x) = (1.2 \times 10^{-8})(1.2 \times 10^{-8}) = 1.4 \times 10^{-16}$

Test 4–2

The solubility equilibrium for $Bi_2S_3(s)$ is:

$$Bi_2S_3(s) \rightleftarrows 2Bi^{3+} + 3S^{2-}$$

and

$$K_{sp} = [Bi^{3+}]^2[S^{2-}]^3$$

Initial Concentrations   *Equilibrium Concentrations*

$[Bi^{3+}]_0 = 0$ $\xrightarrow[\text{dissolve}]{\text{Let } x \text{ moles/}\ell \ Bi_2S_3}$ $[Bi^{3+}] = 2x$
$[S^{2-}]_0 = 0$ $[S^{2-}] = 3x$

Note: x $Bi_2S_3 \rightarrow 2x$ $Bi^{3+} + 3x$ S^{2-}.
Solubility = $x = 1.0 \times 10^{-15}$ moles/ℓ
$[Bi^{3+}] = 2x = 2(1.0 \times 10^{-15}) = 2.0 \times 10^{-15}$ moles/ℓ
$[S^{2-}] = 3x = 3(1.0 \times 10^{-15}) = 3.0 \times 10^{-15}$ moles/ℓ
$K_{sp} = [Bi^{3+}]^2[S^{2-}]^3 = (2.0 \times 10^{-15})^2(3.0 \times 10^{-15})^3$
$\quad\quad = (4.0 \times 10^{-30})(27 \times 10^{-45}) = 1.1 \times 10^{-73}$

Test 4–3

The equilibrium that occurs when $Ag_2CrO_4(s)$ dissolves is:

$$Ag_2CrO_4(s) \rightleftarrows 2Ag^+(aq) + CrO_4^{2-}(aq)$$
$$K_{sp} = [Ag^+]^2[CrO_4^{2-}] = 9.0 \times 10^{-12}$$

Initial Concentrations   *Equilibrium Concentrations*

$[Ag^+]_0 = 0$ $\xrightarrow[\text{dissolve}]{\text{Let } x \text{ moles/}\ell \ Ag_2CrO_4(s)}$ $[Ag^+] = 2x$
$[CrO_4^{2-}]_0 = 0$ $[CrO_4^{2-}] = x$

$$(x \ Ag_2CrO_4(s) \rightarrow 2x \ Ag^+ + x \ CrO_4^{2-})$$

$$9.0 \times 10^{-12} = K_{sp} = [Ag^+]^2[CrO_4^{2-}] = (2x)^2(x) = 4x^3$$

$$x^3 = \frac{9.0 \times 10^{-12}}{4} = 2.25 \times 10^{-12}$$

$$x = \sqrt[3]{2.25 \times 10^{-12}} = 1.3 \times 10^{-4}$$

Solubility $= x = 1.3 \times 10^{-4}$ mole/ℓ

Test 4–4

Solubility of CuS
$CuS(s) \rightleftarrows Cu^{2+} + S^{2-}$
$K_{sp} = [Cu^{2+}][S^{2-}] = 8.5 \times 10^{-45}$
Let x = solubility. At equilibrium: $[Cu^{2+}] = x$ and $[S^{2-}] = x$ so

$$8.5 \times 10^{-45} = [Cu^{2+}][S^{2-}] = (x)(x)$$
$$x^2 = 8.5 \times 10^{-45}$$
$$x = 9.2 \times 10^{-23} \text{ moles}/\ell = \text{solubility}$$

Solubility of Ag$_2$S
$Ag_2S(s) \rightleftarrows 2Ag^+ + S^{2-}$
$K_{sp} = [Ag^+]^2[S^{2-}] = 1.6 \times 10^{-49}$
Let the solubility $= x$.
$x \ Ag_2S(s) \rightarrow 2x \ Ag^+ + x \ S^{2-}$
At equilibrium: $[Ag^+] = 2x$ and $[S^{2-}] = x$ so
$$1.6 \times 10^{-49} = [Ag^+]^2[S^{2-}] = (2x)^2(x)$$
$$4x^3 = 1.6 \times 10^{-49}$$
$$x^3 = \frac{1.6 \times 10^{-49}}{4} = 4.0 \times 10^{-50}$$
$$x = 3.4 \times 10^{-17} \text{ moles}/\ell = \text{solubility}$$

Solubility of Bi$_2$S$_3$(s)
$Bi_2S_3(s) \rightleftarrows 2Bi^{3+} + 3S^{2-}$
$K_{sp} = [Bi^{3+}]^2[S^{2-}]^3 = 1.1 \times 10^{-73}$
Let x = solubility.
$x \ Bi_2S_3(s) \rightarrow 2x \ Bi^{3+} + 3x \ S^{2-}$
At equilibrium: $[Bi^{3+}] = 2x$ and $[S^{2-}] = 3x$ so

$$1.1 \times 10^{-73} = [Bi^{3+}]^2[S^{2-}]^3 = (2x)^2(3x)^3 = 108 \ x^5$$

$$x^5 = \frac{1.1 \times 10^{-73}}{1.1 \times 10^{-2}} = 1.0 \times 10^{-75}$$

$$x = 1.0 \times 10^{-15} \text{ moles}/\ell = \text{solubility}$$

The solubilities of the three salts are:

Salt	K_{sp}	Solubility (moles/ℓ)
CuS	8.3×10^{-45}	9.2×10^{-23}
Ag$_2$S	1.6×10^{-49}	3.4×10^{-17}
Bi$_2$S$_3$	1.1×10^{-73}	1.0×10^{-15}

The order of solubilities is:

$$Bi_2S_3(s) \; > \; Ag_2S(s) \; > \; CuS(s)$$
$$\text{most soluble} \qquad\qquad \text{least soluble}$$

This is the reverse of the order of the K_{sp} values. This is an important result. The K_{sp} values for salts that produce different numbers of ions (and, thus, which have different powers in the equilibrium constant expression) cannot be used directly to predict relative solubilities.

Test 4–5

Solubility of $Ag_3PO_4(s)$ in Water
The equilibrium is:

$$Ag_3PO_4(s) \rightleftarrows 3Ag^+ + PO_4^{3-}$$

and the equilibrium expression is:

$$K_{sp} = [Ag^+]^3[PO_4^{3-}] = 1.8 \times 10^{-18}$$

Initial Concentrations		*Equilibrium Concentrations*
$[Ag^+]_0 = 0$	Let x moles/ℓ ——$Ag_3PO_4(s)$—→ dissolve	$[Ag^+] = 3x$
$[PO_4^{3-}]_0 = 0$		$[PO_4^{3-}] = x$

$$1.8 \times 10^{-18} = K_{sp} = [Ag^+]^3[PO_4^{3-}] = (3x)^3(x)$$

$$27x^4 = 1.8 \times 10^{-18}$$

$$x^4 = \frac{1.8 \times 10^{-18}}{27} = 6.7 \times 10^{-20}$$

$$x = 1.6 \times 10^{-5} = \text{solubility}$$

Solubility of $Ag_3PO_4(s)$ in 1.0 M Na_3PO_4
The equilibrium is:

$$Ag_3PO_4(s) \rightleftarrows 3Ag^+ + PO_4^{3-}$$

and the equilibrium expression is:

$$K_{sp} = [Ag^+]^3[PO_4^{3-}] = 1.8 \times 10^{-18}$$

Initial Concentrations
(before any Ag_3PO_4 dissolves)   *Equilibrium Concentrations*

$[Ag^+]_0 = 0$	Let x moles/ℓ ——Ag_3PO_4—→ dissolve	$[Ag^+] = 3x$
$[PO_4^{3-}]_0 = 1.0\ M$		$[PO_4^{3-}] = 1.0 + x$
(from 1.0 M Na_3PO_4)		

$$1.8 \times 10^{-18} = K_{sp} = [Ag^+]^3[PO_4^{3-}] = (3x)^3(1.0 + x)$$

Assuming that $1.0 \gg x$ and thus that $1.0 + x \approx 1.0$ gives:

$$1.8 \times 10^{-18} \approx (3x)^3(1.0)$$
$$27x^3 \approx 1.8 \times 10^{-18}$$
$$x^3 \approx 6.7 \times 10^{-20}$$
$$x \approx 4.1 \times 10^{-7} \text{ moles/}\ell$$

The assumption is valid. Solubility $= 4.1 \times 10^{-7}$ moles/ℓ. Note that Ag_3PO_4 is significantly less soluble in $1.0\,M\,Na_3PO_4$ than in pure water because of the common ion effect.

Test 4–6

The mixed solution contains the ions: Cu^+, NO_3^-, Na^+, Cl^-. We must first calculate the concentrations of Cu^+ and Cl^- in the mixed solution, which has a volume of 250.0 mℓ:

$$[Cu^+]_0 = \frac{\text{mmoles } Cu^+}{\text{m}\ell \text{ of solution}} = \frac{(50.0 \text{ m}\ell)(1.0 \times 10^{-2}\,M)}{(250.0 \text{ m}\ell)} = 2.0 \times 10^{-3}\,M$$

$$[Cl^-]_0 = \frac{\text{mmoles } Cl^-}{\text{m}\ell \text{ of solution}} = \frac{(200.0 \text{ m}\ell)(1.0 \times 10^{-4}\,M)}{(250.0 \text{ m}\ell)} = 8.0 \times 10^{-5}\,M$$

The solid of interest here is $CuCl(s)$, which has the following ion product:

$$Q = [Cu^+]_0[Cl^-]_0$$
$$Q = (2.0 \times 10^{-3})(8.0 \times 10^{-5}) = 1.6 \times 10^{-7}$$
$$K_{sp} = 1.8 \times 10^{-7}$$
$$Q < K_{sp}$$

No precipitation of $CuCl(s)$.

Test 4–7

First consider formation of $AgCl(s)$. The ion product expression is:

$$Q_{AgCl} = [Ag^+]_0[Cl^-]_0$$

where $[Ag^+]_0 = 1.0 \times 10^{-4}\,M$. Let $Q = K_{sp} = 1.6 \times 10^{-10} = (1.0 \times 10^{-4})[Cl^-]_0$; then

$$[Cl^-]_0 = \frac{1.6 \times 10^{-10}}{1.0 \times 10^{-4}} = 1.6 \times 10^{-6} \text{ M}$$

$AgCl(s)$ will form when $[Cl^-] > 1.6 \times 10^{-6}\,M$.

Consider $PbCl_2$. The ion product expression is:

$$Q = [Pb^{2+}]_0[Cl^-]_0^2$$

where $[Pb^{2+}]_0 = 1.0 \times 10^{-2}\,M$. Let $Q = K_{sp} = 1.0 \times 10^{-4} = (1.0 \times 10^{-2})[Cl^-]_0^2$; then

$$[Cl^-]_0^2 = \frac{1.0 \times 10^{-4}}{1.0 \times 10^{-2}} = 1.0 \times 10^{-2}$$

$$[Cl^-]_0 = 1.0 \times 10^{-1} \; M$$

$PbCl_2(s)$ will form when $[Cl^-] > 1.0 \times 10^{-1} \; M$. As Cl^- is added, $AgCl(s)$ will form first when $[Cl^-] > 1.6 \times 10^{-6} \; M$.

Test 4–8

pH = 9.00
$[H^+] = 10^{-pH} = 1.00 \times 10^{-9}$

$$[S^{2-}] = \frac{1.3 \times 10^{-21}}{[H^+]^2} = \frac{1.3 \times 10^{-21}}{(1.00 \times 10^{-9})^2} = \frac{1.3 \times 10^{-21}}{1.0 \times 10^{-18}} = 1.3 \times 10^{-3} \; M$$

Test 4–9

The pH is 1.00; thus $[H^+] = 1.00 \times 10^{-1} \; M$
Since the solution is saturated with H_2S,

$$[S^{2-}] = \frac{1.3 \times 10^{-21}}{[H^+]^2} = \frac{1.3 \times 10^{-21}}{(1.00 \times 10^{-1})^2} = 1.3 \times 10^{-19}$$

Calculate Q for each salt:

<u>FeS(s)</u>: $Q = [Fe^{2+}]_0[S^{2-}]_0 = (1.0 \times 10^{-2})(1.3 \times 10^{-19}) = 1.3 \times 10^{-21}$
$Q < K_{sp}$, so no FeS(s) forms.

<u>NiS(s)</u>: $Q = [Ni^{2+}]_0[S^{2-}]_0 = (1.0 \times 10^{-2})(1.3 \times 10^{-19}) = 1.3 \times 10^{-21}$
$Q > K_{sp}$, so NiS(s) forms

Chapter 5

Test 5–1

A. $HNO_2 \rightleftarrows H^+ + NO_2^-$

$$K_a = \frac{[H^+][NO_2^-]}{[HNO_2]} = 4.0 \times 10^{-4}$$

B. $[HNO_2]_0 = 2.00 \times 10^{-3} \; M$
$[NO_2^-]_0 = 0$
$[H^+]_0 \approx 0$ Ignore water as a contributor to $[H^+]$.

C. x = moles/ℓ of HNO_2 that dissociate

D. $[HNO_2] = 2.00 \times 10^{-3} - x$
$[NO_2^-] = x$
$[H^+] = x$

E. $4.0 \times 10^{-4} = K_a = \dfrac{[H^+][NO_2^-]}{[HNO_2]} = \dfrac{(x)(x)}{2.00 \times 10^{-3} - x}$

F. Assume $2.00 \times 10^{-3} - x \approx 2.00 \times 10^{-3}$

$$\frac{x^2}{2.00 \times 10^{-3}} \approx 4.0 \times 10^{-4}$$

$$x^2 \approx 8.0 \times 10^{-7}$$

$$x \approx 8.9 \times 10^{-4}$$

G. Compare x to 2.00×10^{-3}:

$$\frac{8.9 \times 10^{-4}}{2.00 \times 10^{-3}} \times 100 = 45\%$$

This clearly violates the 5% rule. That is,

$$2.00 \times 10^{-3} - x \neq 2.00 \times 10^{-3}$$

Thus the quadratic formula must be used.

H. $$\frac{x^2}{2.00 \times 10^{-3} - x} = 4.0 \times 10^{-4}$$

$$x^2 = (2.00 \times 10^{-3} - x)(4.0 \times 10^{-4}) = 8.0 \times 10^{-7} - (4.0 \times 10^{-4})x$$
$$x^2 + (4.0 \times 10^{-4})x - 8.0 \times 10^{-7} = 0$$
$$a = 1, b = 4.0 \times 10^{-4}, c = -8.0 \times 10^{-7}$$

$$x = \frac{-b \pm \sqrt{b^2 - 4ac}}{2a} =$$

$$\frac{-4.0 \times 10^{-4} \pm \sqrt{(4.0 \times 10^{-4})^2 - 4(1)(-8.0 \times 10^{-7})}}{2(1)}$$

$x = 7.0 \times 10^{-4}$ (ignore the negative root)
$[H^+] = x = 7.0 \times 10^{-4}$
$pH = 3.15$

Test 5–2

A. Since the HNO_3 added produces $2 \times 10^{-8}\ M\ H^+$, which is close to the amount produced by water, both sources of H^+ must be taken into account. Use the charge balance equation:

$$[H^+] = [NO_3^-] + [OH^-]$$
$$[NO_3^-] = 2.0 \times 10^{-8}\ M$$

$$[OH^-] = \frac{K_w}{[H^+]}$$

$$[H^+] = [NO_3^-] + \frac{K_w}{[H^+]} = 2.0 \times 10^{-8} + \frac{1.0 \times 10^{-14}}{[H^+]}$$

$$[H^+] - \frac{1.0 \times 10^{-14}}{[H^+]} = 2.0 \times 10^{-8}$$

Using the quadratic formula:

$$[H^+] = 1.1 \times 10^{-7}\ M$$
$$pH = -\log(1.1 \times 10^{-7}) = 6.96$$

B. 1. The ions present are: Na^+, OH^-, H^+
    2. The charge balance equation is
        $[Na^+] + [H^+] = [OH^-]$
    3. $[Na^+] = 1.0 \times 10^{-7}\ M$ (from $1.0 \times 10^{-7}\ M$ NaOH)
    4. $[H^+][OH^-] = K_w$; $[H^+] = \dfrac{K_w}{[OH^-]}$
    5. For this solution

$$[Na^+] + [H^+] = [OH^-] = [Na^+] + \frac{K_w}{[OH^-]}$$

$$[OH^-] - \frac{K_w}{[OH^-]} = [Na^+] = 1.0 \times 10^{-7}\ M$$

$$[OH^-] - \frac{1.0 \times 10^{-14}}{[OH^-]} = 1.0 \times 10^{-7}\ M$$

By trial and error: $[OH^-] = 1.6 \times 10^{-7}$
$[H^+][OH^-] = K_w = [H^+](1.6 \times 10^{-7}) =$
$\qquad 1.0 \times 10^{-14}$

$$[H^+] = \frac{1.0 \times 10^{-14}}{1.6 \times 10^{-7}} = 6.3 \times 10^{-8}$$

$pH = 7.20$

$\left.\vphantom{\begin{array}{c}1\\2\\3\\4\end{array}}\right\}$ The quadratic formula may also be used.

C. The HCl solution contains the ions: H^+, Cl^-, and OH^-. The charge balance equation is

$$[H^+] = [Cl^-] + [OH^-]$$

In this case, $[Cl^-] = 0.10\ M$ (from the HCl). Since the $[OH^-]$ will be smaller than $10^{-7}\ M$ (the acid shifts the water equilibrium to the left):

$$[Cl^-] \gg [OH^-]$$
$$[H^+] = [Cl^-] + [OH^-] \approx [Cl^-] = 0.10\ M$$
$$pH = 1$$

This answer was obtained by ignoring the contribution of water to the $[H^+]$, since it is negligible in this case.

Test 5–3

$$6.2 \times 10^{-10} = K_a = \frac{[H^+]^2 - K_w}{[HA]_0 - \dfrac{[H^+]^2 - K_w}{[H^+]}}$$

$$= \frac{(2.5 \times 10^{-5})^2 - 1.00 \times 10^{-14}}{(1.0) - \dfrac{(2.5 \times 10^{-5})^2 - 1.00 \times 10^{-14}}{2.5 \times 10^{-5}}}$$

$$= \frac{6.25 \times 10^{-10} - 1.00 \times 10^{-14}}{(1.0) - \dfrac{6.25 \times 10^{-10} - 1.00 \times 10^{-14}}{2.5 \times 10^{-5}}} = \frac{6.25 \times 10^{-10}}{1.0 - \dfrac{6.25 \times 10^{-10}}{2.5 \times 10^{-5}}}$$

$$= \frac{6.25 \times 10^{-10}}{1.0}$$

The two sides of the equation are equal within round-off errors. In this problem, the full equation and the "normal equation" give the same answer. It is not necessary to consider water as a source of H^+ here. The 1.0 M HCN produces much more H^+ than does H_2O.

Test 5–4

A. The dissociation equilibrium for phenol is

$$C_6H_5OH \rightleftarrows C_6H_5O^- + H^+$$

$$K_a = \frac{[H^+]\,[C_6H_5O^-]}{[C_6H_5OH]} = 1.3 \times 10^{-10}$$

Doing the problem using the normal steps leads to the expression

$$1.3 \times 10^{-10} = \frac{(x)(x)}{2.0 \times 10^{-4} - x} \approx \frac{x^2}{2.0 \times 10^{-4}}$$

$x^2 \approx 2.6 \times 10^{-14}$

$x \approx 1.6 \times 10^{-7}\ M = [H^+]$ from phenol without considering water.

B. $1.6 \times 10^{-7}\ M$ is less than $10^{-6}\ M$. Thus water must be considered in calculating the correct value of the $[H^+]$.

C. The full equation must be used.

D. The $[H^+]$ from phenol considered alone is $1.6 \times 10^{-7}\ M$. Water will contribute something to this. A reasonable guess might be $[H^+] = 2.0 \times 10^{-7}\ M$.

E. $$K_a = 1.3 \times 10^{-10} = \frac{[H^+]^2 - K_w}{[HA]_0 - \dfrac{[H^+]^2 - K_w}{[H^+]}}$$

$$= \frac{[H^+]^2 - 1.0 \times 10^{-14}}{2.0 \times 10^{-4} - \dfrac{[H^+]^2 - 1.0 \times 10^{-14}}{[H^+]}}$$

Use successive approximations. Substitute guessed value of $2.0 \times 10^{-7}\ M$ for $[H^+]$ into the dominator:

$$1.3 \times 10^{-10} = \frac{[H^+]^2 - 1.0 \times 10^{-14}}{2.0 \times 10^{-4} - \dfrac{(2.0 \times 10^{-7})^2 - 1.0 \times 10^{-14}}{2.0 \times 10^{-7}}}$$

$$= \frac{[H^+]^2 - 1.0 \times 10^{-14}}{2.0 \times 10^{-4} - 1.5 \times 10^{-7}}$$

Solving for $[H^+]$ gives

$$[H^+] = 1.9 \times 10^{-7}\ M$$

Substituting this value back into the equation shows that it is the correct value.

Test 5–5

A. Since $K_{a_1} \gg K_{a_2}$, assume that only H_2CO_3 is a significant source of H^+ in this solution. This assumption allows the treatment of this acid to be the same as for a normal monoprotic acid:

$$H_2CO_3 \rightleftharpoons H^+ + HCO_3^-$$

$$K_{a_1} = \frac{[H^+][HCO_3^-]}{[H_2CO_3]} = 4.3 \times 10^{-7}$$

Initial Concentrations   *Equilibrium Concentrations*

$[H_2CO_3]_0 = 0.10\ M$ $\xrightarrow[\substack{\text{Let } x \text{ moles/}\ell \\ \text{—}H_2CO_3\text{—} \\ \text{dissociate}}]{}$ $[H_2CO_3] = 0.10 - x$

$[HCO_3^-]_0 = 0$ $[HCO_3^-] = x$

$[H^+]_0 \approx 0$ $[H^+] = x$

$$4.3 \times 10^{-7} = \frac{[H^+][HCO_3^-]}{[H_2CO_3]} = \frac{(x)(x)}{0.10 - x} \approx \frac{x^2}{0.10}$$

$$x^2 \approx (0.10)(4.3 \times 10^{-7}) = 4.3 \times 10^{-8}$$

$$x \approx 2.1 \times 10^{-4} = [H^+]$$

$$pH = 3.68$$

B. Use K_{a_2}:

$$5.6 \times 10^{-11} = K_{a2} = \frac{[CO_3^{2-}][H^+]}{[HCO_3^-]}$$

From part A,
   $[H^+] = 2.1 \times 10^{-4}\ M$
   $[HCO_3^-] = 2.1 \times 10^{-4}\ M$

$$5.6 \times 10^{-11} = \frac{[CO_3^{2-}][H^+]}{[HCO_3^-]} = \frac{[CO_3^{2-}](2.1 \times 10^{-4})}{2.1 \times 10^{-4}} = [CO_3^{2-}]$$

$$[CO_3^{2-}] = 5.6 \times 10^{-11}\ M$$

Test 5–6

$H_2SO_4 \xrightarrow{\hspace{1cm}} H^+ + HSO_4^-$ K_a large

$HSO_4^- \rightleftharpoons H^+ + SO_4^{2-}$ $K_a = 1.2 \times 10^{-2}$

The major species in 5.0 M H_2SO_4 are:

$$H^+, HSO_4^-, H_2O$$

from complete dissociation of H_2SO_4

Initial Concentrations

$[HSO_4^-]_0 = 5.0 \ M$

$[H^+]_0 = 5.0 \ M$

$[SO_4^{2-}]_0 = 0$

Equilibrium Concentrations

$[HSO_4^-] = 5.0 - x$

$[H^+] = 5.0 + x$

$[SO_4^{2-}] = x$

$1.2 \times 10^{-2} = \dfrac{[H^+][SO_4^{2-}]}{[HSO_4^-]} = \dfrac{(5.0 + x)(x)}{5.0 - x} \approx \dfrac{(5.0)(x)}{5.0} = x$

$x \approx 1.2 \times 10^{-2}$

Assumption is valid.

$[H^+] = 5.0$

$pH = -\log(5.0) = -0.70$

$[SO_4^{2-}] = x = 1.2 \times 10^{-2} \ M$

Test 5–7

A. The major species in solution are: Na^+, $H_2AsO_4^-$, H_2O. The pH will be controlled by $H_2AsO_4^-$ acting both as an acid and as a base. Thus

$$pH = \frac{pK_1 + pK_2}{2} = \frac{2.30 + 7.08}{2} = \frac{9.38}{2} = 4.69$$

B. The major species in solution are: Na^+, $HAsO_4^{2-}$, H_2O. The pH will be controlled by $HAsO_4^{2-}$ acting both as an acid and as a base.

$$pH = \frac{pK_2 + pK_3}{2} = \frac{7.08 + 9.22}{2} = \frac{16.30}{2} = 8.15$$

C. The major species in solution are: Na^+, $H_2AsO_4^-$, $HAsO_4^{2-}$, H_2O. The strongest acid is $H_2AsO_4^-$. The strongest base is $HAsO_4^{2-}$. The dominant equilibrium is

$H_2AsO_4^- \rightleftarrows H^+ + HAsO_4^{2-}$

$K_{a_2} = \dfrac{[H^+][HAsO_4^{2-}]}{[H_2AsO_4^-]} = 8.3 \times 10^{-8}$

Initial Concentrations

$[H_2AsO_4^-]_0 = 0.100 \ M$

$[HAsO_4^{2-}]_0 = 0.100 \ M$

$[H^+]_0 \approx 0$

Let x moles/ℓ

$\xrightarrow[\text{dissociate}]{H_2AsO_4}$

Equilibrium Concentrations

$[H_2AsO_4^-] = 0.100 - x$

$[HAsO_4^{2-}] = 0.100 + x$

$[H^+] = x$

$8.3 \times 10^{-8} = K_{a_2} = \dfrac{[H^+][HAsO_4^{2-}]}{[H_2AsO_4^-]} = \dfrac{(x)(0.100 + x)}{0.100 - x} \approx \dfrac{(x)(0.100)}{0.100}$

$x = 8.3 \times 10^{-8} = [H^+]$

$pH = -\log(8.3 \times 10^{-8}) = 7.08$

Test 5–8

The major species in solution are: $H_2C_8H_4O_4$ and H_2O. $H_2C_8H_4O_4$ is a diprotic acid, but since $K_{a_1} \gg K_{a_2}$, assume that the stronger acid dominates:

$$H_2C_8H_4O_4 \rightleftarrows H^+ + HC_8H_4O_4^-$$

$$K_{a_1} = \frac{[H^+][HC_8H_4O_4^-]}{[H_2C_8H_4O_4]} = 1.3 \times 10^{-3}$$

Initial Concentrations
$[H_2C_8H_4O_4]_0 = 1.00\ M$
$[HC_8H_4O_4^-]_0 = 0$
$[H^+]_0 \approx 0$

Let x moles/ℓ
⟶$H_2C_8H_4O_4$⟶
dissociate

Equilibrium Concentrations
$[H_2C_8H_4O_4] = 1.00 - x$
$[HC_8H_4O_4^-] = x$
$[H^+] = x$

$$1.3 \times 10^{-3} = \frac{[H^+][HC_8H_4O_4^-]}{[H_2C_8H_4O_4]} = \frac{(x)(x)}{1.00 - x} \approx \frac{x^2}{1.00}$$

$x^2 \approx (1.00)(1.3 \times 10^{-3})$
$x \approx 3.6 \times 10^{-2}$

$$\frac{3.6 \times 10^{-2}}{1.00} \times 100 = 3.6\% \text{ so the assumption is valid.}$$

$x = [H^+] = 3.6 \times 10^{-2}$
$pH = -\log(3.6 \times 10^{-2}) = 1.44$

Test 5–9

$$H_2C_8H_4O_4 \rightleftarrows H^+ + HC_8H_4O_4^-$$

$$K_{a_1} = \frac{[H^+][HC_8H_4O_4^-]}{[H_2C_8H_4O_4]} = 1.3 \times 10^{-3}$$

Initial Concentrations

$[H_2C_8H_4O_4]_0 = \dfrac{75.0\ \text{mmole}}{125.0\ \text{m}\ell}$
$= 0.600\ M$

$[HC_8H_4O_4^-]_0 = \dfrac{25.0\ \text{mmole}}{125.0\ \text{m}\ell}$
$= 0.200\ M$

$[H^+]_0 \approx 0$

Let x moles/ℓ
⟶$H_2C_8H_4O_4$⟶
dissociate

Equilibrium Concentrations

$[H_2C_8H_4O_4] = 0.600 - x$

$[HC_8H_4O_4^-] = 0.200 + x$

$[H^+] = x$

$$1.3 \times 10^{-3} = K_{a_1} = \frac{[H^+][HC_8H_4O_4^-]}{[H_2C_8H_4O_4]} = \frac{(x)(0.200 + x)}{0.600 - x} \approx \frac{(x)(0.200)}{0.600}$$

$$x \approx \frac{(0.600)}{(0.200)} (1.3 \times 10^{-3}) = 3.9 \times 10^{-3}$$

Assumption is valid.
$[H^+] = 3.9 \times 10^{-3}$
$pH = -\log(3.9 \times 10^{-3}) = 2.41$

Test 5–10

The reaction is

$$OH^- \quad + \quad H_2C_8H_4O_4 \quad \rightarrow \quad HC_8H_4O_4^- \quad + \quad H_2O$$

	OH⁻	H₂C₈H₄O₄	HC₈H₄O₄⁻	H₂O
Before the reaction	50.0 mmole	100.0 mmole	0	—
After the reaction	0	50.0 mmole	50.0 mmole	—

When the reaction has gone to completion, the solution contains (major species):

$$H_2C_8H_4O_4, \ HC_8H_4O_4^-, \ Na^+, \ H_2O$$

The equilibrium that controls the pH will involve both $H_2C_8H_4O_4$ and $HC_8H_4O_4^-$:

Initial Concentrations

$$[H_2C_8H_4O_4]_0 = \frac{50.0}{150.} $$
$$= 0.333 \ M$$

$$[HC_8H_4O_4^-]_0 = \frac{50.0}{150.}$$
$$= 0.333 \ M$$

$$[H^+]_0 \approx 0$$

Let x moles/ℓ
$$\xrightarrow[\text{dissociate}]{H_2C_8H_4O_4}$$

Equilibrium Concentrations

$$[H_2C_8H_4O_4] = 0.333 - x$$

$$[HC_8H_4O_4^-] = 0.333 + x$$

$$[H^+] = x$$

$$1.3 \times 10^{-3} = K_{a_1} = \frac{[H^+][HC_8H_4O_4^-]}{[H_2C_8H_4O_4]} = \frac{(x)(0.333 + x)}{0.333 - x} = \frac{(x)(0.333)}{0.333}$$

$$x = 1.3 \times 10^{-3} \ M = [H^+] = K_{a_1}$$
$$pH = pK_{a_1} = 2.89.$$

Note that this is halfway to the first stoichiometric point where $pH = pK_{a_1}$.

Test 5–11

At this point, $(150.0 \ m\ell)(1.00 \ M) = 150.0$ mmoles of OH^- have been added. This will react with the 100.0 mmoles of $H_2C_8H_4O_4$ to produce 50.0 mmoles of $C_8H_4O_4^{2-}$ and 50.0 mmoles of $HC_8H_4O_4^-$. When the reaction with OH^- is complete, the solution contains

$$HC_8H_4O_4^-, \ C_8H_4O_4^{2-}, \ Na^+, \ H_2O$$

As in part E, K_{a_2} must be used to solve for the $[H^+]$.

Take a shortcut by noting that this point in the titration corresponds to the halfway point between the first and second equivalence points (the amounts of $HC_8H_4O_4^-$ and $C_8H_4O_4^{2-}$ are equal). At this point

$$pH = pK_{a_2} = -\log(3.9 \times 10^{-6}) = 5.41$$

Test 5–12

The solution contains: Na^+, $C_8H_4O_4^{2-}$, H_2O. The dominant reaction will be

$$C_8H_4O_4^{2-} + H_2O \rightleftarrows HC_8H_4O_4^- + OH^-$$

$$K_b = \frac{K_w}{K_{a_2}} = \frac{1.0 \times 10^{-14}}{3.9 \times 10^{-6}} = 2.6 \times 10^{-9}$$

Initial Concentrations

$$[C_8H_4O_4^{2-}]_0 = \frac{100.0 \text{ mmoles}}{300.0 \text{ m}\ell}$$
$$= 0.333 \ M$$

$$[HC_8H_4O_4^-]_0 = 0$$
$$[OH^-]_0 \approx 0$$

$$\xrightarrow[\text{react with } H_2O]{\text{Let } x \text{ moles}/\ell \\ C_8H_4O_4^{2-}}$$

Equilibrium Concentrations

$$[C_8H_4O_4^{2-}] = 0.333 - x$$

$$[HC_8H_4O_4^-] = x$$
$$[OH^-] = x$$

$$2.6 \times 10^{-9} = K_b = \frac{[HC_8H_4O_4^-][OH^-]}{[C_8H_4O_4^{2-}]} = \frac{(x)(x)}{0.333 - x} \approx \frac{x^2}{0.333}$$

$$x^2 \approx (0.333)(2.6 \times 10^{-9}) = 8.7 \times 10^{-10}$$
$$x \approx 2.9 \times 10^{-5}$$
$$[OH^-] = x = 2.9 \times 10^{-5}$$
$$[H^+][OH^-] = K_w = 1.0 \times 10^{-14}$$
$$[H^+](2.9 \times 10^{-5}) = 1.0 \times 10^{-14}$$

$$[H^+] = \frac{1.0 \times 10^{-14}}{2.9 \times 10^{-5}} = 3.4 \times 10^{-10} \ M$$

$$pH = 9.47$$

Test 5–13

A. Since equal volumes are mixed, the concentrations are halved.

$$[Pb^{2+}]_0 = \frac{1.0 \times 10^{-3}}{2} = 5.0 \times 10^{-4} \ M$$

$$[Cl]_0 = \frac{1.0 \times 10^{-2}}{2} = 5.0 \times 10^{-3} \ M$$

For $PbCl_2(s)$, $Q = [Pb^{2+}]_0[Cl^-]_0^2$
$$= (5.0 \times 10^{-4})(5.0 \times 10^{-3})^2$$
$$= 1.25 \times 10^{-8}$$

$Q < K_{sp}$; no $PbCl_2(s)$ forms.

B. $[Pb^{2+}] = [Pb^{2+}]_0 = 5.0 \times 10^{-4} \ M$
$[Cl^-] = [Cl^-]_0 = 5.0 \times 10^{-3} \ M$

Test 5–14

A. $[Mg^{2+}]_0 = \dfrac{\text{mmoles } Mg^{2+}}{\text{m}\ell \text{ of solution}} = \dfrac{(150.0 \text{ m}\ell)(1.00 \times 10^{-2} \ M)}{400.0 \text{ m}\ell} = 3.75 \times 10^{-3} \ M$

$[F^-]_0 = \dfrac{\text{mmoles } F^-}{\text{m}\ell \text{ of solution}} = \dfrac{(250.0 \text{ m}\ell)(1.00 \times 10^{-1} \ M)}{400.0 \text{ m}\ell} = 6.25 \times 10^{-2} \ M$

$Q = [Mg^{2+}]_0[F^-]_0^2 = (3.75 \times 10^{-3})(6.25 \times 10^{-2})^2 = 1.46 \times 10^{-5}$
$Q > K_{sp}$; $MgF_2(s)$ will form

B. Run the precipitation reaction to completion

	Mg^{2+}	$+$	$2F^-$	$\rightarrow$	$MgF_2(s)$
Before the reaction	$(150.0)(1.00 \times 10^{-2})$ $= 1.5$ mmoles		$(250.0)(1.00 \times 10^{-1})$ $= 25.0$ mmoles		—
After the reaction	0		$25.0 - 2(1.50)$ $= 22.0$ mmoles		—

C. Initial concentrations (after the reaction in B has gone to completion):
$[Mg^{2+}]_0 = 0$

$$[F^-]_0 = \frac{22.0 \text{ mmoles}}{400.0 \text{ m}\ell} = 5.50 \times 10^{-2} \ M$$

D. Let x moles/ℓ $MgF_2(s)$ dissolve to come to equilibrium.
$x MgF_2(s) \rightarrow x Mg^{2+} + 2x F^-$

E. Equilibrium concentrations: $[Mg^{2+}] = x$
$[F^-] = 5.50 \times 10^{-2} \ M + 2x$

F. $6.4 \times 10^{-9} = K_{sp} = [Mg^{2+}][F^-]^2 = (x)(5.50 \times 10^{-2} + 2x)^2$
Assume $5.50 \times 10^{-2} \gg 2x$, so
$6.4 \times 10^{-9} \approx (x)(5.50 \times 10^{-2})^2$

$$x \approx \frac{6.4 \times 10^{-9}}{(5.50 \times 10^{-2})^2} = 2.1 \times 10^{-6} \ M$$

The assumption is valid.

G. $[Mg^{2+}] = x = 2.1 \times 10^{-6} \ M$
$[F^-] = 5.50 \times 10^{-2} \ M + 2x = 5.50 \times 10^{-2} \ M$

Test 5–15

A. $[Ag^+]_0 = \dfrac{(150.0 \text{ m}\ell)(1.0 \times 10^{-3} \ M)}{350.0 \text{ m}\ell} = 4.29 \times 10^{-4} \ M$

$[S_2O_3^{2-}]_0 = \dfrac{(200.0 \text{ m}\ell)(5.0 \ M)}{350.0 \text{ m}\ell} = 2.86 \ M$

B. Since $[S_2O_3^{2-}]_0 \gg [Ag^+]_0$ and since K_1 and K_2 are both large, the dominant species will be $Ag(S_2O_3)_2^{3-}$. The net reaction will be

$$Ag^+ + 2S_2O_3^{2-} \rightarrow Ag(S_2O_3)_2^{3-}$$

In this example:
$4.29 \times 10^{-4} \ M \ Ag + 2(4.29 \times 10^{-4} \ M)S_2O_3^{2-} \rightarrow 4.29 \times 10^{-4} \ M \ Ag(S_2O_3)_2^{3-}$

$[Ag(S_2O_3)_2^{3-}] \approx 4.29 \times 10^{-4} \ M$

C. $[S_2O_3^{2-}] = [S_2O_3^{2-}]_{original}$ − amount consumed
$$= 2.86\ M - 2(4.29 \times 10^{-4}\ M) = 2.86\ M$$

D. Calculate $[Ag(S_2O_3)^-]$ from K_2:

$$3.9 \times 10^4 = K_2 = \frac{[Ag(S_2O_3)_2^{3-}]}{[Ag(S_2O_3)^-][S_2O_3^{2-}]} = \frac{4.29 \times 10^{-4}}{[Ag(S_2O_3)^-](2.86)}$$

$$[Ag(S_2O_3)^-] = \frac{4.29 \times 10^{-4}}{(3.9 \times 10^4)(2.86)} = 3.8 \times 10^{-9}\ M$$

Calculate $[Ag^+]$ from K_1:

$$7.4 \times 10^8 = K_1 = \frac{[Ag(S_2O_3)^-]}{[Ag^+][S_2O_3^{2-}]} = \frac{3.8 \times 10^{-9}}{[Ag^+](2.86)}$$

$$[Ag^+] = \frac{3.8 \times 10^{-9}}{(7.4 \times 10^8)(2.86)} = 1.8 \times 10^{-18}\ M$$

E. These results show that $[Ag(S_2O_3)_2^{3-}] \gg [Ag(S_2O_3)^-] \gg [Ag^+]$. The assumptions are valid.

Test 5–16

$$[NH_3]_{original} = \frac{3.00\ M}{2} = 1.50\ M$$

$$[Cu^{2+}]_{original} = \frac{2.00 \times 10^{-3}\ M}{2} = 1.00 \times 10^{-3}\ M$$

Since $[NH_3]_{original} \gg [Cu^{2+}]_{original}$ and since K_1, K_2, K_3, and K_4 are all large, $Cu(NH_3)_4^{2+}$ will be the dominant species. The net reaction will be

$$Cu^{2+} + 4NH_3 \rightarrow Cu(NH_3)_4^{2+}$$

In this case

$1.00 \times 10^{-3}\ M\ Cu^{2+}$ plus $4(1.00 \times 10^{-3}\ M)NH_3$ will produce $1.00 \times 10^{-3}\ M$
$Cu(NH_3)_4^{2+}$

At equilibrium:

$[Cu(NH_3)_4^{2+}] \approx 1.00 \times 10^{-3}\ M$
$[NH_3] = [NH_3]_0 - NH_3$ consumed $= 1.50\ M - 4(1.00 \times 10^{-3}\ M) = 1.50\ M$

Calculate $[Cu(NH_3)_3^{2+}]$ from K_4:

$$1.55 \times 10^2 = K_4 = \frac{[Cu(NH_3)_4^{2+}]}{[Cu(NH_3)_3^{2+}][NH_3]} = \frac{1.00 \times 10^{-3}}{[Cu(NH_3)_3^{2+}](1.50)}$$

$$[Cu(NH_3)_3^{2+}] = \frac{1.00 \times ^{-3}}{[Cu(NH_3)_3^{2+}](1.50)} = 4.30 \times 10^{-6}$$

Calculate $[Cu(NH_3)_2^{2+}]$ from K_3:

$$1.00 \times 10^3 = K_3 = \frac{[Cu(NH_3)_3^{2+}]}{[Cu(NH_3)_2^{2+}][NH_3]} = \frac{4.30 \times 10^{-6}}{[Cu(NH_3)_2^{2+}](1.50)}$$

$$[Cu(NH_3)_3^{2+}] = \frac{4.30 \times 10^{-6}}{(1.00 \times 10^3)(1.50)} = 2.87 \times 10^{-9} \, M$$

Calculate $[Cu(NH_3)^{2+}]$ from K_2:

$$3.88 \times 10^3 = K_2 = \frac{[Cu(NH_3)_2^{2+}]}{[Cu(NH_3)^{2+}][NH_3]} = \frac{2.87 \times 10^{-9}}{[Cu(NH_3)^{2+}](1.50)}$$

$$[Cu(NH_3)^{2+}] = \frac{2.87 \times 10^{-9}}{(3.88 \times 10^3)(1.50)} = 4.93 \times 10^{-13} \, M$$

Calculate $[Cu^{2+}]$ from K_1:

$$1.86 \times 10^4 = \frac{[Cu(NH_3)^{2+}]}{[Cu^{2+}][NH_3]} = \frac{4.93 \times 10^{-13}}{[Cu^{2+}](1.50)}$$

$$[Cu^{2+}] = \frac{4.93 \times 10^{-13}}{(1.86 \times 10^4)(1.50)} = 1.77 \times 10^{-17} \, M$$

The assumptions are valid. $Cu(NH_3)_4^{2+}$ is clearly the dominant copper-containing component.

Test 5–17

The reactions to be considered are:

$$Ag_3PO_4(s) \rightleftharpoons 3Ag^+ + PO_4^{3-} \qquad K_{sp} \qquad = 1.8 \times 10^{-18}$$

$$PO_4^{3-} + H_2O \rightleftharpoons HPO_4^{2-} + OH^- \qquad K_b = \frac{K_w}{K_{a_3}} = \frac{1.00 \times 10^{-14}}{4.8 \times 10^{-13}} = 2.1 \times 10^{-2}$$

The reaction of HPO_4^{2-} with water to form $H_2PO_4^-$ need not be considered, since it is a much weaker base than PO_4^{3-}.

The problem contains four unknowns. So far we have two equations (the two equilibrium expressions). More relationships are clearly needed. One relationship that is almost always useful is the material balance equation. Since both the Ag^+ and the PO_4^{3-} come from $Ag_3PO_4(s)$, the following relationship holds:

$$[Ag^+] = 3 \text{ times concentration of phosphate in all forms}$$

Since the assumption has been made that $H_2PO_4^-$ and H_3PO_4 are unimportant,

$$[Ag^+] = 3\{[PO_4^{3-}] + [HPO_4^{2-}]\}$$

When two terms are to be added, consider whether it is reasonable to suppose that one term is much larger than the other. What about the relative values of

$[PO_4{}^{3-}]$ and $[HPO_4{}^{2-}]$ at equilibrium? Both species are involved in the K_b expression:

$$K_b = \frac{K_w}{K_{a_3}} = 2.1 \times 10^{-2} = \frac{[OH^-][HPO_4{}^{2-}]}{[PO_4{}^{3-}]}$$

Note that the ratio of the concentrations of $HPO_4{}^{2-}$ and $PO_4{}^{3-}$ depends on the $[OH^-]$. Can we estimate a reasonable value of $[OH^-]$?

$[OH^-]$ will definitely be greater than $10^{-7}\ M$ ($PO_4{}^{3-}$ is a base). Suppose $[OH^-] = 10^{-5}\ M$. Then

$$\frac{[HPO_4{}^{2-}]}{[PO_4{}^{3-}]} = \frac{K_b}{[OH^-]} = \frac{2.1 \times 10^{-2}}{10^{-5}} = 2.1 \times 10^3 = 2100$$

In this case

$$[HPO_4{}^{2-}] \gg [PO_4{}^{3-}]$$

On the other hand, if $[OH^-] = 10^{-2}\ M$

$$\frac{[HPO_4{}^{2-}]}{[PO_4{}^{3-}]} = \frac{2.1 \times 10^{-2}}{10^{-2}} = 2.1$$

and

$$[HPO_4{}^{2-}] \approx 2[PO_4{}^{3-}]$$

So arbitrarily assume that the $[OH^-]$ at equilibrium will be small enough so that

$$[HPO_4{}^{2-}] \gg [PO_4{}^{3-}]$$

What this assumption really means is that essentially all of the $PO_4{}^{3-}$ produced when $Ag_3PO_4(s)$ dissolves will react with water to produce $HPO_4{}^{2-}$ so that the net reaction will be

$$Ag_3PO_4(s) + H_2O(\ell) \rightleftarrows 3Ag^+ + HPO_4{}^{2-} + OH^-$$

which is the sum of the reactions

$$Ag_3PO_4(s) \rightleftarrows 3Ag^+ + PO_4{}^{3-} \qquad K_{sp} = 1.8 \times 10^{-18}$$
$$PO_4{}^{3-} + H_2O \rightleftarrows HPO_4{}^{2-} + OH^- \qquad K_b = 2.1 \times 10^{-2}$$

When reactions are summed, equilibrium constants are multiplied:

$$K = [Ag^+]^3[HPO_4{}^{2-}][OH^-] = K_{sp}K_b$$
$$= (1.8 \times 10^{-18})(2.1 \times 10^{-2}) = 3.8 \times 10^{-20}$$

Now let x = solubility of Ag_3PO_4 according to the above reaction:

xAg_3PO_4 reacts with xH_2O to produce $3xAg^+$ plus $xHPO_4^{2-}$ plus xOH^-

Thus at equilibrium

$$[Ag^+] = 3x$$
$$[HPO_4^{2-}] = [OH^-] = x$$
$$K = [Ag^+]^3[HPO_4^{2-}][OH^-] = (3x)^3(x)(x) = 3.8 \times 10^{-20}$$
$$27x^5 = 3.8 \times 10^{-20}$$
$$x^5 = \frac{3.8 \times 10^{-20}}{27} = 1.4 \times 10^{-21}$$
$$x = 6.7 \times 10^{-5} = \text{solubility}$$

Now check the assumption that $[HPO_4^{2-}] \gg [PO_4^{3-}]$:

$$K_b = \frac{[OH^-][HPO_4^{2-}]}{[PO_4^{3-}]} = 2.1 \times 10^{-2}$$

$$\frac{[HPO_4^{2-}]}{[PO_4^{3-}]} = \frac{K_b}{[OH^-]} = \frac{2.1 \times 10^{-2}}{6.7 \times 10^{-5}} = 3.1 \times 10^2 = 310$$
$$\nwarrow \text{ from above}$$

$$[HPO_4^{2-}] \gg [PO_4^{3-}]$$

The assumptions are correct.

The solubility of Ag_3PO_4 in water is 6.7×10^{-5} moles/ℓ. Compare this to the calculated value of 1.6×10^{-5} moles/ℓ when the basicity of PO_4^{3-} is ignored.

Test 5–18

A. $CuS(s) \rightleftarrows Cu^{2+} + S^{2-}$ $\qquad\qquad K_{sp} = 8.5 \times 10^{-45}$

$S^{2-} + H^+ \rightleftarrows HS^-$ $\qquad\qquad K = \dfrac{1}{K_{a_2}} = 7.75 \times 10^{12}$

$HS^- + H^+ \rightleftarrows H_2S$ $\qquad\qquad K = \dfrac{1}{K_{a_1}} = 9.80 \times 10^6$

B. S^{2-} and HS^- are both effective bases (each reacts with H^+ to produce an equilibrium that lies far to the right—see A above). This means that essentially all of the S^{2-} that is released into the solution as $CuS(s)$ dissolves will end up as H_2S. The conclusion is that H_2S will be the dominant sulfur-containing species.

C.   The net reaction is

$$CuS(s) + 2H^+ \rightarrow H_2S + Cu^{2+}$$

D. $K = \dfrac{[H_2S][Cu^{2+}]}{[H^+]^2} = \dfrac{K_{sp}}{K_{a_1} \cdot K_{a_2}} = 8.2 \times 10^{-25}$

$$CuS(s) \quad + \quad 2H^+ \quad \rightarrow \quad H_2S \quad + \quad Cu^{\cdot}$$

$xCuS(s)$ reacts with $2xH^+$ to produce xH_2S plus xCu^{2+}

At equilibrium: $[Cu^{2+}] = x$

$\quad [H_2S] = x$

$\quad [H^+] = 10.0 - $ amount consumed $= 10.0 - 2x$

$\quad\quad\quad\quad\quad\nwarrow$ initial concentration

$$6.5 \times 10^{-25} = \frac{[H_2S][Cu^{2+}]}{[H^+]^2} = \frac{(x)(x)}{(10.0 - 2x)^2}$$

Note that K is small, which means that $2x$ will be small compared to 10.0. Thus

$$6.5 \times 10^{-25} = \frac{(x)(x)}{(10 - 2x)^2} \approx \frac{x^2}{(10)^2}$$

$$x^2 \approx 6.5 \times 10^{-23}$$

$$x = 8.1 \times 10^{-12} \text{ moles}/\ell$$

Check the assumption that H_2S is dominant:

$$[H^+] = 10.0 - 2x = 10.0 - 2(8.1 \times 10^{-12}) = 10.0 \ M$$

Using K_{a_1}:

$$K_{a_1} = 1.02 \times 10^{-7} = \frac{[H^+][HS^-]}{[H_2S]}$$

$$\frac{[H_2S]}{[HS^-]} = \frac{[H^+]}{K_{a_1}} = \frac{(10.0)}{(1.02 \times 10^{-7})} = 9.8 \times 10^7$$

Thus $[H_2S] \gg [HS^-]$.

Using K_{a_2}:

$$K_{a_2} = 1.29 \times 10^{-13} = \frac{[H^+][S^{2-}]}{[HS^-]}$$

$$\frac{[HS^-]}{[S^{2-}]} = \frac{[H^+]}{K_{a_2}} = \frac{(10.0)}{(1.29 \times 10^{-13})} = 7.8 \times 10^{13}$$

Thus $[HS^-] \gg [S^{2-}]$.

In summary: $[H_2S] \gg [HS^-] \gg [S^{2-}]$. H_2S is dominant. The solubility of CuS in 10.0M H^+ is 8.1×10^{-12} moles/ℓ.

Test 5–19

A. $AgI(s) \rightleftarrows Ag^+ + I^-$ $\quad\quad\quad\quad\quad\quad\quad\quad\quad K_{sp} = 1.5 \times 10^{-16}$

$\quad Ag^+ + S_2O_3^{2-} \rightleftarrows Ag(S_2O_3)^- \quad\quad\quad K_1 = 7.4 \times 10^8$

$\quad Ag(S_2O_3)_2^{3-} + S_2O_3^{2-} \rightleftarrows Ag(S_2O_3)_2^{3-} \quad K_2 = 3.9 \times 10^4$

B. $Ag(S_2O_3)_2{}^{3-}$ will be dominant.

C. $AgI(s) + 2S_2O_3{}^{2-} \rightleftarrows Ag(S_2O_3)_2{}^{3-} + I^-$

D. $K = \dfrac{[Ag(S_2O_3)_2{}^{3-}][I^-]}{[S_2O_3{}^{2-}]^2} = K_{sp}K_1K_2 = 4.3 \times 10^{-3}$

E.   Let x = solubility of $AgI(s)$ at equilibrium

$$[I^-] = [Ag(S_2O_3)_2{}^{3-}] = x$$
$$[S_2O_3{}^{2-}] = 5.0\ M - 2x$$

$$4.3 \times 10^{-3} = K = \frac{[Ag(S_2O_3)_2{}^{3-}][I^-]}{[S_2O_3{}^{2-}]^2} = \frac{(x)\,(x)}{(5.0 - 2x)^2}$$

Assume $5.0 - 2x \approx 5.0$, so

$$4.3 \times 10^{-3} \approx \frac{x^2}{(5.0)^2}$$

$$x^2 \approx (5.0)^2(4.3 \times 10^{-3}) = 1.1 \times 10^{-1}$$
$$x \approx 3.3 \times 10^{-1}$$

Check the assumption:

$$2x = 2(0.33) = 0.66$$

$$\frac{0.66}{5.0} \times 100 = 13.2\%$$

The approximation is not valid. The expression

$$\frac{x^2}{(5.0 - 2x)^2} = 4.3 \times 10^{-3}$$

must be solved directly (take the square root of both sides).
This gives:

$$x = 0.29\ \text{mole}/\ell$$
$$[S_2O_3{}^{2-}] = 5.0 - 2x = 5.0 - 0.58 = 4.4\ M$$

Now check the original assumption that $[Ag(S_2O_3)_2{}^{3-}]$ is dominant.
   Using K_2:

$$K_2 = \frac{[Ag(S_2O_3)_2{}^{3-}]}{[Ag(S_2O_3)^-][S_2O_3{}^{2-}]} = 3.9 \times 10^4$$

$$\frac{[Ag(S_2O_3)_2{}^{3-}]}{[Ag(S_2O_3)^-]} = K_2[S_2O_3{}^{2-}] = (3.9 \times 10^4)(4.4) = 1.7 \times 10^5$$

Thus $[Ag(S_2O_3)_2{}^{3-}] \gg [Ag(S_2O_3)^-]$.
   Using K_1:

$$K_1 = \frac{[Ag(S_2O_3)^-]}{[Ag^+][S_2O_3{}^{2-}]} = 7.4 \times 10^8$$

$$\frac{[Ag(S_2O_3)^-]}{[Ag^+]} = K_1[S_2O_3{}^{2-}] = (7.4 \times 10^8)\,(4.4) = 3.3 \times 10^9$$

Thus $[Ag(S_2O_3)^-] \gg [Ag^+]$.

Summary:

$$[Ag(S_2O_3)_2{}^{3-}] \gg [Ag(S_2O_3)^-] \gg [Ag^+]$$

The solubility of $AgI(s)$ in 5.0 M $Na_2S_2O_3$ is 0.29 mole/ℓ.

Chapter 6

Test 6–1

A. $(568 \text{ cal}) \left(\dfrac{4.184 \text{ J}}{1 \text{ cal}} \right) = 2380 \text{ J}$

B. $(135 \text{ J}) \left(\dfrac{1 \text{ cal}}{4.184 \text{ J}} \right) = 32.3 \text{ cal}$

Test 6–2

A. 1. $(136 \text{ J}) \left(\dfrac{1 \text{ kJ}}{10^3 \text{ J}} \right) = 0.136 \text{ kJ}$

   2. $(1868 \text{ cal}) \left(\dfrac{4.184 \text{ J}}{1 \text{ cal}} \right) = 7816 \text{ J}$

   3. $(7816 \text{ J}) \left(\dfrac{1 \text{ kJ}}{10^3 \text{ J}} \right) = 7.816 \text{ kJ}$

B. 1. $(28 \text{ cal}) \left(\dfrac{1 \text{ kcal}}{10^3 \text{ cal}} \right) = 0.028 \text{ kcal}$

   2. $(1325 \text{ J}) \left(\dfrac{1 \text{ cal}}{4.184 \text{ J}} \right) = 316.7 \text{ cal}$

   $(316.7 \text{ cal}) \left(\dfrac{1 \text{ kcal}}{10^3 \text{ cal}} \right) = 0.3167 \text{ kcal}$

Test 6–3

A. $\Delta H^0 = \Delta H_f{}^0\,(F_2(g)) + \Delta H_f{}^0(XeF_4(s)) - \Delta H_f{}^0(XeF_6(g))$
      $= 0 - 251 \text{ kJ} - (-294 \text{ kJ})$
      $= 43 \text{ kJ}$

B. $T = 25 + 273 = 298$ K

$$\Delta S_{surr} = -\frac{\Delta H}{T} = -\frac{43 \text{ kJ}}{298 \text{ K}}$$

$$= -0.14 \frac{\text{kJ}}{\text{K}}$$

Test 6–4

A. The process is endothermic.

B. $\Delta S_{surr} = -\dfrac{\Delta H}{T}$. ΔH is positive; thus ΔS_{surr} is negative.

Test 6–5

1,2	3,4
1,3	2,4
2,3	1,4
2,4	1,3
3,4	1,2
4,1	2,3

Test 6–6

One would be very surprised to find the cards in the original order. This would be possible, but *very* improbable. There are thousands of ways for the deck to be disordered, but only one way to be ordered (your definition). Thus the chances of picking the cards up out of order are much greater than those of picking them up in order.

Test 6–7

A. There are many more ways to arrange the two independent balls than the unit (two glued together). This situation is closely related to the change in positional disorder occurring in the process

$$2Cl(g) \rightarrow Cl_2(g)$$

There are many more arrangements possible for the independent Cl atoms than when they are bound together as a Cl_2 molecule. Thus positional disorder decreases in the above process and ΔS will be negative.

B. Positional disorder
    1. decreases; ΔS should be negative
    2. increases; ΔS should be positive
    3. little change; ΔS should be small
    4. decreases; ΔS will be negative
    5. little change; ΔS should be small

$$\text{CuS(s)} \quad + \quad \text{2H}^+ \quad \rightarrow \quad \text{H}_2\text{S} \quad + \quad \text{Cu}^{2+}$$

xCuS(s) reacts with $2x$H$^+$ to produce xH$_2$S plus xCu^{2+}

At equilibrium: $\quad$ $[\text{Cu}^{2+}] = x$

$[\text{H}_2\text{S}] = x$

$[\text{H}^+] = 10.0 -$ amount consumed $= 10.0 - 2x$

$\quad\quad\quad\quad\quad\quad\quad$ ↖ initial concentration

$$6.5 \times 10^{-25} = \frac{[\text{H}_2\text{S}][\text{Cu}^{2+}]}{[\text{H}^+]^2} = \frac{(x)(x)}{(10.0 - 2x)^2}$$

Note that K is small, which means that $2x$ will be small compared to 10.0. Thus

$$6.5 \times 10^{-25} = \frac{(x)(x)}{(10 - 2x)^2} \approx \frac{x^2}{(10)^2}$$

$$x^2 \approx 6.5 \times 10^{-23}$$

$$x = 8.1 \times 10^{-12} \text{ moles}/\ell$$

Check the assumption that H$_2$S is dominant:

$$[\text{H}^+] = 10.0 - 2x = 10.0 - 2(8.1 \times 10^{-12}) = 10.0 \, M$$

Using K_{a_1}:

$$K_{a_1} = 1.02 \times 10^{-7} = \frac{[\text{H}^+][\text{HS}^-]}{[\text{H}_2\text{S}]}$$

$$\frac{[\text{H}_2\text{S}]}{[\text{HS}^-]} = \frac{[\text{H}^+]}{K_{a_1}} = \frac{(10.0)}{(1.02 \times 10^{-7})} = 9.8 \times 10^7$$

Thus $[\text{H}_2\text{S}] \gg [\text{HS}^-]$.

$\quad$ Using K_{a_2}:

$$K_{a_2} = 1.29 \times 10^{-13} = \frac{[\text{H}^+][\text{S}^{2-}]}{[\text{HS}^-]}$$

$$\frac{[\text{HS}^-]}{[\text{S}^{2-}]} = \frac{[\text{H}^+]}{K_{a_2}} = \frac{(10.0)}{(1.29 \times 10^{-13})} = 7.8 \times 10^{13}$$

Thus $[\text{HS}^-] \gg [\text{S}^{2-}]$.

$\quad$ In summary: $[\text{H}_2\text{S}] \gg [\text{HS}^-] \gg [\text{S}^{2-}]$. H$_2$S is dominant. The solubility of CuS in 10.0M H$^+$ is 8.1×10^{-12} moles/ℓ.

Test 5–19

A. $\text{AgI(s)} \rightleftarrows \text{Ag}^+ + \text{I}^-$ $\qquad\qquad\qquad$ $K_{sp} = 1.5 \times 10^{-16}$

$\quad$ $\text{Ag}^+ + \text{S}_2\text{O}_3{}^{2-} \rightleftarrows \text{Ag}(\text{S}_2\text{O}_3)^-$ $\qquad$ $K_1 = 7.4 \times 10^8$

$\quad$ $\text{Ag}(\text{S}_2\text{O}_3)_2{}^{3-} + \text{S}_2\text{O}_3{}^{2-} \rightleftarrows \text{Ag}(\text{S}_2\text{O}_3)_2{}^{3-}$ $\qquad$ $K_2 = 3.9 \times 10^4$

B. $Ag(S_2O_3)_2^{3-}$ will be dominant.

C. $AgI(s) + 2S_2O_3^{2-} \rightleftharpoons Ag(S_2O_3)_2^{3-} + I^-$

D. $K = \dfrac{[Ag(S_2O_3)_2^{3-}][I^-]}{[S_2O_3^{2-}]^2} = K_{sp}K_1K_2 = 4.3 \times 10^{-3}$

E. Let $x = $ solubility of $AgI(s)$ at equilibrium

$$[I^-] = [Ag(S_2O_3)_2^{3-}] = x$$
$$[S_2O_3^{2-}] = 5.0\ M - 2x$$

$$4.3 \times 10^{-3} = K = \frac{[Ag(S_2O_3)_2^{3-}][I^-]}{[S_2O_3^{2-}]^2} = \frac{(x)\,(x)}{(5.0 - 2x)^2}$$

Assume $5.0 - 2x \approx 5.0$, so

$$4.3 \times 10^{-3} \approx \frac{x^2}{(5.0)^2}$$

$$x^2 \approx (5.0)^2(4.3 \times 10^{-3}) = 1.1 \times 10^{-1}$$

$$x \approx 3.3 \times 10^{-1}$$

Check the assumption:

$$2x = 2(0.33) = 0.66$$

$$\frac{0.66}{5.0} \times 100 = 13.2\%$$

The approximation is not valid. The expression

$$\frac{x^2}{(5.0 - 2x)^2} = 4.3 \times 10^{-3}$$

must be solved directly (take the square root of both sides).
This gives:

$$x = 0.29\ \text{mole}/\ell$$
$$[S_2O_3^{2-}] = 5.0 - 2x = 5.0 - 0.58 = 4.4\ M$$

Now check the original assumption that $[Ag(S_2O_3)_2^{3-}]$ is dominant.
Using K_2:

$$K_2 = \frac{[Ag(S_2O_3)_2^{3-}]}{[Ag(S_2O_3)^-][S_2O_3^{2-}]} = 3.9 \times 10^4$$

$$\frac{[Ag(S_2O_3)_2^{3-}]}{[Ag(S_2O_3)^-]} = K_2[S_2O_3^{2-}] = (3.9 \times 10^4)(4.4) = 1.7 \times 10^5$$

Thus $[Ag(S_2O_3)_2^{3-}] \gg [Ag(S_2O_3)^-]$.
Using K_1:

$$K_1 = \frac{[Ag(S_2O_3)^-]}{[Ag^+][S_2O_3^{2-}]} = 7.4 \times 10^8$$

$$\frac{[Ag(S_2O_3)^-]}{[Ag^+]} = K_1[S_2O_3^{2-}] = (7.4 \times 10^8)\,(4.4) = 3.3 \times 10^9$$

Thus $[Ag(S_2O_3)^-] \gg [Ag^+]$.

Summary:

$$[Ag(S_2O_3)_2^{3-}] \gg [Ag(S_2O_3)^-] \gg [Ag^+]$$

The solubility of AgI(s) in 5.0 M Na$_2$S$_2$O$_3$ is 0.29 mole/ℓ.

Chapter 6

Test 6–1

A. $(568 \text{ cal}) \left(\dfrac{4.184 \text{ J}}{1 \text{ cal}} \right) = 2380 \text{ J}$

B. $(135 \text{ J}) \left(\dfrac{1 \text{ cal}}{4.184 \text{ J}} \right) = 32.3 \text{ cal}$

Test 6–2

A. 1. $(136 \text{ J}) \left(\dfrac{1 \text{ kJ}}{10^3 \text{ J}} \right) = 0.136 \text{ kJ}$

2. $(1868 \text{ cal}) \left(\dfrac{4.184 \text{ J}}{1 \text{ cal}} \right) = 7816 \text{ J}$

3. $(7816 \text{ J}) \left(\dfrac{1 \text{ kJ}}{10^3 \text{ J}} \right) = 7.816 \text{ kJ}$

B. 1. $(28 \text{ cal}) \left(\dfrac{1 \text{ kcal}}{10^3 \text{ cal}} \right) = 0.028 \text{ kcal}$

2. $(1325 \text{ J}) \left(\dfrac{1 \text{ cal}}{4.184 \text{ J}} \right) = 316.7 \text{ cal}$

$(316.7 \text{ cal}) \left(\dfrac{1 \text{ kcal}}{10^3 \text{ cal}} \right) = 0.3167 \text{ kcal}$

Test 6–3

A. $\Delta H^0 = \Delta H_f^0\,(F_2(g)) + \Delta H_f^0(XeF_4(s)) - \Delta H_f^0(XeF_6(g))$
    $= 0 - 251 \text{ kJ} - (-294 \text{ kJ})$
    $= 43 \text{ kJ}$

B. $T = 25 + 273 = 298$ K

$$\Delta S_{surr} = -\frac{\Delta H}{T} = -\frac{43 \text{ kJ}}{298 \text{ K}}$$

$$= -0.14 \frac{\text{kJ}}{\text{K}}$$

Test 6–4

A. The process is endothermic.

B. $\Delta S_{surr} = -\frac{\Delta H}{T}$. ΔH is positive; thus ΔS_{surr} is negative.

Test 6–5

1,2	3,4
1,3	2,4
2,3	1,4
2,4	1,3
3,4	1,2
4,1	2,3

Test 6–6

One would be very surprised to find the cards in the original order. This would be possible, but *very* improbable. There are thousands of ways for the deck to be disordered, but only one way to be ordered (your definition). Thus the chances of picking the cards up out of order are much greater than those of picking them up in order.

Test 6–7

A. There are many more ways to arrange the two independent balls than the unit (two glued together). This situation is closely related to the change in positional disorder occurring in the process

$$2Cl(g) \rightarrow Cl_2(g)$$

There are many more arrangements possible for the independent Cl atoms than when they are bound together as a Cl_2 molecule. Thus positional disorder decreases in the above process and ΔS will be negative.

B. Positional disorder
1. decreases; ΔS should be negative
2. increases; ΔS should be positive
3. little change; ΔS should be small
4. decreases; ΔS will be negative
5. little change; ΔS should be small

Test 6–8

A. 1. Since the process is endothermic, ΔS_{surr} will be negative:

$$\Delta S_{surr} = -\frac{\Delta H}{T} = -\frac{178\ kJ}{298\ K} = -0.597\ \frac{kJ}{K}$$

Since the number of gas molecules increases, ΔS will be positive.

2. ΔS_{surr} will be positive:

$$\Delta S_{surr} = -\frac{\Delta H}{T} = -\frac{-283\ kJ}{298\ K} = 0.950\ \frac{kJ}{K}$$

ΔS will be negative, since the number of gaseous molecules decreases.

B. 1. $CO_2(g)$ has higher entropy.
   2. 1 mole of $N_2(g)$ at 1.0×10^{-2} atm has higher entropy since the volume must be larger than for 1 mole of $N_2(g)$ at 1 atm.
   3. $Na(\ell)$ has higher entropy.

C. To accommodate the operation of an order-producing cell with the Second Law of Thermodynamics, we must remember that ΔS_{univ}, not ΔS_{system}, must be positive for a process to be spontaneous. Processes where ΔS is negative are often spontaneous because of a large, positive value for ΔS_{surr}. Operation of a cell is such a process.

Test 6–9

A. The number of gas molecules decreases. Thus ΔS^0 should be negative.

B. $\Delta S^0 = \Sigma S^0$ (products) $- \Sigma S^0$ (reactants)
$= 2S^0_{NO_2(g)} - 2S^0_{NO(g)} - S^0_{O_2(g)}$
$= 2$ moles $(240\ J/K{\cdot}mole) - 2$ moles $(211\ J/K{\cdot}mole) - 1$ mole $(205\ J/K{\cdot}mole)$
$= 480\ J/K - 422\ J/K - 205\ J/K$
$= -147\ J/K$

C. The sign of ΔS^0 agrees with the prediction.

D. $NO_2(g)$ is more complex than $NO(g)$ and should have a higher value of S^0.

Test 6–10

A. 1. $\Delta H^0 = 2\Delta H_f^0\ (SO_3(g)) - 2\Delta H_f^0\ (SO_2(g)) - \Delta H_f^0\ (O_2(g))$
$= 2$ mole $(-396\ kJ/mole) - 2$ mole $(-297\ kJ/mole) - 0$
$= -792\ kJ + 594\ kJ$
$= -198\ kJ$
   2. ΔS^0 is expected to be negative, since 3 molecules of gas become 2 molecules.

$$\Delta S^0 = 2S^0_{SO_3(g)} - 2S^0_{SO_2(g)} - S^0_{O_2}$$

$$= 2 \text{ mole } (257 \text{ J/K·mole}) - 2 \text{ mole } (248 \text{ J/K·mole}) - 1 \text{ mole } (205 \text{ J/K·mole})$$

$$= 514 \text{ J/K} - 496 \text{ J/K} - 205 \text{ J/K}$$

$$= -187 \text{ J/K}$$

$\bar{3}.$ $\Delta G^0 = \Delta H^0 - T\Delta S^0$

$$= -198 \text{ kJ} - (298 \text{ K}) \left(-187 \frac{J}{K} \right) \left(\frac{1 \text{ kJ}}{10^3 \text{ J}} \right)$$

$$= -198 \text{ kJ} + 55.7 \text{ kJ} = -142 \text{ kJ}$$

B. The process is spontaneous, since ΔG is negative.

C. ΔS^0 (which is dominated by changes in positional probability) is negative and is thus unfavorable. Because ΔH^0 is negative, ΔS_{surr} is positive and favors spontaneity. Since $|\Delta H^0| > |T\Delta S^0|$, ΔG^0 is negative and the process is spontaneous.

Test 6–11

The boiling point of liquid hydrogen is $-253°$ C or 20 K. For the process

$$H_2(\ell) \rightarrow H_2(g)$$

at the boiling point

$$\Delta G = 0 \text{ and } \Delta H = 903 \text{ J/mole}$$

Thus

$$\Delta G = \Delta H_{vap} - T_{B.P.}\Delta S_{vap} = 0$$

$$\Delta S_{vap} = \frac{\Delta H_{vap}}{T_{B.P.}} = \frac{903 \text{ J/mole}}{20 \text{ K}} = 45 \frac{J}{\text{mole K}}$$

Test 6–12

$T = 273 - 20 = 253 \text{ K}$
$\Delta H = 6025 \text{ J/mole}$
$\Delta S = 22.1 \text{ J/K·mole}$
$\Delta G = \Delta H - T\Delta S = 6,025 \text{ J/mole} - (253 \text{ K}) (22.1 \text{ J/K·mole})$
$\Delta G = 6025 \text{ J/mole} - 5591 \text{ J/mole} = 434 \text{ J/mole}$

Note that ΔG is positive for the process

$$H_2O(s) \rightarrow H_2O(\ell)$$

which means that it occurs spontaneously in the opposite direction at $-20°$ C.

Test 6–13

A. 1a. At 373 K, $G_{H_2O(\ell)} = G_{H_2O(g)}$ and

$$\Delta G = \Delta H - T\Delta S = 0$$

$$\Delta S = \frac{\Delta H}{T} = \frac{43,900 \text{ J}}{373 \text{ K}} = 118 \frac{\text{J}}{\text{K}}$$

1b. The system is at equilibrium at 100° C so $\Delta G = 0$.

2. $\Delta G = \Delta H - T\Delta S = 0$ at $T = 373$ K. ΔH is positive, and ΔS is positive. At $T > 373$ K, the magnitude of $T\Delta S$ is greater than that of ΔH. Thus at $T > 373$ K, ΔG is negative.

B. 1a. At the melting point, $G_{CHCl_3(s)} = G_{CHCl_3(\ell)}$ and $\Delta G = 0$ for the process

$$CHCl_3(s) \rightarrow CHCl_3(\ell)$$

$$\Delta G = 0 = \Delta H - T\Delta S$$

$$= (9.2 \text{ kJ}) \left(\frac{10^3 \text{ J}}{\text{kJ}} \right) - T \left(43.9 \frac{\text{J}}{\text{K}} \right)$$

$$= 9200 \text{ J} - T \left(43.9 \frac{\text{J}}{\text{K}} \right)$$

$$9200 \text{ J} = T \left(43.9 \frac{\text{J}}{\text{K}} \right)$$

$$T = \frac{9200}{43.9} \text{ K} = 210 \text{ K}$$

The melting point is 210 K or $-63°$ C.

1b. The process

$$CHCl_3(s) \rightarrow CHCl_3(\ell)$$

is endothermic (ΔH is positive), which is unfavorable (ΔS_{surr} is negative). On the other hand, ΔS is positive. Thus high T (in this case $T > 210$ K) favors melting, and low temperature favors the reverse process.

Test 6–14

Reaction (1) must be reversed:

$$CO_2(g) \rightarrow C_{(s)}^{diamond} + O_2(g) \qquad \Delta G^0 = -(-397 \text{ kJ}) = 397 \text{ kJ}$$

Now add to (2) to give

$$C_{(s)}^{graphite} + O_2(g) + CO_2(g) \rightarrow C_{(s)}^{diamond} + O_2(g) + CO_2(g)$$
$$\Delta G = 397 \text{ kJ} - 394 \text{ kJ} = 3 \text{ kJ}$$

Thus for the process

$$C_{(s)}^{graphite} \rightarrow C_{(s)}^{diamond}$$

we find that $\Delta G = 3$ kJ.

Test 6–15

A. $\Delta G^0 = \Delta G_f^0 \, (P_4O_{10}(s)) + 6\Delta G_f^0(H_2O(\ell)) - 4\Delta G_f^0 \, (PH_3) - 8\Delta G_f^0(O_2(g))$
$\qquad = 1 \text{ mole } (-2697.8 \text{ kJ/mole}) + 6 \text{ mole } (-237.2 \text{ kJ/mole}) -$
$\qquad \quad 4 \text{ mole } (13.4 \text{ kJ/mole}) - 8(0)$
$\qquad = -2697.8 \text{ kJ} - 1423.2 \text{ kJ} - 53.6 \text{ kJ}$
$\qquad = -4175 \text{ kJ}$

B. The combustion reaction for glucose is

$$C_6H_{12}O_6(s) + 6O_2(g) \rightarrow 6CO_2(g) + 6H_2O(g)$$

Note that many times in considering combustion reactions, water is assumed to be in the liquid phase ($\Delta G_f^0(H_2O(\ell)) = -237$ kJ/mole). In this example, water is assumed to be in the gas phase.

$\Delta G^0_{reaction} = \Sigma\Delta G_f^0 \text{ (products)} - \Sigma\Delta G_f^0 \text{ (reactant)}$
$\Delta G^0_{reaction} = -2830 \text{ kJ} = 6 \text{ moles } (-394 \text{ kJ/mole})$
$\qquad\qquad\qquad + 6 \text{ moles } (-229 \text{ kJ/mole}) - 6 \text{ moles } (0) - \Delta G_f^0 \text{ (glucose)}$

$\Delta G_f^0 \text{ (glucose)} = +2830 \text{ kJ} - 2364 \text{ kJ} - 1374 \text{ kJ}$
$\qquad\qquad\qquad\quad = -908 \text{ kJ/mole}$

Test 6–16

A. $\Delta G^0 = \Delta H^0 - T\Delta S^0 \qquad T = 25 + 273 = 298 \text{ K}$
$\qquad = -112 \text{ kJ} - (298 \text{ K}) \, (-147 \text{ J/K})$
$\qquad = -112 \text{ kJ} + 43800 \text{ J}$

$\qquad = -112 \text{ kJ} + (43800 \text{ J}) \left(\dfrac{1 \text{ kJ}}{10^3 \text{ J}} \right)$

$\qquad = -112 \text{ kJ} + 43.8 \text{ kJ}$
$\qquad = -68 \text{ kJ}$

B. $\Delta G = \Delta G^0 + 2.303RT \log Q$

$\qquad Q = \dfrac{P_{NO_2}^2}{P_{NO}^2 P_{O_2}} = \dfrac{(3.8)^2}{(2.5)^2(1.3)} = 1.8$

$\qquad \Delta G = -68 \text{ kJ} + (2.303) \, (8.315 \text{ J/K}) \, (298 \text{ K}) \log (1.8)$
$\qquad\qquad = -68 \text{ kJ} + 1460 \text{ J}$

$\qquad\qquad = -68 \text{ kJ} + (1460 \text{ J}) \left(\dfrac{1 \text{ kJ}}{10^3 \text{ J}} \right) = -68 \text{ kJ} + 1.5 \text{ kJ} = -66.5 \text{ kJ}$

$\qquad\qquad = -67 \text{ kJ}$

C. $\Delta G^0 = \Delta H^0 - T\Delta S^0$
   $T = 65 + 273 = 338$ K
   Assume ΔH^0 and ΔS^0 do not depend upon temperature.

   $$\Delta G^0 = -112 \text{ kJ} - (338)\left(-147\,\frac{J}{K}\right)\left(\frac{1 \text{ kJ}}{10^3 \text{ K}}\right)$$

   $$= -112 \text{ kJ} + 49.7 \text{ kJ}$$
   $$= -62 \text{ kJ}$$

Test 6–17

A. 1. a. This reaction describes the formation of two moles of HCl from its elements. Thus

   $$\Delta H^0 = 2\Delta H_f^0(\text{HCl}) = 2(-92) = -184 \text{ kJ}$$

   b. $\Delta S^0 = 2S_{\text{HCl}}^0 - S_{\text{H}_2}^0 - S_{\text{Cl}_2}^0$
      $= 2(187) - 131 - 223 = 20$ J/K
   c. $\Delta G^0 = \Delta H^0 - T\Delta S^0$
      $T = 25 + 273 = 298$

   $$\Delta G^0 = -184 \text{ kJ} - (298 \text{ K})\left(20\,\frac{J}{K}\right)\left(\frac{1 \text{ kJ}}{10^3 \text{ J}}\right)$$

   $$= -184 \text{ kJ} - 6 \text{ kJ} = -190 \text{ kJ}$$

   2. ΔG^0 is very negative. This means that the free energy of HCl at one atmosphere and 25° C is much lower than that for H_2 and Cl_2 under the same conditions. Thus the mixture will shift far right to come to equilibrium.
   3. $\Delta G^0 = -2.303RT \log K$

   $$-190 \text{ kJ} = -2.303\left(8.315\,\frac{J}{K}\right)\left(\frac{1 \text{ kJ}}{10^3 \text{ J}}\right)(298 \text{ K}) \log K$$

   $$= -5.71 \text{ kJ} \log K$$
   $\log K = 33.3$
   $K = 2 \times 10^{33}$

B. 1. a. $\Delta H^0 = \Delta H_f^0(\text{HS}^-) + \Delta H_f^0(\text{H}^+) - \Delta H_f^0(\text{H}_2\text{S})$
      $= 1 \text{ mole } (-18 \text{ kJ/mole}) + 0 - 1 \text{ mole } (-21 \text{ kJ/mole})$
      $= 3 \text{ kJ}$
   b. $\Delta S^0 = S_{\text{H}^+}^0 + S_{\text{HS}^-}^0 - S_{\text{H}_2\text{S}}^0$
      $= 0 + 1 \text{ mole } (63 \text{ J/K·mole}) - 1 \text{ mole } (206 \text{ J/K·mole})$
      $= -143$ J/K
   c. $\Delta G^0 = \Delta H^0 - T\Delta S^0$
      $T = 25 + 273 = 298$ K

   $$\Delta G^0 = 3 \text{ kJ} - (298 \text{ K})(-143 \text{ J/K})\left(\frac{1 \text{ kJ}}{10^3 \text{ J}}\right)$$

   $$= 3 \text{ kJ} + 42.6 \text{ kJ}$$
   $$= 45.6 \text{ kJ} = 46 \text{ kJ}$$

d. $\Delta G^0 = -2.30RT \log K$

$$46 \text{ kJ} = -2.303\left(8.315\frac{\text{J}}{\text{K}}\right) \left(\frac{1 \text{ kJ}}{10^3 \text{ J}}\right) (298 \text{ K}) \log K$$

$$\log K = -\frac{46}{5.7} = -8.1$$

$$K = 8.5 \times 10^{-9}$$

2. The calculated value for ΔS^0 is -143 J/K. This seems strange in view of the fact that in the reaction

$$H_2S \rightleftarrows H^+ + HS^-$$

two "particles" are being created from one "particle." This looks like an increase in positional disorder, so that one might expect ΔS^0 to be positive. Why is ΔS^0 actually very negative?

The complicating factor in this reaction is hydration. An uncharged molecule is producing two ions, which will be strongly hydrated (water molecules will attach to them). The hydration phenomenon produces a strong ordering effect on the water. ΔS^0 in this case will be the net effect of a disordering process ($H_2S \rightarrow H^+ + HS^-$) and an ordering process (hydration of the ions). The latter must be dominant.

This is an important case, since it often applies for dissociation of acids in water.

Chapter 7

Test 7–1

A. The half-reaction involving magnesium must be reversed.

$$Mg \rightarrow Mg^{2+} + 2e^- \qquad -\mathscr{E}^0 = -(-2.37) = 2.37 \text{ V}$$

Also, since the two half-reactions involve different numbers of electrons, they must be multiplied by integers as follows:

$$
\begin{array}{ll}
2(Al^{3+} + 3e^- \rightarrow Al) & \mathscr{E}^0 = -1.66 \text{ V} \\
\underline{3(Mg \rightarrow Mg^{2+} + 2e^-)} & \underline{-\mathscr{E}^0 = 2.37 \text{ V}} \\
2Al^{3+} + 3Mg \rightarrow 2Al + 3Mg^{2+} & \mathscr{E}^0_{\text{cell}} = -1.66 + 2.37 \\
& \phantom{\mathscr{E}^0_{\text{cell}}} = 0.71 \text{ V}
\end{array}
$$

where the six electrons on both sides have been cancelled out.

B. Half-reaction (2) must be reversed and both half reactions must be multiplied by integers to make the number of electrons equal:

$$
\begin{array}{ll}
2(MnO_4^- + 5e^- + 8 H^+ \rightarrow Mn^{2+} + 4H_2O) & \mathscr{E}^0 = 1.51 \text{ V} \\
\underline{5(ClO_3^- + H_2O \rightarrow ClO_4^- + 2H^+ + 2e^-)} & \underline{-\mathscr{E}^0 = -1.19 \text{ V}} \\
2MnO_4^- + 10e^- + 16H^+ + 5ClO_3^- + 5H_2O \rightarrow & \\
2Mn^{2+} + 8H_2O + 5ClO_4^- + 10H^+ + 10e^- &
\end{array}
$$

Cancelling species common to both sides gives

$$2MnO_4^- + 6H^+ + 5ClO_3^- \rightarrow 2Mn^{2+}$$
$$+ 3H_2O + 5ClO_4^-$$

$\mathscr{E}^0_{cell} = 1.51 - 1.19$
$= 0.32$ V

Test 7–2

A.   To achieve a cell with a positive $\mathscr{E}^0$ value, the Cu^{2+}, Cu reaction can be reversed.

$$\frac{\begin{array}{l} Cu \rightarrow Cu^{2+} + 2e^- \\ 2(Ce^{4+} + e^- \rightarrow Ce^{3+}) \end{array}}{Cu + 2Ce^{4+} \rightarrow Cu^{2+} + 2Ce^{3+}}$$

$-\mathscr{E}^0 = -0.34$
$\mathscr{E}^0 = 1.70$ V
$\overline{\mathscr{E}^0_{cell} = 1.36}$ V

In the working cell Cu is oxidized (anode) and Ce^{4+} is reduced (cathode). The cell diagram is

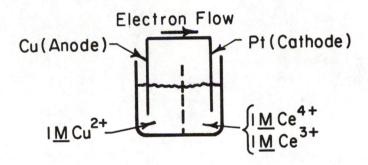

B.   The cell reaction is

$$\frac{\begin{array}{l} 2(Al \rightarrow 3e^- + Al^{3+}) \\ 3(Mn^{2+} + 2e^- \rightarrow Mn) \end{array}}{2Al + 3Mn^{2+} \rightarrow 2Al^{3+} + 3Mn}$$

$-\mathscr{E}^0 = 1.66$ V
$\mathscr{E}^0 = -1.18$ V
$\overline{\mathscr{E}^0_{cell} = 0.48}$ V

The cell diagram is

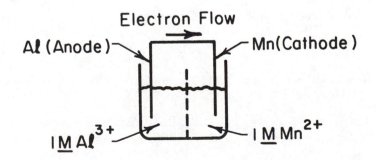

Test 7–3

Nature wants to equalize the concentrations of Fe^{2+} in both compartments. This can be accomplished by transferring electrons from the left to the right compartments. Fe^{2+} will be formed in the left compartment and Fe will be plated out in the right compartment.

Test 7–4   Note: An extra significant figure is carried here.

A. 1. Charge passed through the solution

$$57.5 \frac{coul}{sec} \times 16.8 \ min \times \frac{60.0 \ sec}{min} = 5.796 \times 10^4 \ coul$$

2. Moles of electrons passed through the solution

$$5.796 \times 10^{-4} \ coul \times \frac{1 \ mole \ of \ electrons}{96,486 \ coul} = 6.007 \times 10^{-1} \ mole$$

3. Moles of Cr formed

$$6.007 \times 10^{-1} \ mole \ of \ electrons \times \frac{1 \ mole \ Cr}{3 \ moles \ of \ electrons}$$
$$= 2.002 \times 10^{-1} \ mole \ of \ Cr$$

4. Grams of Cr formed

$$2.002 \times 10^{-1} \ mole \ Cr \times \frac{51.996 \ g \ Cr}{mole \ Cr} = 10.4 \ g \ Cr$$

B. 1. Moles of Cl_2 formed

$$26.5 \ g \times \frac{1 \ mole \ Cl_2}{2(35.453) \ g \ Cl_2} = 3.737 \times 10^{-1} \ mole \ Cl_2$$

2. Moles of electrons
The reaction in this case is an oxidation

$$2Cl^- \rightarrow Cl_2 + 2e^-$$

and Cl_2 is produced at the anode. Each mole of Cl_2 releases two moles of electrons.

$$3.737 \times 10^{-1} \ mole \ of \ Cl_2 \times \frac{2 \ moles \ electrons}{mole \ Cl_2}$$
$$= 7.475 \times 10^{-1} \ mole \ of \ electrons$$

3. Coulombs of charge

$$7.475 \times 10^{-1} \ mole \ of \ electrons \times \frac{96,486 \ coul}{mole \ of \ electrons} = 7.212 \times 10^4 \ coul$$

4. Time required
   Amps × seconds = coulombs

   $$\left(15.0\,\frac{coul}{sec}\right)(time) = 7.212 \times 10^4 \text{ coul}$$

   $time = 4.81 \times 10^3 \text{ seconds}$

Test 7–5

A. Work $= q\mathscr{E} = 3.00$ moles of electrons $\times \dfrac{96{,}486 \text{ coul}}{\text{mole of electrons}} \times 1.18 \text{ J/coul}$

   $= 3.42 \times 10^5 \text{ J}$

B. Work (maximum) $= q\mathscr{E}_{max} = -\Delta G$

   $\Delta G = -5.86 \times 10^5 \text{ J}$

   $q = 3.00$ moles of electrons $\times \dfrac{96{,}486 \text{ coul}}{\text{mole of electrons}}$

   $= 2.89 \times 10^5 \text{ coulombs}$

   $$\mathscr{E}_{max} = \frac{-\Delta G}{q} = \frac{-(-5.86 \times 10^5 \text{ J})}{(2.89 \times 10^5 \text{ coul})} = 2.03 \text{ V}$$

C. Work (maximum) $= -\Delta G = 5.86 \times 10^5 \text{ J}$

Test 7–6

The Nernst equation (25° C) is

$$\mathscr{E} = \mathscr{E}^0 - \frac{0.0592}{n} \log Q$$

$\mathscr{E}^0 = 1.36 \text{ V}$
$n = 2$

$$Q = \frac{[Ce^{3+}]^2[Cu^{2+}]}{[Ce^{4+}]^2} = \frac{(1.0 \times 10^{-4})^2(1.0 \times 10^{-2})}{(3.0)^2} = 1.11 \times 10^{-11}$$

$$\mathscr{E}_{cell} = 1.36 - \frac{0.0592}{2} \log (1.11 \times 10^{-11})$$

$$= 1.36 - \frac{0.0592}{2} (-10.95) = 1.36 + 3.2 \times 10^{-1}$$

$$= 1.36 + 0.32 = 1.68 \text{ V}$$

Note that in this case both product concentrations are much lower than 1.0 *M* and the reactant concentration is greater than 1.0 *M*. Both of these effects increase the cell potential, and for this cell the potential is significantly larger than $\mathscr{E}^0$.

Test 7–7

The balanced cell reaction is

$$Cr \rightarrow Cr^{3+} + 3e^- \qquad\qquad -\mathscr{E}^0 = 0.74 \text{ V}$$
$$\underline{3(TiO^{2+} + 2H^+ + e^- \rightarrow Ti^{3+} + H_2O)} \qquad \underline{\mathscr{E}^0 = 0.10 \text{ V}}$$
$$Cr + 3TiO^{2+} + 6H^+ \rightarrow Cr^{3+} + 3Ti^{3+} + 3H_2O \qquad \mathscr{E}^0{}_{cell} = 0.84 \text{ V}$$

The Nernst equation is

$$\mathscr{E}_{cell} = \mathscr{E}^0_{cell} - \frac{0.0592}{n} \log Q$$

$$= 0.84 - \frac{0.0592}{3} \log \frac{[Ti^{3+}]^3[Cr^{3+}]}{[TiO^{2+}]^3[H^+]^6}$$

$$= 0.84 - \frac{0.0592}{3} \log \frac{(5.0 \times 10^{-2})^3(1.0 \times 10^{-4})}{(1.0 \times 10^{-1})^3(1.0)^6}$$

$$= 0.84 - \frac{0.0592}{3} \log (1.25 \times 10^{-5})$$

$$= 0.84 - \frac{0.0592}{3} (-4.90) = 0.84 + 0.097 = 0.94 \text{ V}$$

Test 7–8   Note: An extra significant figure is carried here.

A. 1. $\mathscr{E}^0 = 0.33 \text{ V}$
$n = 2$
$$\log K = \frac{n\mathscr{E}^0}{0.0592} = \frac{2(0.33)}{0.0592} = 11.15$$
$K = 1.4 \times 10^{11}$

2. $\mathscr{E}^0 = 0.71 \text{ V.}$
$n = 6$
$$\log K = \frac{n\mathscr{E}^0}{0.0592} = \frac{(6)(0.71)}{0.0592} = 71.96$$
$K = 9.1 \times 10^{71}$

3. $\mathscr{E}^0 = 0.32 \text{ V.}$
$n = 10$
$$\log K = \frac{n\mathscr{E}^0}{0.0592} = \frac{(10)(0.32)}{0.0592} = 54.05$$
$K = 1.1 \times 10^{54}$

B.   In this case (2) must be reversed and multiplied by 5.

$$2IO_3^- + 12H^+ + 10e^- \rightarrow I_2 + 6H_2O \qquad\qquad \mathscr{E}^0 = 1.19 \text{ V}$$

$$\underline{5(SO_2 + 2H_2O \rightarrow 2e^- + 4H^+ + SO_4^{2-}) \qquad\qquad -\mathscr{E}^0 = -0.17 \text{ V}}$$

$$2IO_3^- + 5SO_2 + 4H_2O \rightarrow 8H^+ + 5SO_4^{2-} + I_2$$

$$\mathscr{E}^0 = 1.19 - 0.17 = 1.02 \text{ V}$$

$$n = 10$$

$$\log K = \frac{n\mathscr{E}^0}{0.0592} = \frac{(10)(1.02)}{0.0592} = 172.30$$

$$K = 2.0 \times 10^{172}$$

ANSWERS TO EXERCISES

CHAPTER 1

1. a. $K = \dfrac{[H_2O]^2}{[H_2]^2[O_2]}$

    b. $K = \dfrac{[H_2O]^2}{[H_2]^2}$

    c. $K = \dfrac{[NO_2]^4[H_2O]^6}{[NH_3]^4[O_2]^7}$

2. $K = \dfrac{[PCl_5]}{[PCl_3][Cl_2]}$

3. a. 11 ℓ/mole   b. 9.0×10^{-2} mole/ℓ
4. left
5. right
6. $[SO_2] = 0.34$ mole/ℓ
7. a. 1.7×10^{-3} atm^{-2} b. smaller
8. a. 45.2   b. 45.2
9. $[HI] = 4.30$ moles/ℓ $[I_2] = 4.10$ moles/ℓ
10. 1.0×10^1 ℓ/mole
11. a. $[CO_2] = 8.0 \times 10^{-3}$ mole/ℓ c. 4.0×10^{-2}
     b. 4.0×10^{-2} d. 6.7×10^{-1} atm
12. 1.7×10^{12} ℓ/mole
13. 6.9×10^{10} atm^{-1}
14. a. shifts left   c. no change
     b. shifts left   d. shifts right
15. 2.4×10^{-2} mole/ℓ
16. a. No $Q > K$
     b. will shift left
     c. $2x$ = moles/ℓ of NH_3 formed to reach equilibrium (other choices are possible)
     d. $[NH_3] = 2.0 \times 10^{-4} + 2x$; $[N_2] = 2.0 \times 10^{-1} - x$; $[H_2] = 2.0 \times 10^{-2} - 3x$
17. $K_P = \dfrac{P^2_{NO_2}}{P_{N_2O_4}} = \dfrac{(6.10 \times 10^{-2})^2}{1.33 \times 10^{-2}} = 2.80 \times 10^{-1}$ atm

54. $[PCl_5] = 1.8 \times 10^{-3}$ mole/ℓ
     $[PCl_3] = 6.5 \times 10^{-2}$ mole/ℓ
     $[Cl_2] = 2.5 \times 10^{-3}$ mole/ℓ

55. $[NO_2] = 7.2 \times 10^{-2}$ mole/ℓ
     $[N_2O_4] = 6.4 \times 10^{-2}$ mole/ℓ

56. $[NH_3] = 4.6 \times 10^{-3}$ atm
     $[N_2] = 1.0 \times 10^{-1}$ atm
     $[H_2] = 4.9 \times 10^{-1}$ atm

57. a. left
     b. $[NH_3] = 1.0 \times 10^{-3}$ atm
         $[N_2] = 1.3 \times 10^{-1}$ atm
         $[H_2] = 1.7 \times 10^{-1}$ atm
58. $[HI] = 2.35$ moles/ℓ
     $[H_2] = [I_2] = 0.377$ mole/ℓ
59. a. shifts right
     b. $[HI] = 2.62$ moles/ℓ
         $[H_2] = 0.241$ mole/ℓ
         $[I_2] = 0.741$ mole/ℓ

60. $[Cl_2]$ = 9.6×10^{-2} mole/ℓ
    $[PCl_5]$ = 1.84×10^{-1} mole/ℓ
    $[PCl_3]$ = 4.6×10^{-2} mole/ℓ
61. $[HI]$ = 6.90×10^{-1} mole/ℓ
    $[H_2]$ = 1.55×10^{-1} mole/ℓ
    $[I_2]$ = 5.0×10^{-3} mole/ℓ

62. a. No $Q > K$
    b. will shift left
    c. $[ClO]$ = 3.0×10^{-2} mole/ℓ
        $[Cl_2]$ = 2.3×10^{-5} mole/ℓ
        $[O_2]$ = 2.5×10^{-1} mole/ℓ

CHAPTER 2

1. a. HNO_2, H_2O
        $HNO_2 \rightleftarrows H^+ + NO_2^-$
    b. H^+, NO_3^-, H_2O
        H^+ from complete dissociation of HNO_3
    c. C_5H_5N, H_2O
        $C_5H_5N + H_2O \rightleftarrows C_5H_5NH^+ + OH^-$
    d. Na^+, CN^-, H_2O
        $CN^- + H_2O \rightleftarrows HCN + OH^-$
    e. $HCHO_2$, Na^+, CHO_2^-, H_2O
        $HCHO_2 \rightleftarrows H^+ + CHO_2^-$ or
        $CHO_2^- + H_2O \rightleftarrows HCHO_2 + OH^-$
    f. Na^+, OH^-, H_2O
        OH^- from complete dissociation of NaOH
    g. $Pu^{3+}(aq)$, NO_3^-, H_2O
        $Pu(OH_2)_6^{3+} \rightleftarrows Pu(OH)(OH_2)_5^{2+} + H^+$
    h. $HOCl$, H_2O
        $HOCl \rightleftarrows H^+ + OCl^-$
    i. $(CH_3)_3N$, H_2O
        $(CH_3)_3N + H_2O \rightleftarrows (CH_3)_3NH^+ + OH^-$
    j. H^+, Cl^-, H_2O
        H^+ from dissolved HCl
    k. K^+, OH^-, H_2O
        OH^- from dissolved KOH
    l. HNO_2, Na^+, NO_2^-, H_2O
        $HNO_2 \rightleftarrows H^+ + NO_2^-$
    m. HF, Na^+, F^-, H_2O
        $HF \rightleftarrows H^+ + F^-$
    n. CH_3NH_2, H_2O
        $CH_3NH_2 + H_2O \rightleftarrows CH_3NH_3^+ + OH^-$
    o. $Al^{3+}(aq)$, NO_3^-, H_2O
        Assume $Al^{3+}(aq)$ is $Al(OH_2)_6^{3+}$ since the K_a for $Al(OH_2)_6^{3+}$ is
        given. $Al(OH_2)_6^{3+} \rightleftarrows Al(OH)(OH_2)_5^{2+} + H^+$
2. a. 1.70
    b. 2.00
    c. 9.57
    d. 11.10
    e. 3.44
    f. 14.00
    g. 4.48

      h. 3.73
      i. 11.86
      j. 1.00
      k. 11.00
      l. 3.10
      m. 3.54
      n. 12.17
      o. 3.43

3.   b

4. $K_a = 1.0 \times 10^{-7}$

5.   a. 2.49
      b. 2.11
      c. 2.63

6.   8.44

7.   9.26

8.   a. 4.98
      b. 4.70

CHAPTER 3

1. a. (1) H^+, Cl^-, Na^+, OH^-, H_2O
          (2) $H^+ + OH^- \rightarrow H_2O$
          (3) Na^+, OH^-, H_2O
          (4) Excess OH^- will determine pH
    b. (1) Na^+, OH^-, HOAc, H_2O
          (2) $OH^- + HOAc \rightarrow H_2O + OAc^-$
          (3) HOAc, OAc^-, Na^+, H_2O
          (4) $HOAc \rightleftharpoons H^+ + OAc^-$ or
               $OAc^- + H_2O \rightleftharpoons HOAc + OH^-$
    c. (1) H^+, Cl^-, NH_3, H_2O
          (2) $NH_3 + H^+ \rightarrow NH_4^+$
          (3) NH_3, NH_4^+, Cl^-, H_2O
          (4) $NH_4^+ \rightleftharpoons NH_3 + H^+$ or
               $NH_3 + H_2O \rightleftharpoons NH_4^+ + OH^-$
    d. (1) H^+, Cl^-, Na^+, CN^-, H_2O
          (2) $H^+ + CN^- \rightarrow HCN$
          (3) HCN, CN^-, Na^+, Cl^-, H_2O
          (4) $HCN \rightleftharpoons H^+ + CN^-$ or
               $CN^- + H_2O \rightleftharpoons HCN + OH^-$
    e. (1) Na^+, OH^-, $HCHO_2$, H_2O
          (2) $OH^- + HCHO_2 \rightarrow H_2O + CHO_2^-$
          (3) $HCHO_2$, CHO_2^-, Na^+, H_2O
          (4) $HCHO_2 \rightleftharpoons H^+ + CHO_2^-$ or
               $CHO_2^- + H_2O \rightleftharpoons HCHO_2 + OH^-$
    f. (1) C_6H_5COOH, Na^+, OH^-, H_2O
          (2) $C_6H_5COOH + OH^- \rightarrow C_6H_5COO^- + H_2O$
          (3) $C_6H_5COO^-$, Na^+, OH^-, H_2O
          (4) excess OH^- from NaOH

g. (1) H^+, NO_3^-, C_5H_5N, H_2O
   (2) $H^+ + C_5H_5N \rightarrow C_5H_5NH^+$
   (3) C_5H_5N, $C_5H_5NH^+$, NO_3^-, H_2O
   (4) $C_5H_5NH^+ \rightleftarrows C_5H_5N + H^+$ or
       $C_5H_5N + H_2O \rightleftarrows C_5H_5NH^+ + OH^-$

h. (1) NH_3, H^+, Cl^-, H_2O
   (2) $NH_3 + H^+ \rightarrow NH_4^+$
   (3) NH_3, NH_4^+, Cl^-, H_2O
   (4) $NH_4^+ \rightleftarrows NH_3 + H^+$ or
       $NH_3 + H_2O \rightleftarrows NH_4^+ + OH^-$

2. a. 12.70
   b. 4.60
   c. 9.86
   d. 9.21
   e. 4.22
   f. 13.65
   g. 6.10
   h. 9.26

3. a. 0.70
   b. 1.10
   c. 1.30
   d. 7.00
   e. 12.60

4. a. 13.30
   b. 13.11
   c. 12.88
   d. 12.52
   e. 7.00
   f. 1.65

5. a. (1) 4.95
      (2) 8.91

   (3) 9.21
   (4) 11.02
   (5) 12.60
   b. $K_a \approx 10^{-12}$

6. a. (1) yellow
      (2) 3.30
      (3) yellow to
          yellow-orange
   b. (1) red
      (2) 5.30
      (3) red to
          red-orange
   c. 4.3

7. a. 11.28
   b. 10.21
   c. 9.73
   d. 9.26
   e. 5.33
   f. 1.65

CHAPTER 4

1. 5.3×10^{-12}
2. 6.9×10^{-9}
3. 3.9×10^{-5} mole/ℓ
4. 8.9×10^{-4} mole/ℓ
5. 1.1×10^{-29}
6. a. 8.8×10^{-7} mole/ℓ
   b. 7.7×10^{-11} mole/ℓ
7. 1.0×10^{-10}
8. a. 1.6×10^{-9} mole/ℓ
   b. 1.6×10^{-20} mole/ℓ
9. 5.2×10^{-9} mole/ℓ
10. a. $CaF_2(s)$
    b. $FePO_4(s)$
11. $AgCN(s)$ will form
12. $Ce(IO_3)_3(s)$ will form

13. $[S^{2-}]$ greater than 7.0×10^{-15} mole/ℓ
14. $CaSO_4(s)$ will not form
15. $CuCl(s)$ will form
16. $PbF_2(s)$ will not form
17. $[Ag^+]$ greater than 5.6×10^{-5} mole/ℓ
18. 2.6×10^{-13}

CHAPTER 5

1. 2.51
2. 6.89
3. 2.28
4. 6.69
5. 0.65
6. a. 1.70   b. 4.69
   c. 2.30   d. 11.11
7. 0.04
8. a. 1.36   b. 2.03
9. 2.32
10. $[Ce^{3+}] = 8.2 \times 10^{-6} \, M$
    $[IO_3^-] = 3.5 \times 10^{-2} \, M$
11. $[BeF_4^{2-}] = 5.0 \times 10^{-5} \, M$
    $[F^-] = 4.0 \, M$
    $[BeF_3^-] = 4.6 \times 10^{-7} \, M$
    $[BeF_2] = 1.9 \times 10^{-10} \, M$
    $[BeF^+] = 8.2 \times 10^{-15} \, M$
    $[Be^{2+}] = 2.6 \times 10^{-20} \, M$
12. 6.0×10^{-2} mole/ℓ
13. 8.7×10^{-16} mole/ℓ
14. 1.3×10^{-1} mole/ℓ
    (The answer is 1.27×10^{-1} mole/ℓ assuming one extra significant figure.)
15. 2.5×10^{-4} mole/ℓ
16. 2.0×10^{-6} mole/ℓ

CHAPTER 6

1. Negative; $\Delta S_{surr} = -130$ J/K·mole
2. Negative; $\Delta S_{surr} = -13.4$ J/K·mole
3. Negative; $\Delta S_{surr} = -1.46$ kJ/K·mole
4. Positive; $\Delta S_{surr} = 147$ J/K·mole
5. Positive; $\Delta S_{surr} = 309$ J/K·mole
6. Positive; $\Delta S_{surr} = 1.62$ kJ/K·mole
7. Negative
8. Positive
9. Positive, since H_2O is more complex than H_2
10. Near zero
11. Positive, since H_2O is more complex than H_2

12. Positive
13. Negative
14. Negative
15. Negative
16. Positive
17. -119 J/K
18. 4 J/K

19. 116 J/K
20. -242 J/K
21. 190 J/K
22. -113 J/K
23. 119 J/K
24. 57 J/K
25. 149 kJ/mole

26. $\Delta G^0 = -458$ kJ; $\Delta S^0 = -89$ J/K;
    $\Delta H^0 = -485$ kJ; $K = 1.9 \times 10^{80}$

27. $\Delta G^0 = 360$ kJ; $\Delta S^0 = 141$ J/K;
    $\Delta H^0 = 402$ kJ; $K = 8.0 \times 10^{-64}$

28. $\Delta G^0 = 6$ kJ; $\Delta S^0 = 176$ J/K;
    $\Delta H^0 = 58$ kJ; $K = 8.9 \times 10^{-2}$

29. $\Delta G^0 = -8890$ kJ; $\Delta S^0 = -2970$ J/K;
    $\Delta H^0 = -9775$ kJ; $K = 10^{1560}$

30. $\Delta G^0 = -962$ kJ; $\Delta S^0 = 181$ J/K;
    $\Delta H^0 = -908$ kJ; $K = 10^{169}$

31. 18.1 kJ

32. a. $\Delta G^0 = 53$ kJ
    b. No, ΔG^0 is positive
    c. $T = 725$ K

33. a. Positive, since ΔS_{surr} is negative
    b. Increase

34. Spontaneous at 6000 K (ΔG^0 is negative)

35. True
36. False
37. False
38. True

39. True
40. False
41. True

CHAPTER 7

1.

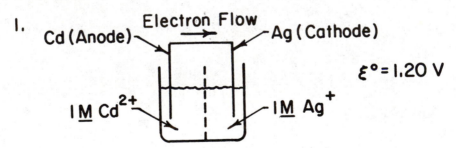

2.

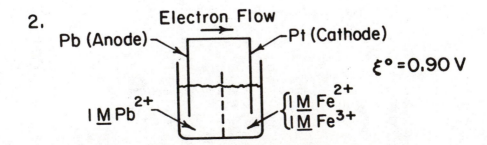

3.

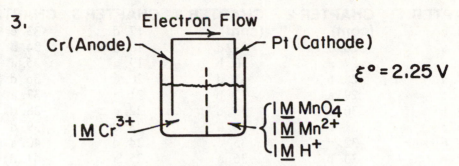

$\xi° = 2.25$ V

4.

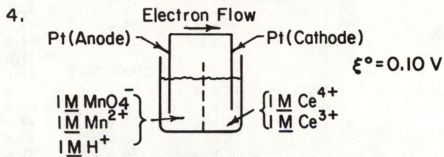

$\xi° = 0.10$ V

5.

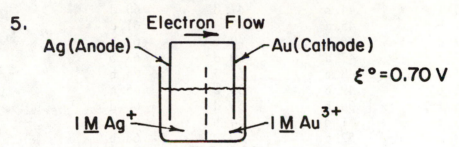

$\xi° = 0.70$ V

6. 6.0×10^{-4} mole

7. 7.62×10^{-2} g

8. $\mathcal{E}^0 = 0.32$ V

9. Negative

10. $Zn \rightarrow Zn^{2+} + 2e^-$

11. $\mathcal{E} = 0.32 - \dfrac{0.0592}{2} \log \dfrac{0.100}{1.0 \times 10^{-5}} = 0.20$ V

12. $\mathcal{E}^0 = -1.61$ V

13. $K = 4.1 \times 10^{-55}$

14. No

15. Ni

16. $\mathcal{E}^0 = -0.11$ V

17. $K = 5.1 \times 10^{-10}$

18. $Au^{3+}(aq) + 3Tl(s) \rightarrow 3Tl^+(aq) + Au(s)$

19. $\mathcal{E}^0 = 1.84$ V

20. Tl(anode); Au(cathode)

21. $\mathcal{E} = 1.84 - \dfrac{0.0592}{3} \log \dfrac{(1.0 \times 10^{-4})^3}{1.0 \times 10^{-2}} = 2.04$ V

22. $\mathcal{E}^0 = 0.04$ V

23. $K = 5.7 \times 10^6$

24. $\Delta G^0 = -38.5$ kJ

CHAPTER 1	CHAPTER 2 (cont)	CHAPTER 3 (cont)	CHAPTER 5	CHAPTER 7
24. c	26. a	29. d	17. d	33. c
25. a	27. a	30. b	18. d	34. a
26. a	28. b	31. d	19. a	35. a
27. a	29. a	32. b	20. e	36. d
28. e	30. e[1]	33. d	21. c	37. a
29. b	31. c	34. a	22. c	38. d
30. c	32. d	35. c	23. d	39. d
31. c	33. b	36. a	24. d	40. a
32. c	34. c	37. c	25. a	41. d
33. b	35. b	38. d	26. d	42. b
34. c	36. c	39. a	27. d	43. a
35. 1) c	37. d	40. c	28. a	44. b
2) c	38. a	41. a		45. a
3) b	39. b	42. d	**CHAPTER 6**	46. e[4]
4) b	40. d[2]	43. a	55. b	47. b
36. c	41. c	44. b[3]	56. a	48. b
37. b	42. c	45. a	57. b	49. c
38. b	43. c	46. b	58. a	50. d
39. a	44. b	47. d	59. b	51. a
40. a	45. a	48. d	60. d	
41. b	46. c	49. b	61. c	
42. d	47. a	50. d	62. b	
43. c	48. c	51. a	63. b	
44. b	49. c	52. c	64. b	
45. b	50. b	53. d	65. a	
46. c	51. d	54. b	66. d	
47. c	52. c		67. c	
48. a			68. b	
49. c		**CHAPTER 4**	69. c	
50. d	**CHAPTER 3**	23. a	70. b	
51. b	13. c	24. e	71. a	
52. b	14. a	25. a	72. c	
53. c	15. a	26. a	73. d	
	16. b	27. a		
CHAPTER 2	17. d	28. a		
16. c	18. e	29. c		
17. c	19. b	30. d		
18. d	20. b	31. d		
19. b	21. d	32. b		
20. a	22. c	33. d		
21. c	23. c	34. b		
22. d	24. c	35. a		
23. a) c	25. d			
b) d	26. b			
24. c	27. c			
25. a	28. c			

[1]answer is $1.95 \times 10^{-6} M$
[2]answer is $2.0 \times 10^{-4} M$
[3]not using quadratic formula   2 3 4 5 6 7 8 9 0
[4]answer is $6.4 \times 10^{-3} J$